Pictured Key Nature Series

How To Know

THE MOSSES AND LIVERWORTS

Pictured-Keys for determining many of the North American Mosses and Liverworts, with suggestions and aids for their study.

Revised Edition

HENRY S. CONARD, Ph.D., Sc.D.

Emeritus Professor of Botany, Grinnell College
Visiting Research Professor in Botany
State University of Iowa

WM. C. BROWN COMPANY PUBLISHERS

135 SOUTH LOCUST STREET • DUBUQUE, IOWA 52003

Library of Congress Catalog Card Number: 59-1321

THE PICTURED-KEY NATURE SERIES

"How to Know the Insects," Jaques, 1947
"Living Things—How to Know Them," Jaques, 1946
"How to Know the Trees," Jaques, 1946
"Plant Families—How to know Them," Jaques, 1948
"How to Know the Economic Plants," Jaques, 1948, 1958
"How to Know the Spring Flowers," Cuthbert, 1943, 1949
"How to Know the Mosses and Liverworts," Conard, 1944, 1956
"How to Know the Land Birds," Jaques, 1947
"How to Know the Fall Flowers," Cuthbert, 1948
"How to Know the Immature Insects," Chu, 1949
"How to Know the Protozoa," Jahn, 1949
"How to Know the Mammals," Booth, 1949
"How to Know the Beetles," Jaques, 1951
"How to Know the Spiders," Kaston, 1952
"How to Know the Grasses," Pohl, 1953
"How to Know the Fresh-Water Algae," Prescott, 1954
"How to Know the Western Trees," Baerg, 1955
"How to Know the Seaweeds," Dawson, 1956
"How to Know the Freshwater Fishes," Eddy, 1957
"How to Know the Weeds," Jaques, 1959
"How to Know the Water Birds," Jaques-Ollivier, 1960
"How to Know the Butterflies," Ehrlich, 1961
"How to Know the Eastern Land Snails," Burch, 1962
"How to Know the Grasshoppers," Helfer, 1963
"How to Know the Cacti," Dawson, 1963

Other Subjects in Preparation

Printed in U.S.A.

CONTENTS

INTRODUCTION

"All mosses look alike to me." "All grasses look alike to me." "All Negroes look alike to me." "All Chinese . . ." That is only because we do not know them well enough. To a Chinese student who has just come to the States, all Americans look alike. On acquaintance we find just as many different appearances and behaviors amongst non-caucasians as amongst caucasians, once our attention is not distracted by the conspicuous differences in color of skin.

The different kinds of mosses are pretty obvious when we have learned where to look for the differences. Nobody would say these plants look alike:

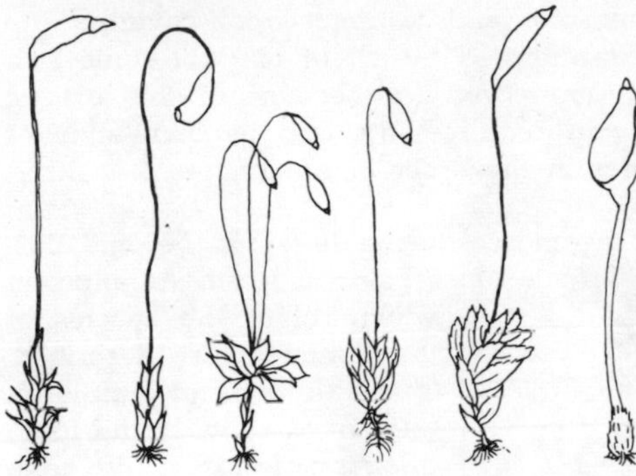

Figure 1. From left to right: *Ceratodon purpureus, Funaria hygrometrica, Rhodobryum roseum, Bryum caespiticium, Aulacomnium heterostichum, Buxbaumia aphylla.*

Or these leaves:

Figure 2. From left to right: *Aulacomnium heterostichum, Leptobryum pyriforme, Mnium cuspidatum, Drepanocladus aduncus, Rhytidiadelphus triquetrus.*

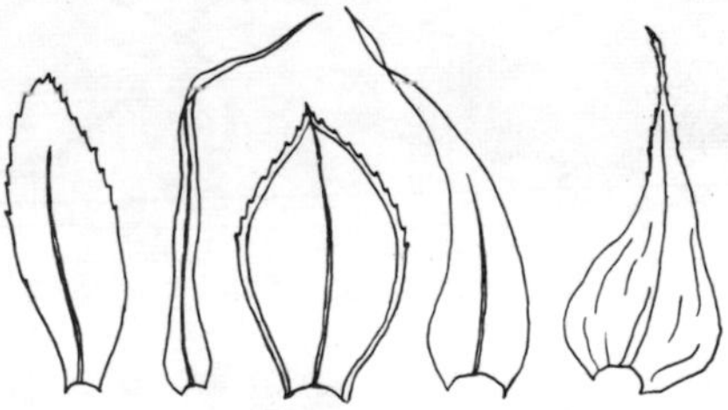

Or even these capsules:

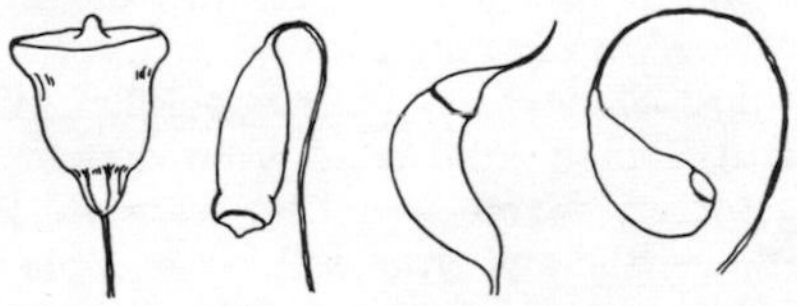

Figure 3. From left to right: *Physcomitrium turbinatum, Bryum argenteum, Dicranella heteromalla, Funaria hygrometrica.*

(I have often wondered if our ideas of gnomes and pyxies were drawn from the sober erect mosses, and the curved capsules with their impish pointed caps.) A great many mosses do look alike. Some kinds are so common and abundant that they are seen practically everywhere. We pick up the same identical thing in every continent. A great many of the mosses of North America are found also in Europe.

So there are not too many mosses in any local area for a person to learn to know in a reasonable time. One hundred species in a county is a near average. Chester County, Pennsylvania, has about 150 species. The State of Iowa has about 250 true mosses and 50 liverworts. Several of these have been collected but once. Probably only 150 are found in sufficient quantity to be represented in ten large herbaria; 135 species have recently been distributed to such institutions; thirty species of liverworts have been distributed.

The elegant touch that mosses lend to landscape, covering the naked earth with greenness, is admitted by all of us. On some rich estates mosses are cultivated and cared for because of this artistic value. Each species has its own requirements and its own style of beauty, and its own significance in the order of nature.

We need, now, to know the mosses. And that has become possible, since the completion of Grout's Moss Flora of North America, in which all of the species of the Continent are described. This little book of ours is an attempt to simplify the identification of mosses. We have culled out the most distinctive recognition characters, and these are shown in pictures adjacent to the verbal descriptions.

It has long been customary for students of mosses to send specimens to specialists to get their identification corroborated or corrected. This is almost necessary for a beginner. Here is how it is done: you collect enough to make two good specimens. A number is assigned to this collection; this same number to appear on the wrapper of each of the two specimens. One specimen is presented to the specialist for keeps; you keep the other. In return for your gift, the specialist sends back word that your No......... is...................
The author of these keys will be glad to pose as your specialist. Or, better, join the American Bryological Society and send your specimen to the Curator of Mosses of the Society. You will also receive the Bryologist, the quarterly journal of the Society, you will be eligible to publish therein, and you will be helping to support the only American moss journal.

Finally, a Pictured-Key owes its value chiefly to the pictures. This book was made possible by the constant cooperation of my wife, Louisa Sargent Conard, M.A., formerly Assistant Professor of Botany in Grinnell College. She has made nearly all of the pictures, large and small. It is really her book! I am also indebted to three students who worked through many weary hours, and whose drawings are initialed. Each drawing has been approved by the author; if errors are found, the responsibility is his.

In making the pictures we have drawn freely upon all of the sources mentioned herein. In most cases actual specimens from the 10,000 in our herbarium, often several specimens, have been examined, and the drawings have been determined by this actual evidence.

And, of course, I am indebted immeasurably to my good friend the Editor, Professor H. E. Jaques, whose advice and assistance all along have been absolutely essential.

If you like the book, tell your friends. If not, tell us.

Lake Hamilton, Florida
October 1, 1956

Henry S. Conard

Dr. Conard has been for many years an outstanding teacher and high-ranking scientist. He knows much about many of Nature's creatures. One of his very special fields has been the Mosses and the Liverworts. We published the first edition of his book in 1944. Its appearance resulted in an increased interest in these lovely little plants. The "Moss Clinic" which Dr. Conard conducted for several summers brought moss enthusiasts and specimens from the widely scattered corners of North America.

In this revised edition he has improved the keys and illustrations and added many species not included in the earlier book.

H. E. Jaques
Editor

An enlarged photograph of the "flowers" of *Mnium cuspidatum*.

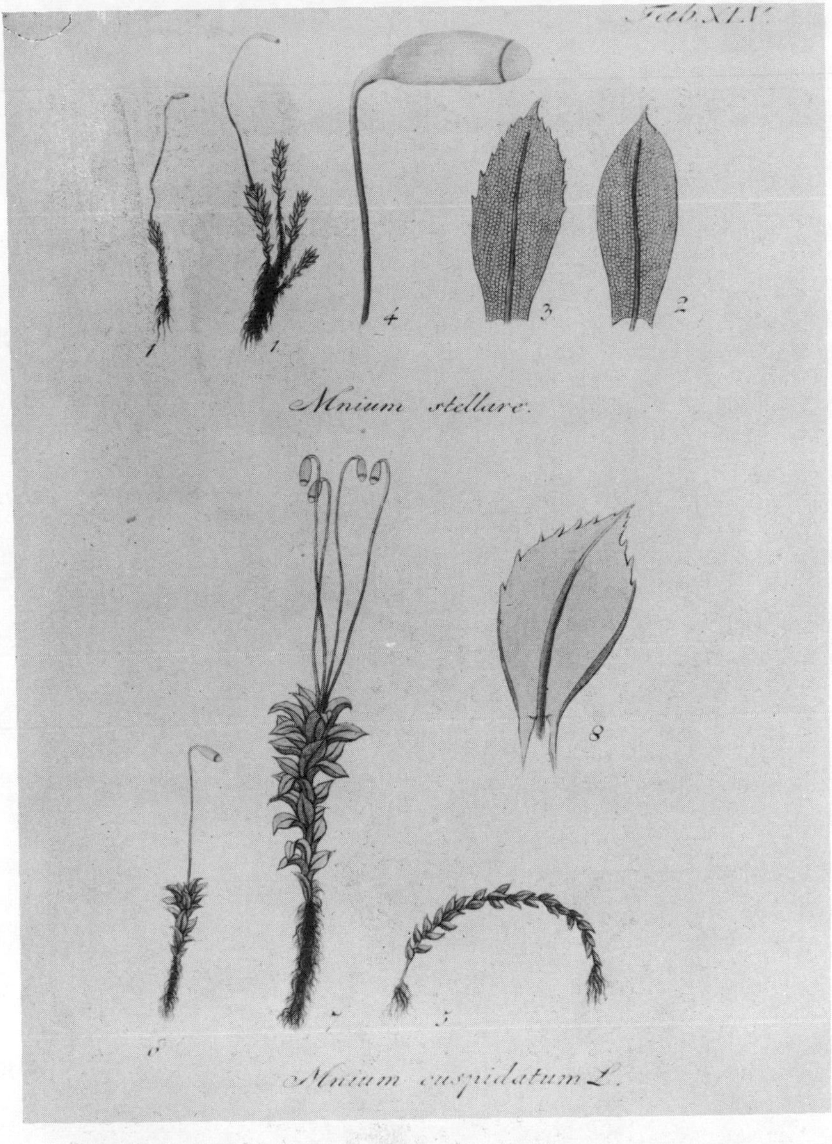

Plate 45 from Species muscorum frondosorum by J. Hedwig, Leipzig 1801. This plate gives the name to our commonest moss (northeast), *Mnium cuspidatum* Hedw. Although Linnaeus, 1753, used the name cuspidatum for it, the Botanical Congress of 1930 ruled that names of true mosses should begin with Hedwig 1801. The figure with 4 capsules is our *Mnium medium*.

Thick mats of *Polytrichium juniperinum* are common.

ABOUT MOSSES

WHAT THEY ARE NOT

The gray-green festoons that dangle from trees in the South, the "Spanish Moss", is not a moss. It is a near relative of the pineapple, with the same kind of hairs on the leaves, with flowers, and with silky seeds. No Moss has either flowers or seeds.

Figure 4.
Spanish moss.

Similar festoons in the Northeast, where ". . . the murmuring pines and the hemlocks" are "bearded with moss", are made of lichens. They bear flat discs containing the spores. Many other leafless gray-green lichens are called mosses, for example "reindeer moss." Of course the moss roses, moss pink, flowering moss and any other "moss" with flowers, is not a moss.

Figure 5.
Usnea.

Figure 6.
Reindeer lichen,
Cladonia.

Figure 7.
Portulaca.

Figure 8.
Seaweed.

Nor are there any Mosses in sea water. These are algae. Several Mosses grow in *fresh* water; they have stems with regularly arranged leaves. The Pictured-Key, "Plant Families", explains all of this.

WHAT THEY ARE

This book attempts to enlarge upon the chapters in "Plant Families" relating to Bryophytes (Atracheata).

1. They are small plants 1/16 inch to 24 inches tall, mostly a few inches. Some are flat, scale-like growths (thallus plants) on earth or rocks or trees. Most of them have stem and leaves, the latter variously

but regularly attached to the stem. Run through the pictures in this book to get a general idea.

2. All of the members of this great phylum are photosynthetic. They manufacture their own food out of constituents of earth and air, by means of chlorophyll, with the aid of sunlight. They are green, at least in part.

$$6CO_2 + 6H_2O + \text{sunlight} = C_6H_{12}O_6 + 6O_2 + \text{stored energy}$$

3. All of them are propagated and disseminated by spores, one-celled particles of living matter with a firm protective wall.

4. At another period in their lives all are propagated by male and female germ cells, which fuse into a single cell (zygote) as in nearly all other plants and in animals. From this single-celled zygote an embryo develops and grows to its own maturity.

LIFE CYCLE

The whole life of a moss runs this way: a spore, in a favorable spot, swells with water, bursts its shell, and puts forth a slender, branching, many-celled green thread, called protonema. This growth may cover several inches or feet of ground; it looks like a green alga. It

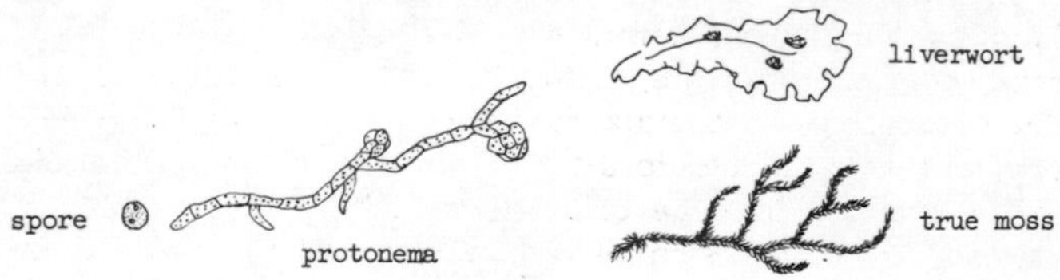

Figure 9

is distinguished by having some of the partitions in the thread oblique, and by having branches going down into the ground, colorless or brown in color. In due time buds (or a bud) appear on this protonema, and each bud grows out as a leafy stem or flattened scale. In either case it is anchored and fed by numerous threads that grow into the soil (rhizoids). Thus we get new moss plants where previously there was none.

When such a plant comes to maturity it produces male and/or female germ cells. The male germ cells are minute colorless coiled bodies, driven by two cilia. They can swim about in a drop of dew or rain for an hour or so. They are produced in oval sacs called antheridia (singular, antheridium) (Fig. 10). The antheridia are borne in a cluster of leaves, or in a pocket of the scale-like thallus. The egg cell is borne in the bottom of a long-necked vase called an archegonium. When the egg is ready for fertilization, the neck of the archegonium becomes a tube of mucilage, the tip opens, and the mucilage exudes, disseminating cane sugar (or some protein in liverworts). This exudate is overwhelmingly attractive to the spiral sperm. Every sperm coming within the scent of it dashes directly into the neck of the archegonium and swims to the egg. One sperm fuses with the egg, and a new being is initiated.

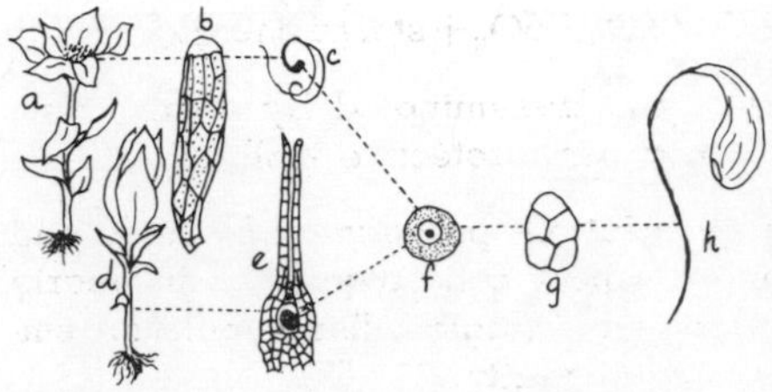

Figure 10. a, male plant; b. antheridium; c, sperm; d, female plant; e, archegonium containing the egg; f, zygote, the union of sperm and egg; g, embryo; h, mature sporophyte of *Funaria*.

This new duplex cell remains in the archegonium while it divides into two, then into 4, 8, 16, many cells, and gradually shapes itself into the beginnings of a stalk (seta) and spore-case (capsule). At its maturity, the seta shoots forth, bursting the archegonium and pushing up the capsule into the air, whence the spores are liberated and float away. When the seta of a true moss (Musci) bursts the archegonium, the tip of the latter remains as a cover or cap over the tip of the capsule. This cap, the product of the upper end of the archegonium, is called a calyptra. The shapes of calyptras are often very characteristic.

The foot, seta and capsule compose the *sporophyte*. Being derived from a fertilized egg, the sporophyte is a diploid organism, in which heredity operates as in animals and flowers by pairs of genes. The thallus or leafy moss has only one set of genes; it is haploid. But its hereditary characters are just as precise and dependable as if it had its genes in pairs. This is a curious situation, applicable to all the mosses. Besides this, there are hybrid mosses, and triploids, tetraploids and octoploids. The genetics of mosses is a rich field, as yet only slightly explored.

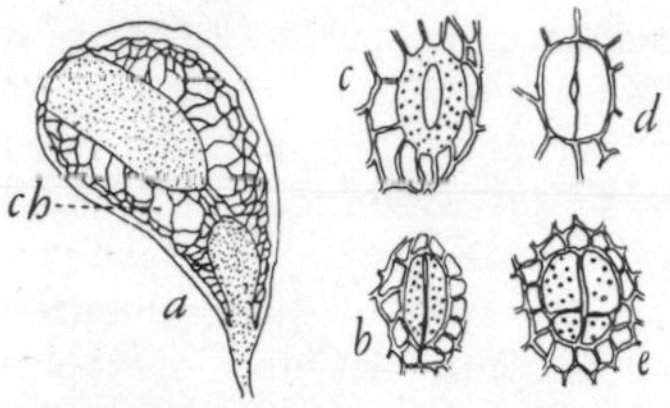

Figure 11. a, section of capsule of *Funaria* showing the netlike chlorophyll tissues; b, young stoma and c, mature stoma of *Funaria*; d, stoma of *Orthotrichum*; e, stoma of *Polytrichum commune*.

The sporophyte (seta and capsule) gets nearly all of its food from the mother plant. Most young sporophytes have a little chlorophyll (leaf-green) by means of which they manufacture a modicum of sugar for food. The capsules of true mosses often have a well developed system of chlorophyll cells and air spaces, served by true stomata, Figure 11.

WHERE MOSSES GROW

Every state in the Union and Canada has its mosses. Iceland and Greenland have many more species. Mexico and tropical America are very rich in species. The evergreen forests of our west coast, from Santa Cruz to Dutch Harbor, have more and bigger mosses than any other part of the Continent.

Most mosses grow among trees. There is no moss among the grasses of the Tallgrass Prairies or the Shortgrass Plains. Moist spots or bare spots or wooded spots among these Plant Associations have their mosses. Some species prefer exposed rocks in full sunshine. They are found at 14,000 feet in Colorado, and on boulders or sand beside the seashore. For some we wade waist-deep in ponds, or reach out from boats.

The kinds in each habitat are characteristic, and the assembly of species in each region is characteristic. Give me a list of the mosses of your region, and I will tell you where you live and what other vegetation is native there. Mosses, like other plants, are social organisms. They have their own associations and associates. They *indicate* the natural conditions of their homes, and give clues to what naturally grows (or grew) there, and what crops can be grown. They even indicate acid or alkaline soils, and what, if any, treatment a soil needs to keep it normal. Unfortunately the indicator value of mosses has been very little studied.

USES

Perhaps no great group of plants has so few uses, commercial or economic uses, as the mosses. The peat mosses (Sphagnum) are used for packing nursery stock. The moss holds moisture in quantity and keeps roots fresh for a journey across the continent. It is gathered from acres of bogs in northern regions, and sold in 50 lb. bales. Clean sprays of Sphagnum are sometimes wrapped in cheesecloth, sterilized and used as packing for seeping wounds. Sphagnum makes much of the peat, which is the fuel of Ireland and northwestern Europe. But the moss peat of Iowa is mostly *Drepanocladus*. Chopped sphagnum is an excellent cover for a seedbed, or an addition to soil to keep it moist and porous.

The big mosses of the west coast are good for packing crockery. They are soft and springy, and sufficiently long-stemmed and abundant.

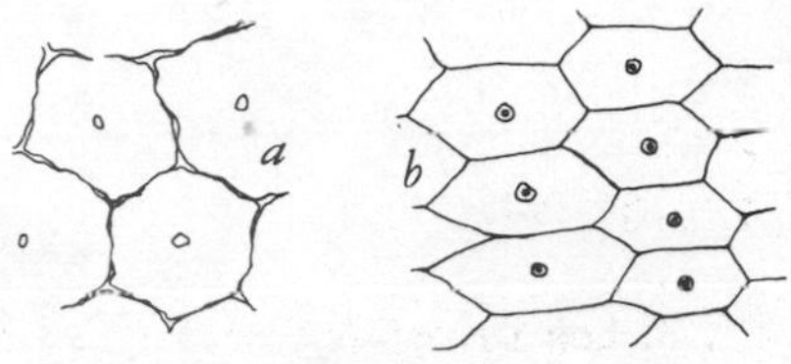

Figure 12. a, section of liver, after Encyclopedia Brittanica; b, surface of *Marchantia*, after Kny.

In ancient and medieval medicine mosses had a place. Because the thallus of several scale-like species is marked in polygonal areas, like a cross section of an animal's liver, these mosses were believed to be good medicine for ailments attributed to malfunction of the liver. The plants were therefore called liverworts, a name that is still used for these plants and their kin. No moss is credited with any medicinal virtues according to modern standards.

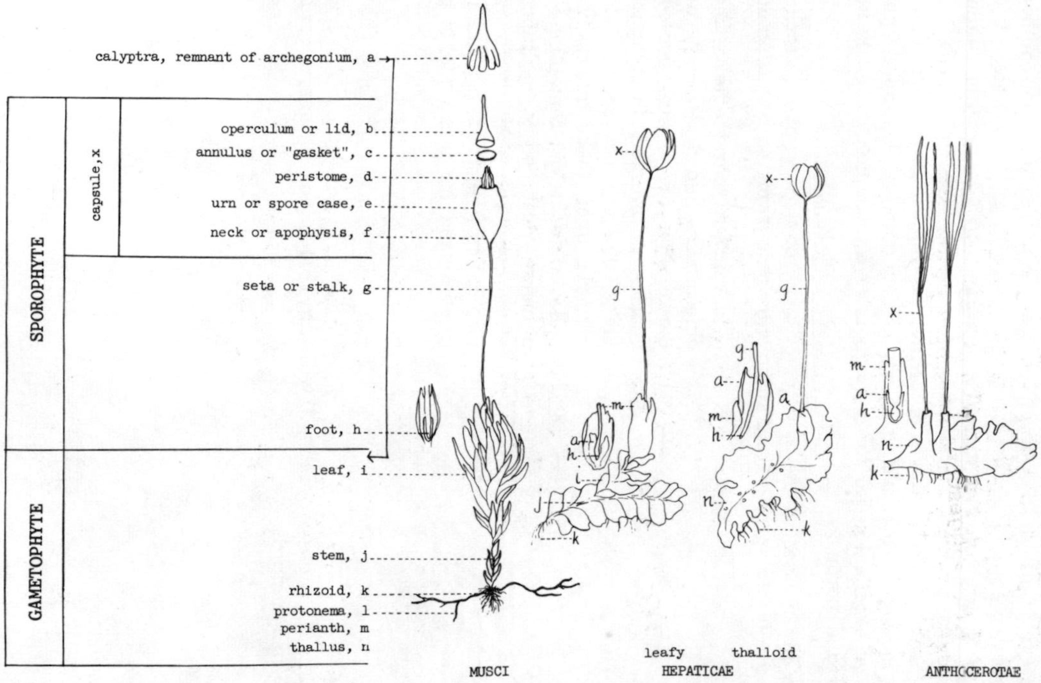

Figure 13. The whole Moss. Left to right: *Ptychomitrium incurvum*, *Lophocolea heterophylla*, *Pellia epiphylla*, *Anthoceros laevis*.

CLASSIFICATION

The plants included here under the general term of "Mosses" are of three distinct types, as shown in Fig. 13. They are all so much alike in structures and life-history that the same terms (with few exceptions) apply to all. The whole group has long been known as Bryophyta, a term which for thirty years has been unsatisfactory. They belong to the great phylum of green land-plants, and are best characterized by their lack of the specialized water-conducting cells (tracheids and tracheae) which make possible the life of larger land-plants. The "Mosses" are best classed as Atracheata (a, without), over against the larger land-plants, the Tracheata.

We divide the Atracheata, then into

Musci or True Mosses,
Hepaticae or Liverworts and
Anthocerotae or Hornworts.

The Anthocerotae includes only one order and one family. The gametophyte is a green thallus or scale, with no distinction of stem and leaf. Fig. 13, *Anthoceros laevis.*

Hepaticae may be described in four Orders:

1. Jungermanniales, the leafy liverworts. Fig. 13. *Lophocolea heterophylla.*
2. Metzgeriales, the thalloid liverworts with stalked capsules. Fig. 13. *Pellia epiphylla.*
3. Sphaerocarpales, tiny thallose forms with antheridia and archegonia in sacs.
4. Marchantiales, with spongy (air-filled) thallus, and tiny sporophytes borne on an umbrella-shaped receptacle, or imbedded in the thallus.

The Musci are much more numerous and require a more extensive classification, the outline of which may be shown here:

Class Musci

Series 1. Sphagnobrya. Order Sphagnales. Family Sphagnaceae.

Series 2. Andreaeobrya. Order Andreaeales. Family Andreaeaceae.

Series 3. Eubrya.

Division 1. Nematodonteae. Peristome teeth made of several or many long cells lying lengthways of the tooth.

Division 2. Arthrodonteae. Teeth with transverse lines or bars (or lacking), each tooth made of the partition wall between certain cells. (Exceptions in Buxbaumiaceae, Encalyptaceae, Splachnaceae.)

1. Haplolepideae. With a single circle of peristome teeth, or various reductions of this.

2. Diplolepideae. With an outer circle of hard teeth and an inner membranous set of segments and/or cilia, or various reductions of this plan.

    1. Acrocarpi: the archegonium and therefore the seta is borne at the tip of an ordinary usually erect leafy stem, with little or no modification of the adjacent leaves. A bud growing out below the "flower" may give the seta the appearance of being lateral.

    2. Pleurocarpi: Stems always abundantly branching, mostly creeping, with the archegonia and therefore the seta borne in a special lateral bud, with leaves very different from the vegetative leaves (perichaetium).

The rest of the classification, so far as it relates to the plants of this book, will appear in the Systematic List following the Pictured-Keys. It has never been possible to make a useful key to mosses by tracing to families. It is universal practice to key mosses and liverworts directly to the genus. In this key members of one genus may appear in widely separated pages. They are all brought together in the Systematic List.

HOW TO STUDY MOSSES

To know the mosses go out and hunt for them. About twelve kinds grow on the prairie-campus where I used to live. Collect all the kinds you can find. If they have no capsules, watch them until they do. But you will soon learn to recognize and identify them by the leaves.

Your equipment will be a carrying sack—any convenient receptacle —with small paper sacks (4 to 8 oz.) or flat pieces of paper. I use newspapers torn to about 5 x 8 or 8 x 10 inches. A hand lens, 10X to 20X, on a shoestring to hang around your neck. An old knife, 3-inch blade. Bring in everything, and as often as you like. Record the date and place of collecting for every specimen.

The working equipment will be a table, dissecting microscope (preferably binocular), compound microscope (obj. 2/3 and 1/6), fine forceps, 2 fine dissecting needles (one of these may be ground down to a knife blade shape), micro-slides and covers (5/8 in. # 2), bottle of water, bottle of dilute glycerine (1/2 water), labels, stiff backed razor blades, scalpel.

Specimens you cannot examine at once are spread out on papers, piled up with blotters between, and weighted with light weights—not over two pounds. When they are dry, they are placed in folders or packets or "pockets." Many collectors adopt a standard size of packet.* If it is just as big as the end of a large shoe-box, the whole collection can be stored, card-catalog fashion, in shoe boxes. Some use a large envelope, such that two catalog rows will go into one standard herbarium shelf. I use several sizes, to suit the specimens, and paste each envelope on a card 5 9/16 x 4 1/4 inches, white for Iowa, manila for North America outside of Iowa, green for Europe (because many of mine are from Ireland), red for the rest of the world. The cards are then stored, catalog fashion, in shoe boxes, or in boxes specially made to fit a herbarium case. Many of us mount the packets by pasting them on standard herbarium sheets, one species to a sheet; finally the sheet is completely covered with packets. These sheets can

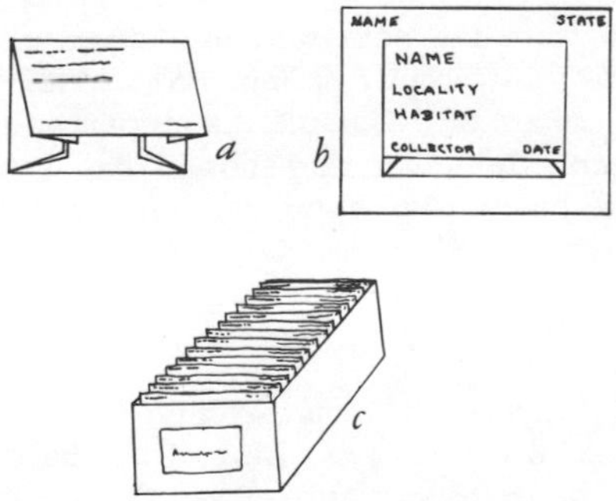

Fig. 14. Filing system. a, envelope; b, envelope pasted on card; c, cards filed in drawer or box.

*See Bryologist 48:198-202, 1945, about envelopes and labels.

be placed in genus covers and stored in the usual way. Mosses do not readily mould, and they are seldom eaten by the insects that so often destroy specimens of flowering plants.

When we are ready to identify a moss, we select a good shoot with a capsule, pluck it out with the forceps and soak it in water until it is "as good as new"—5 minutes to 15 hours as required. A moment in boiling water will do the trick.

Lay a leafy shoot of the soaked moss on a glass slide under the dissecting microscope. Hold it firmly near the apex with a needle or forceps, and scrape the stem rather forcibly from apex toward base to remove a lot of leaves. Remove the stem, spread out the leaves, cover and examine with the compound microscope. If papillae are to be sought, a soaked twig may be examined, mounted in water under a coverglass. By looking with low power at the profile of a fold of a leaf, any papillae that are present will appear as tiny projections from the surface of the fold. Very thin sections of the leaf are desirable. And the experienced eye can detect papillae simply by focusing on the flat surface of a leaf. Fig. 15.

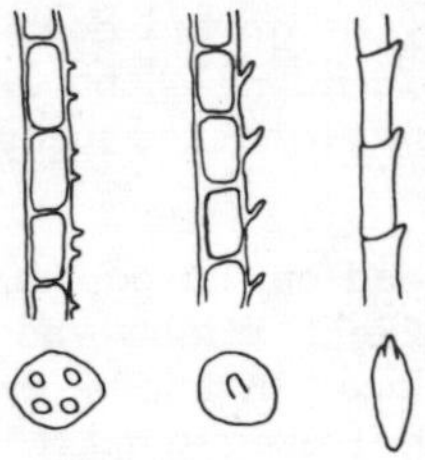

Figure 15

The capsule may be cut off from the seta and laid on a slide. Carefully pry off the lid, if it has not already fallen. Watch for the annulus, or "gasket," as the lid comes off. Cut off the upper end of the capsule, bearing the peristome. Split this ring-shaped end into 2 or more pieces; lay at least one piece with outer side up, and one with inner side up. Cover and examine. Fig. 16. Or, cut the capsule lengthways in half and mount one piece with the outside up, the other with the inside up.

When the slide prepared as directed above is examined, you are likely to find that the peristome is obscured by a blur of air bubbles and spores. This condition can be avoided by boiling the capsule *under water* before dissecting. My practice is to use water at room temperature as directed. Then if the mount is obscured, I hold the slide one or two inches above a lighted match (or alcohol lamp or candle) until the water under the coverglass boils. Then examine and the air bubbles are gone and the spores dispersed. The boiling must be just momentary, and very gentle. Even so the desired pieces of peristome may float out from under the coverglass. If they do they must be coralled and covered again. Only glass covers will do for this; plastic covers crumple.

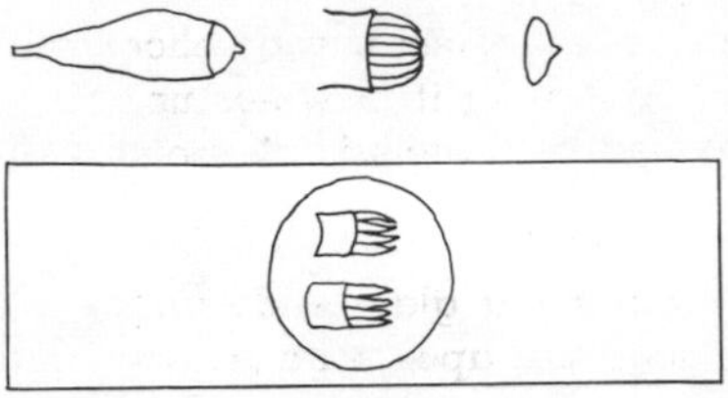

Figure 16

As the water dries away from under the coverglass, replace it with dilute glycerine—a droplet placed at the edge of the cover. Such a glycerine mount will last forever! It may be labeled and stored.

In some cases a cross section of a leaf is absolutely necessary for identification; in many cases a section is very helpful. Lay a wet leaf on a glass slide and hold it with the end of another slide laid so as to cover a part of the leaf. A sharp razor blade simply brought down upon the leaf will cut off the free end. Another cut closer to the upper glass slide will give a cross section. Try several times and drag the best sections to one side (or remove the worse), cover and examine. If the leaf is laid on a piece of stiff transparent plastic (plastic coverglass) the razor blade will last longer.

WHAT TO LOOK FOR

THE LEAF. Is it broad  or narrow  or filiform  ?

Is the margin entire  or toothed  plane  or rolled upward  or rolled backward (revolute) or reflexed  ?

Has it a single midrib (costa)  or double  or none? Does the midrib stop at the middle of the leaf, or near the tip, or does it extend clear to the tip (percurrent)  or does it extend beyond the leaf as an awn or bristle  ? Are the cells isodiametric  or elongate 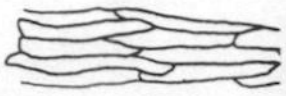 or long-hexagonal 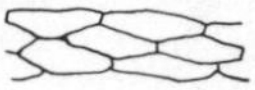 or spindle-shaped  ? Are they smooth or papillose? Are the cells at the basal angles of the leaves (alar cells) just like the rest, or are they small and rectangular (quadrate) or greatly swollen (inflated) and transparent, or swollen and colored golden brown? Does the leaf stop abruptly at the stem, or do the edges of the leaf continue down the stem like wings (decurrent)? Does the margin of the leaf consist of long, thick-walled cells  ?

THE CAPSULE. Is it straight, erect, inclined, nodding, symmetrical, smooth or ribbed, strumose(s)  or contracted under the mouth when dry 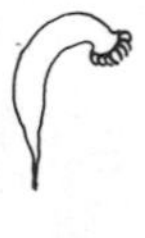 ?

THE SETA. Is it long or short, smooth or rough, and of what color?

THE CALYPTRA: Is it cucullate  or mitrate , **hairy or smooth?**

THE PERISTOME. Is it single or double? Are the teeth entire or split or irregular or absent? Are cilia present or absent? Fig. 17.

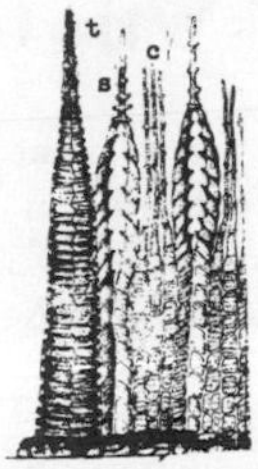

Figure 17. Peristome of *Bryum bimum* with appendiculate cilia, c; segment, s; tooth, t.

SPORES. Sometimes the size of the spores should be measured, or their surface noted: smooth, granulated, prickly, sculptured.

THE ANTHERIDIA. Wherever there is a sporophyte, or seta, there has been an egg in an archegonium. Dissect away the leaves from the base of the seta and we find the dead, unsuccessful archegonia. The antheridia may be found among the archegonia; the plant is *synoicous*. The antheridia may be just below the archegonia, all around; *paroicous*. The antheridia may be in a special cluster or bud somewhere along the stem; *autoicous*. If you find no antheridia on the plant that has archegonia and/or sporophytes, the species is *dioicous;* they will be found on another plant.

The key should do the rest. Each number in the key offers two sets of conditions a and b (sometimes also c and d). The plant cannot be like both a and b. We must decide which statement best describes it. At the end of this statement is a number to which we go next; there we again find two choices, a and b. And so we proceed until we find the genus and species of our moss, and a picture of it. We record the name on the packet—*Polytrichum commune*. And that packet is ready for the herbarium.

On page 38 we find the name *Polytrichum commune* in the Polytrichaceae, and the group Nematodonteae. We may check it on this page by writing the date and place of collecting. Thus, in due time, the Systematic List becomes our check list of species found.

If you can get a good list of the mosses known to inhabit your State, underscore the names of these in the Systematic List, and/or thruout the Key; this will help in identification and will give you a goal toward which to strive. By exchange with hobbyists in other States, your collection may in due time cover the Continent, Europe, South America, or The World.

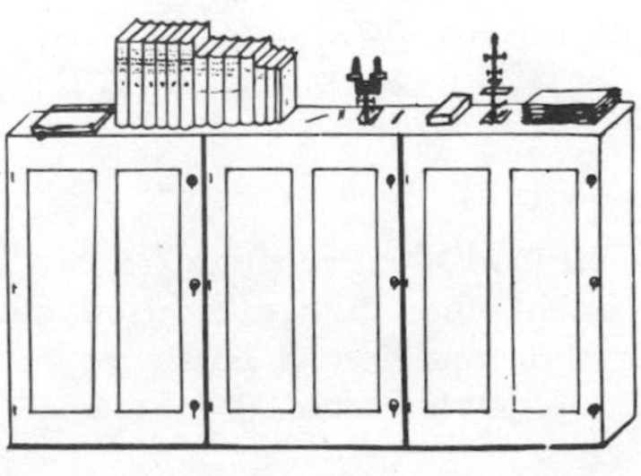

WHAT TO LOOK FOR IN LIVERWORTS

First, some liverworts are mere green scales or ribbons lying on the ground, or floating in water. Others have stems with two rows of leaves. (See Fig. 13.) Of these, some have a third row of small leaflike growths on the under side of the stem (underleaves).

The leaf of a liverwort may be almost perfectly round in outline, or oval or variously lobed or divided. Many species have a notch at the tip of the leaf. The shape of this notch and the shape of the two lobes are important. Sometimes there are two notches (three lobes), or four, or many. In fact the leaf may be completely divided into threadlike rows of cells. (See Figs. 303 to 372.)

The most critical details are (1) how the leaves are attached to the stem, (2) whether the leaf is simple or "complicate bilobed" and (3) whether the walls of the leaf cells are thin or thickened. The leaf is nearly always attached obliquely to the stem. As the stem lies horizontally this means that one edge of the leaf is attached along the upper side of the stem, the other along the lower. If that edge of the leaf that is attached to the upper side of the stem is also nearer to the tip of the stem the arrangement is called *incubous,* and each leaf seems to ride up over the edge of the next leaf toward the tip of the stem. If the reverse is true and the front edge of each leaf runs under the rear edge of the leaf next nearer the tip of the stem the condition is called *succubous.* This is by far the commoner condition. Figs. 18, 19.

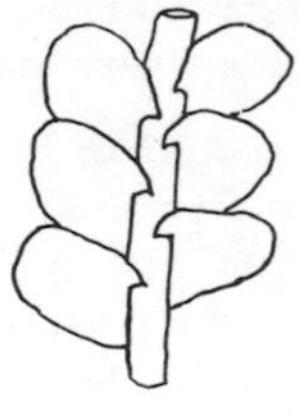

Figure 18. Incubous leaves of *Calypogeia.*

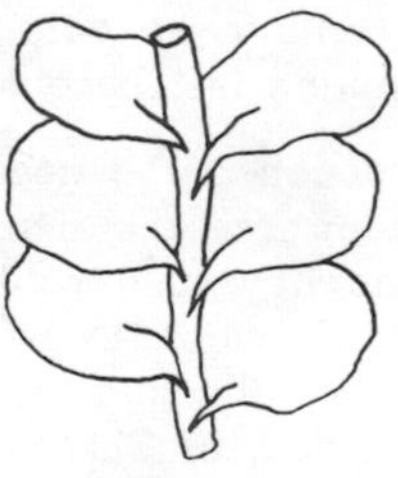

Figure 19. Succubous leaves of *Lophocolea heterophylla.*

2. A "complicate bilobed" leaf is made in two lobes and these are folded close against each other, like a creased piece of paper. If the smaller lobe is upper the condition is easily seen: a small leaf seems to lie upon a larger one. If the smaller lobe is underneath, it can be

seen by looking at the stem from beneath. This smaller lobe may be flat and leaflike, or it may be formed into a hollow sac, or it may lie against the larger lobe so as to enclose a space. This sac or space is a device for holding water. Figs. 20, 21.

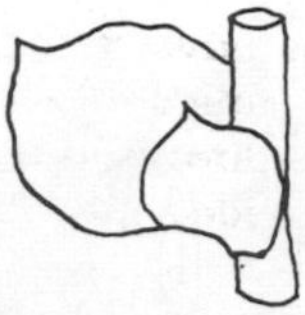

Figure 20. Complicate bilobed leaf with the smaller lobe above the larger; *Scapania undulata.*

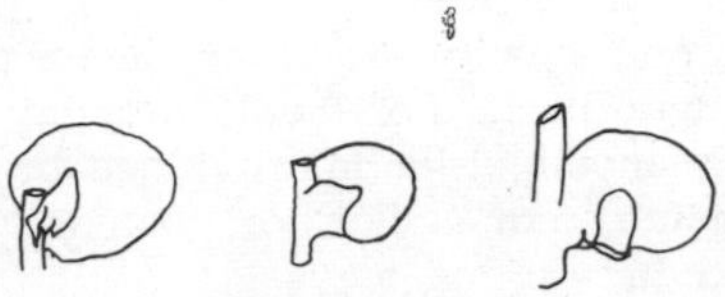

Figure 21. Complicate bilobed leaves seen from below, the smaller lobe being under the larger: From left to right, *Porella, Radula, Frullania.*

3. The cells of the leaf may be equally thin-walled all around (Fig. 22a), or equally thick-walled all around (b), or with the walls thickened in the corners of the cells so as to form small (c), medium (d) or large (e) triangular masses of wall substance. Such triangular masses are called "trigones"; they are sometimes so large as to bulge out into the cells (e).

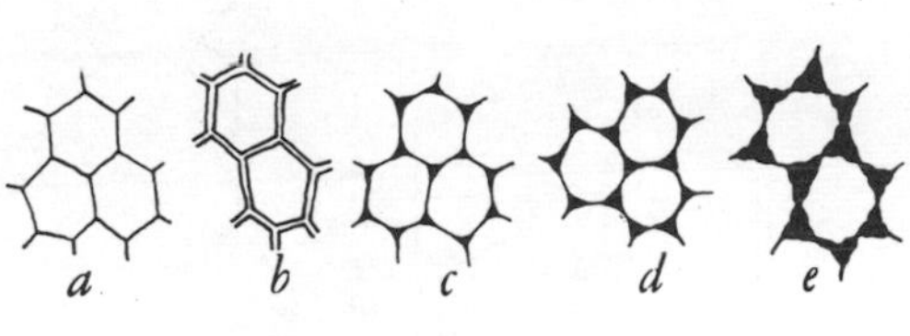

Figure 22.

All liverworts have round or oval or rod-shaped capsules. The round and oval ones are short-lived: they may break to pieces at maturity to let out the spores, or more often they split into four spreading quarters discharging both spores and spirally-banded threads called *elaters*. The seta may be an inch long, but it is weak and watery and quickly withers away. Thus, a collection with open capsules is a rare catch, for you must find it on just the right day.

The capsule originates in an archegonium (See Fig. 10) as in the case of mosses proper (Musci). One or more archegonia are surrounded by a leaf-like sac, the perianth, (Fig. 23). This is a long-lived object, and is more useful for identification than the sporophyte itself. For there are many kinds of perianths: smooth, triangular, ridged or plaited, with the mouth plane, flat, or tubular, and perhaps fringed in various ways.

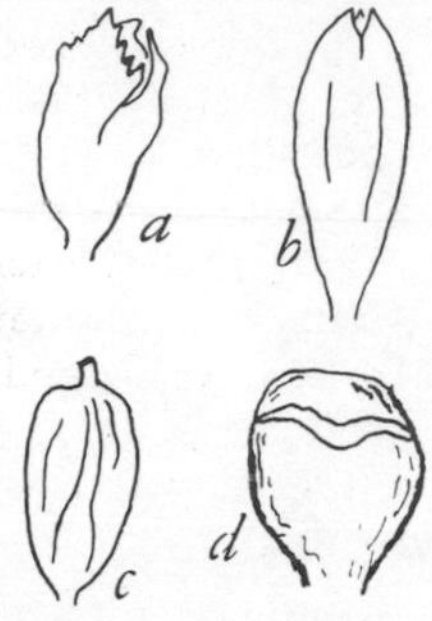

Figure. 23. Perianths of *Lophocolea*, a; *Jungermannia*, b; *Frullania*, c; *Porella*, d.

The leaves adjacent to the perianth are usually quite different from those of the vegetative shoot. These adjacent leaves are called bracts. They are often divided, lobed or toothed, even when the stem-leaves are entire. Frequently we find underleaves as bracts, even when no underleaves occur elsewhere.

Liverworts with perianths can be named fairly readily. Without perianths the problem is much more difficult.

Antheridia, oval or globular bodies containing the male germ cells (sperms), are borne in pits of the surface of the thalloid liverworts. In leafy liverworts they occur, 1 to 3 or 4, in the axil of a leaf. Such leaves usually bulge out over the antheridia, and occur in a group of 6-12 along the stem.

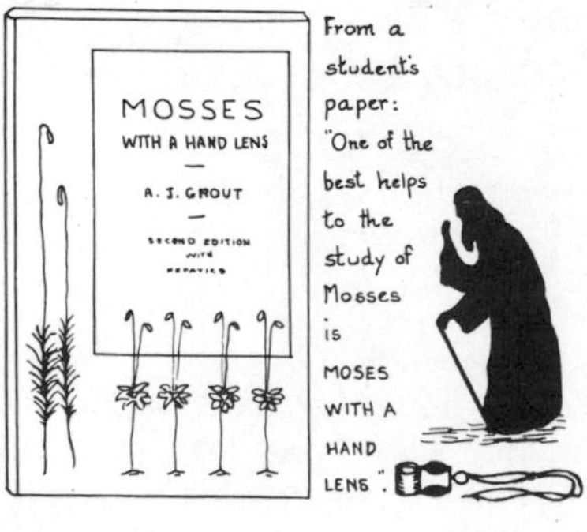

BOOKS AND SPECIMENS AS MEANS OF IDENTIFICATION OF MOSSES AND LIVERWORTS

The achievement of Bryologists is preserved for us in books and collections. This little key is a possibility only because many workers have made their discoveries available. And this Key does not attempt to name every species known from North America. Besides, it is likely that species will be found that have not previously been known from this continent. Probably species new to science are still waiting to be discovered. It is certain that much collecting and identifying will have to be done before we know accurately the ranges of the different species.

The student or hobbyist will want additional books, and reliably named specimens. Here are some titles.

Grout, A. J. *Mosses with a Hand-lens,* ed. 3. Published by the author, Newfane, Vt. Simple keys to mosses and liverworts of New England and the Middle Atlantic States. Helpful anywhere.

———— *Mosses with Hand-lens and Microscope.* Published by the author. Abundant illustrations and excellent text, for mosses east of the 100th meridian and north of North Carolina; mosses only. Indispensably necessary.

———— (Editor). *Moss Flora of North America.* Published by the editor. Newfane, Vt. Three big volumes, describing every species in continental United States, Canada, Alaska, Newfoundland, and Greenland, and illustrating nearly every species that is not pictured in *Mosses with Hand-lens and Microscope.* Indispensable.

One needs these three volumes, and the preceding one. Referred to hereafter as MFNA. The Grout books are sold by Chicago Natural History Museum.

Dixon, H. N., and H. G. Jameson. *Student's Handbook of British Mosses.* A pictured key, with excellent text, covering a majority of our American mosses.

Sullivant, W. S. *Icones Muscorum, and Supplement.* This attempts to describe and to illustrate with superior engravings, the species of Musci not given in Bryologia Europaea. Hard to get.
For liverworts:

Frye, T. C. and L. Clark. *Hepaticae of North America,* University of Washington.

Macvicar, S. M. *Student's Handbook of British Hepatics.* A pictured key, with excellent text, covering a majority of our American liverworts.

Schuster, R. M. *Hepaticae of Central New York.* Amer. Midland Nat. Notre Dame, Ind. 1949.

———— *Liverworts of Minnesota.* Ibid. March, 1953.

———— *Southeastern liverworts*—to appear.

There are excellent keys to liverworts of the States of Washington, Oregon, West Virginia, Tennessee and Florida. Connecticut has a key to mosses and liverworts, now too old to be satisfactory; no pictures. Utah has a key to mosses. For any of these, write to Botany Department, State University.

Collections of named mosses are hard to find. The best American collections that one can hope to get are:
Sullivant & Lesquereux: *Musci Boreali-americani,* Ed. 1 or Ed. 2. Worth about $100.00 a set.

Holzinger: *Musci Acrocarpi Boreali-americani.*
Grout: *North American Musci Pleurocarpi.*

———— *North American Musci Perfecti.*
or, become a member of the American Bryological Society, join the Moss exchange and the Hepatic exchange, and trade your own extra collections for an equal number, of your own choice, from those sent in by other members of the exchange.

A check list of mosses and liverworts of North America is available from the Editor of *The Bryologist.* These are the official lists of the American Bryological Society. The British Bryological Society has similar lists. Exchanges can be arranged with collectors all over the world.

Some books in foreign languages:

Limpricht, K. G. *Die Laubmoose.* Three volumes, with text, keys, and illustrations. Almost indispensable.

Mueller, K. *Die Lebermoose.* Two volumes, with text, keys, and illustrations. Almost indispensable. A new edition is in press.

Bruch, Schimper & Guembel. *Bryologia Europaea.* Six folio volumes with nearly 700 lithographic plates. The great Classic of Bryology. Hard to find. The text is in Latin, German, and French. If you can find a set for less than $200.00, you are lucky.

USING THE KEYS

The keys following are intended to enable a person to determine the names of the mosses and liverworts that he finds. It is assumed that complete fruiting specimens are at hand. But if no sporophytes are available there is still a chance of getting to the proper name, especially with the liverworts. The picture helps at the final identification. Each step in the key involves two questions, rarely three or four. The questions are lettered a, b, (c, d). Suppose we have a specimen of the Common Haircap Moss from our laboratory supplies. We start at number 1a on page 22. Does 1a or 1b better describe our specimen? It fits 1a, so we proceed to 2 as indicated by the figure 2 at the end of the lines for 1a. At 2 we find that 2a best describes our specimen and we go to page 23, Class Musci. Here we begin again with 1a, 1b and 1c. We choose 1c and proceed to 9, and choose 9a, for our plant is erect and the sporophyte is borne at the tip of a leafy shoot. This refers us to 10. Here we choose 10b. We go to 13b, 14b, 29b, 33b, 35b, Family Polytrichaceae. At 36 we choose b, and proceed to 40. The 4-angled capsule takes us to b again, to 44b, Genus Polytrichum. Then 45b, 46b, 47b, 48a, with marginal cells of the lamellae notched. The plant is *Polytrichum commune*. Fig. 50 confirms our conclusion. Maybe your specimen was not labelled correctly. Your laboratory collector or dealer may have given you *P. ohioense* or *P. juniperinum*. You can tell from the pictures and key. Compare your specimen with a named packet in the herbarium, and with descriptions and figures in MFNA.

As an example of a liverwort we may use laboratory material of *Marchantia*. We start as before at number 1 on page 22. We choose 1b because our plant does not have stem and leaves, but is flat and ribbon-like. This refers us to 3. Our plant does not have the capsules of 3a. Its cells have numerous chloroplasts as in 3b. We turn to Hepaticae, page 156. Here we again begin at 1. We choose 1a, 2a, 8a Marchantiaceae, 9. We choose 9a, 10a, and judge from the figure and notes that the plant is *M. polymorpha*. Reference to a well named herbarium, and to a good manual is advised.

HELPS TO THE MOSSES

1. Stems erect; seta from the end of a shoot, with the surrounding leaves little if at all modified. Nematodonteae, Haplolepideae, Acrocarpi.

2. Black or blackish tufts on rocks and trees: *Andreaea, Grimmia, Scouleria, Hedwigia, Ptychomitrium, Rhacomitrium, Orthotrichum, Ulota, Drummondia.*

3. Whitish green, in large spongy patches: *Sphagnum, Leucobryum.* Small, pale green: *Pohlia wahlenbergii;* silvery, *Bryum argenteum.*

4. Leaves papillose: *Orthotrichum, Ulota, Encalypta, Weisia, Pottiaceae, Leskeaceae,* etc.

5. Paraphyllia conspicuous: *Thuidium, Helodium, Hylocomium.*

6. Leaf ending in a hair or bristle: *Acrocarpous, Pottiaceae*, Encalypta, Grimmiaceae, Polytrichum, Bryum; Pleurocarpous, Anomodon, Claopodium, Cirriphyllum, Plagiothecium.*

7. Plant dendroid, that is, like a little tree, with trunk and branches: *Climacium, Mnium menziesii, Porotrichum;* somewhat so, *Bryhnia novae-angliae, Brachythecium rivulare.*

8. Papillose leaves of the families *Pottiaceae** and *Leskeaceae* have a dull surface, without luster. Smooth leaves are usually shiny.

9. Peristome teeth that are divided 1/3 to 2/3 down into two slenderly acute prongs belong in the families *Fissidentaceae** or *Dicranaceae.* If divided to the base into two hair-like divisions try *Ditrichaceae* (leaves smooth), *Pottiaceae* (leaves papillose), *Ptychomitrium, Rhacomitrium.*

10. Habitually submerged or floating: *Fissidens debilis, F. grandifrons, F. rufulus, Scouleria, Bryum weigelii; Eurhynchium rusciforme, Leptodictyum riparium* varieties, *L. vacillans, Hygroamblystegium noterophilum, Hygrohypnum* species, *Fontinalaceae.*

HELPS TO THE LIVERWORTS

1. Thalloid, without distinction of stem and leaf, 1-31. *Marchantiales, Sphaerocarpales, Metzgeriales* (except some *Fossombronias*), *Anthocerotales.*
   Leafy: *Jungermanniales*
   Leaves incubous 37-42
   Leaves succubous 43-64

2. Largest thalloid liverwort: *Conocephalum.* Smallest: *Metzgeria.* Largest leafy liverworts: *Bazzania, Plagiochila.* Smallest: *Blepharostoma, Microlepidozia, Cephaloziella, Cololejeunea, Microlejeunea,* and other *Lejeuneae.*

3. Recent studies call for sections of stem, seta and wall of capsule. These are highly diagnostic, but difficult to come at. Still more difficult, and more diagnostic, are the oil bodies in the cells, and the number of chromosomes, both being seen only in fresh living material. Cf. Schuster in Journ. Hattori Bot. Lab. No. 11, April 1954.

* For family relations see Systematic List, Pages 187-214.

OUTLINE OF THE KEYS

MUSCI

- Sphagnobrya, 1-7
- Andreaeobrya, 8
- Eubrya, True Mosses
  - Acrocarpous species, 1-219
  - Leucobryaceae, 10-12
  - *Buxbaumia*, 13
  - Ordinary leaves, 14-219
    - Leaves 2-ranked, 15-28. *Fissidentaceae*, etc.
    - Leaves 3-many-ranked, 29-219
      - Stemless minute mosses, 29-32
      - Stems demonstrable, 33-219
        - Lamellae or filaments on leaves, 34-48
        - No outgrowths (except gemmae), 49-219
          - With gemma-cups, *Tetraphis*, 49
          - Without cups, 50-219
            - *Diphyscium, Splachnaceae*, 50-51
            - Leaves mamillose, 53-58
            - Leaves papillose, 59-123
            - Leaves smooth, 124-219
              - Corticolous, 124-125
              - Not specifically corticolous, 126-219
                - Very small, 127-136
                - Larger, 137-219
                  - Leaves slender, 139-161
                  - Lanceolate to ovate, 162-219
                    - Blackish. *Grimmiaceae*, 163-180
                    - Green, translucent, 181-219
- Pleurocarpous
  - Leaves papillose, 2-33
  - Leaves smooth, 34-143
    - With paraphyllia, 35-40
    - Without paraphyllia, 41-143
      - With midrib, 42-94
      - Midrib lacking or short, 95-143

HEPATICAE

- Sphaerocarpales, 4a
- Anthocerotales, 4b-7
- Marchantiales, 8-21
- Metzgeriales, 22-30
- Jungermanniales, 32-93
  - Leaves filiform-cleft, 32-34
  - Leaves entire or lobed, 35-93
    - Leaves plane, 35-64
      - Incubous, 37-42
      - Succubous, 43-64
    - Leaves complicate-bilobed, 65-93

PICTURED-KEYS

THE CLASSES OF BRYOPHYTA (ATRACHEATA)

1a Plants with stem and leaves; erect, ascending, prostrate, or hanging from trees. Figs. 13; 24-301; 323-372 2

1b Plants scale-like or ribbon-like, usually fork-branched and flat on the substrate, often in rosettes, without distinction of stem and leaf; green or purplish. Figs. 13; 302-322 3

2a Leaves equally spaced all around the stem, usually with midrib; or in two opposite rows, with or without midrib; margins entire or toothed; never notched at apex or lobed; cells elongate to isodiametric. Sporophyte persisting for weeks or months. No elaters. Figs. 24-301. Class 1 MUSCI .... page 23

2b Leaves in two rows near upper side of stem, without midrib, and with cells isodiametric. Leaves often notched at apex, or lobed, or cut into thread-like lobes, sometimes with a smaller lobe folded against a larger one. Sporophyte short-lived, the capsule raised on a stalk, splitting into four parts, emitting spores and slender elaters with spiral bands. Figs. 323-372. Class 2 HEPATICAE, Order JUNGERMANNIALES .... page 156

3a Plant flat on the ground; each cell with one large chloroplast. Sporophyte persisting for weeks or months, rod-like, projecting from a cylindrical sheath, splitting above into two parts to discharge spores and 2-4-celled irregular elaters. Figs. 303-304. Class 3 ANTHOCEROTAE .... page 157

3b Cells with numerous small chloroplasts. Sporophyte a globular or slightly elongate capsule with or without a fragile watery stalk, lasting only a few days. Figs. 305-322. Class 2 HEPATICAE .... page 156

MUSCI THE MOSSES

1a (b, c) Plants with many spreading, recurved branches along the stem, and clustered at the tip. Leaf cells in one layer, of two kinds: each large empty cell surrounded by narrow cells with chloroplasts. Capsule raised on a pseudopodium, spherical, black, shedding a lid explosively. Peat mosses, Figs. 24-26. Genus *Sphagnum*..2

1b Small blackish mosses on silicious rocks in mountains or far north. Leaf cells small, narrow, very thick-walled. Capsule raised on a pseudopodium, opening by 4 slits in the sides, lengthways, (See Fig. 27). Genus *Andreaea*......................................8

1c All the common mosses. Leaf cells in one or more layers, mostly one; not as in 1a or 1b. Capsule opening by a circular lid (operculum), or merely breaking to pieces. Fig. 24. *Eubrya*...........9

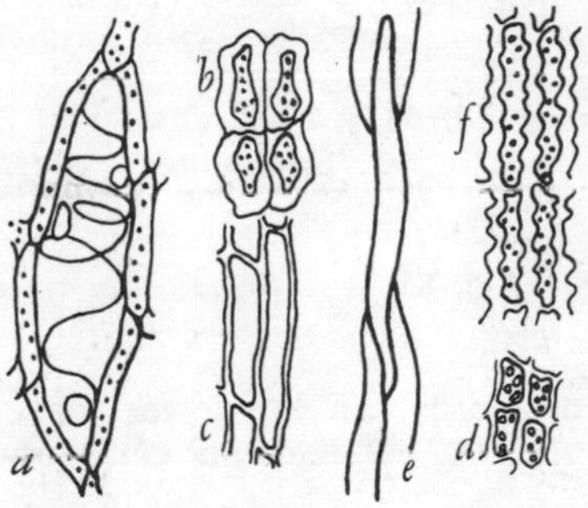

Figure 24

Fig. 24. Cells of leaves. a, *Sphagnum*. b, *Andreaea*. c-f, *Eubrya:* True Mosses. Cells of different shapes are found in different parts of the leaf. Unless otherwise stated the cells described are from the middle of the area between margin and midrib. Cells at the base of the leaf are often characteristic of the species. Those at the basal margin are called alar cells.

2a Stem clothed with 2 or 3 layers of empty cells with spiral lines on the walls. Branchlets stout, in large heads.................3

2b Stems clothed with 1 to 3 layers of empty cells without spiral lines on the walls. Branchlets mostly slender, tapering to a fine point. Often purplish. Chlorophyll cells triangular to trapezoidal in cross section..5

3a Chlorophyll cells in cross section of leaf narrowly elliptical, entirely enclosed by empty cells, Fig. 25..*Sphagnum magellanicum*

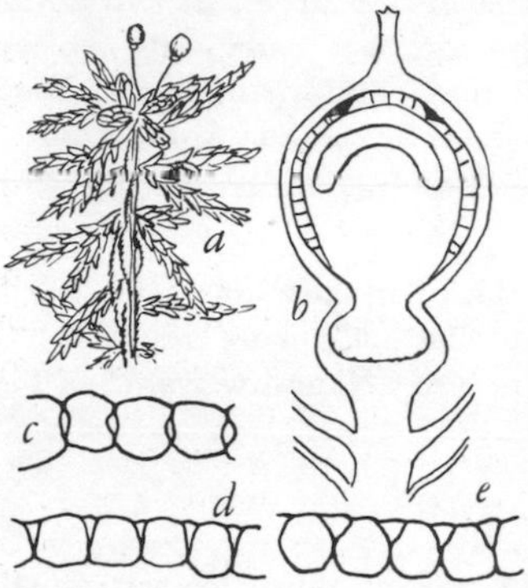

Figure 25

Fig. 25. *Sphagnum magellanicum*. a, plant with capsules; b, capsule, foot and pseudopodium; c, section of leaf; d, section of leaf of *S. palustre;* e, same of *S. affine*. All of these are widespread in the Northern Hemisphere. They grow in big beds and cushions, often covering acres of bog, the living parts up to a foot tall, crowded and supporting one another, associated with cranberries, sundews and some of our loveliest orchids. Four other species have spiral markings on the cortical cells of stems and branches.

3b Chlorophyll cells triangular in cross section, with the base exposed on the upper (ventral) side of the leaf. Fig. 25..................4

4a Cell cavity of chlorophyll cells very narrowly triangular. Fig. 25. ....*Sphagnum palustre*

4b Cell cavity equilaterally triangular. Fig. 25......*Sphagnum affine*

5a Chlorophyll cells exposed only, or mostly, on the lower (dorsal) side of the leaf...............................*Sphagnum cuspidatum*

5b Chlorophyll cells exposed only, or mostly, on the upper (ventral) side of the leaf. Fig. 26...6

6a Apex of stem leaves broad, split into many fibrils. Fig. 26........ ....*Sphagnum girgensohnii*

6b Apex of stem leaves broad or narrow, entire or toothed..........7

7a Stem leaves tongue-shaped, the sides nearly parallel; apical dorsal surface of branch leaves with many strongly ring-margined pores. Fig. 26..*Sphagnum warnstorfii*

7b Stem leaves nearly triangular, the sides slightly curved. Fig. 26. ....*Sphagnum capillaceum*

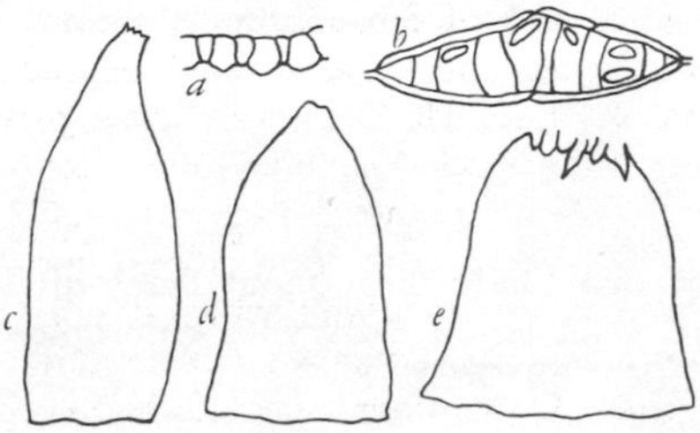

Figure 26

Fig. 26. *Sphagnum capillaceum.* a, section of leaf; b, cell of leaf; c, stem leaf; d, stem leaf of *S. warnstorfii;* e, stem leaf of *S. girgensohnii.* All Sphagnums are useful for packing trees and shrubs for shipment because they take up and hold immense amounts of water. By their growth and decay they form peat. There are 29 other species in North America, all of which lack spiral lines on the outer cells of stems and branches.

8a Leaves with distinct midrib of elongated cells. Fig. 27............ ....*Andreaea rothii*

8b Leaves without midrib. Fig. 27..................*Andreaea rupestris*

Figure 27

Fig. 27. *Andreaea rupestris.* a, plant; b, an open capsule; c, leaf and cells; d, calyptra; e, leaf of *A. rothii.* The five species found in North America are very much alike: shiny brownish black tufts a half inch tall, on igneous rocks, at 3000 ft. in North Carolina, 2000 ft. in Vermont; on rocky shores of Lake Superior. Rare in the Rocky Mountains and Europe.

9a (b, c) Stems erect or obsolete, unbranched, or with branches also erect. (Unbranched spreading runners in *Mnium*). Sporophyte borne at the tip of a leafy shoot (acrocarpous)........................10

9b Stems creeping and branching. Sporophyte borne on a very short branch, subtended by perichaetial leaves that are very different from those of other branches. PLEUROCARPI................Page 97

9c An intermediate group! Stems branching, upright or sprawling. Sporophytes appear lateral because the stem continues growth from a point just below the sporophyte. Considered here along with 9a 10

10a Whitish plants with cells of two kinds throughout the leaf: large empty cells in 2 or 3 layers, with small cells with chloroplasts in between. Figs. 28, 29. LEUCOBRYACEAE..................11

10b Green or blackish plants. If empty cells occur they are at base or apex or margin of leaf....................................13

11a Upper surface of leaf nearly flat. Chlorophyll cells triangular in cross section. On bases of trees, Fla.-Tex. Fig 28............... ....*Octoblepharum albidum*

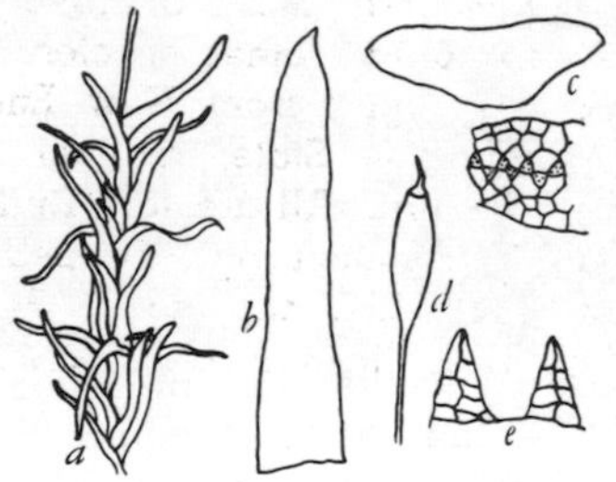

Fig. 28. *Octoblepharum albidum.* a, plant; b, leaf; c, section of leaf; d, capsule; e, peristome. Common in Florida, on humus or dead palmetto trunks, or bases of living trees, often in patches a foot across. Common in all tropical countries. There are 15 other species, in the tropics.

Figure 28

11b Upper part of leaf tubular. Chlorophyll cells four-sided in cross section. Pads and cushions on the ground. Genus *Leucobryum*..12

12a Leaves 4 to 10 mm. long, the tubular portion longer than the flat lower portion. Common northeast. Fig. 29. . . . *Leucobryum glaucum*

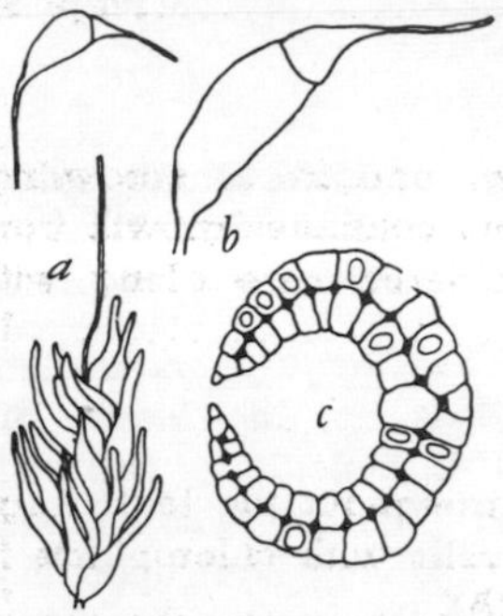

Fig. 29. *Leucobryum glaucum.* a, plant with capsule; b, capsule; c, cross section of leaf. This big cushion-moss often forms spongy discs or sods 3 to 4 inches deep, and covering a whole hillside. Capsules are rarely seen, ripening in autumn. In Florida *Leucobryum albidum* is more common. It is often difficult to distinguish between the two. The peristome teeth are forked as in *Dicranum.*

Figure 29

12b Leaves 4 to 5 mm. long, the tubular portion shorter than the flat basal portion. Va. to Fla. and Tex. . . . . *Leucobryum albidum*

13a Leafless. Seta 1 to 2 cm. tall, directly from the ground, bearing a flat, red-purple capsule obliquely or horizontally. Fig. 30. . . . . *Buxbaumia aphylla*

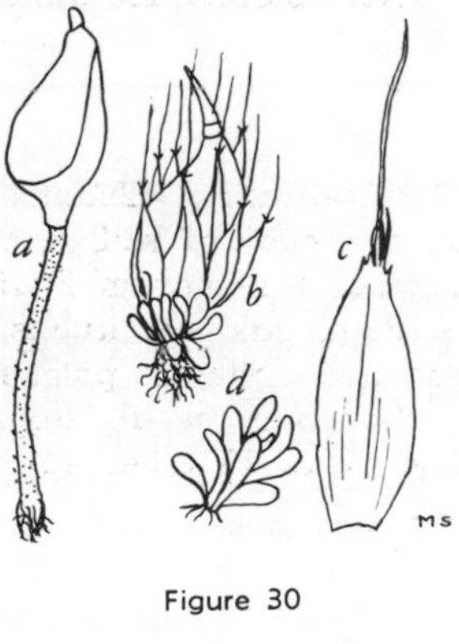

Fig. 30. *Buxbaumia aphylla.* a, plant complete; b, plant of *Diphyscium foliosum;* c, *perichaetial* leaf; d, foliage leaves. This and two other species of *Buxbaumia* are found from New England to Washington State; another is strictly northwestern. All are rare finds. *Diphyscium* is common on dry peaty banks northeast. The capsule of *Buxbaumia* has been likened to a bedbug on a stalk!

Figure 30

13b Plants with leaves, with or without capsules. 14

14a Leaves attached in two rows on opposite sides of the stem, not merely bent over into two rows from various attachments. 15

14b Leaves attached all around the stems, either spreading in all directions or appressed or bent over toward one or two sides. 29

15a (b, c) Leaves apparently split along the lower distal edge from margin to midrib, and embracing the next leaf above (equitant as in Iris). Figs. 33-39. Family FISSIDENTACEAE................16

15b "Leaves" pinnately lobed, growing in caves and old, damp basements, the protonema cells reflecting a golden light. Fig. 31..... ....*Schistostega pennata*

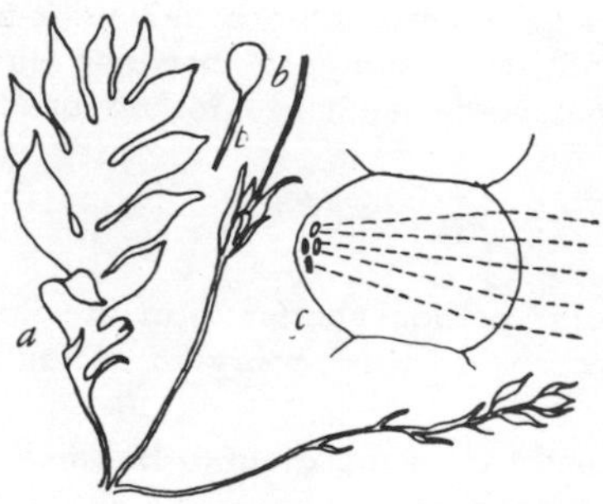

Figure 31

Fig. 31. *Schistostega pennata.* The Luminous Moss. a, the "leaf" or sterile shoot; b, capsule; c, one cell of protonema. The cell is so shaped as to focus incoming light upon the chloroplasts at the inner side of the cell cavity. This light is reflected back, causing a greenish golden glow. Rare in North America, more common in Europe.

15c Leaves filiform, from a sheathing base, the slender portion very rough. Fig. 32...........................*Distichium capillaceum*

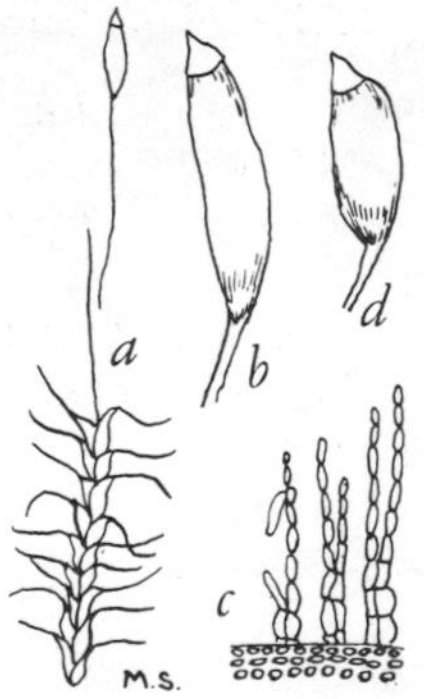

Figure 32

Fig. 32. *Distichium capillaceum.* a, plant; b, capsule; c, peristome; d, capsule of *D. inclinatum.* In silky tufts in cool rocky places, from Greenland and Alaska to New York, Iowa, Colorado and California. The 2-ranked leaves with broad clasping base and filiform blades are enough to identify the genus. The species are best distinguished by the spores: .017-.020 mm., papillose in *D. capillaceum;* .030-.045 mm., warty in *D. inclinatum.* Europe.

16a Leaves very narrowly linear-lanceolate, crowded and almost parallel with the stem. Midrib with a narrow wing along the back. No peristome. Fig. 33........................*Bryoxiphium norvegicum*

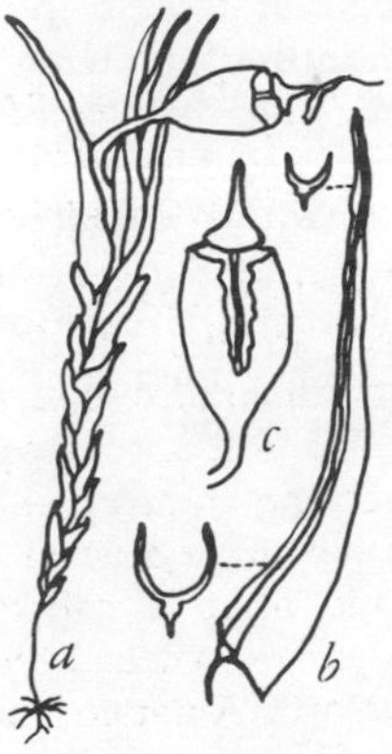

Figure 33

Fig. 33. *Bryoxiphium norvegicum*. a, plant; b, leaf; c, capsule. On shaded sandstone cliffs, usually in dense, closely adhering sheets. Missouri and Kentucky to Greenland and Iceland. Not in Norway! Very rarely fruiting, since in the colonies examined all plants are exclusively archegonial or antheridial.

16b Leaves broader, with midrib in middle of leaf. Peristome of 16 2-cleft teeth. Figs. 34-39. Genus *Fissidens*............................17

17a Growing submerged in running water.........................18

17b On earth, trees or rocks, not normally submerged.............20

18a Leaves large (about 2 mm.), stiff, 2-layered in spots, bordered with elongated cells; border and midrib reddish. Fig. 34.............. ....*Fissidens rufulus*

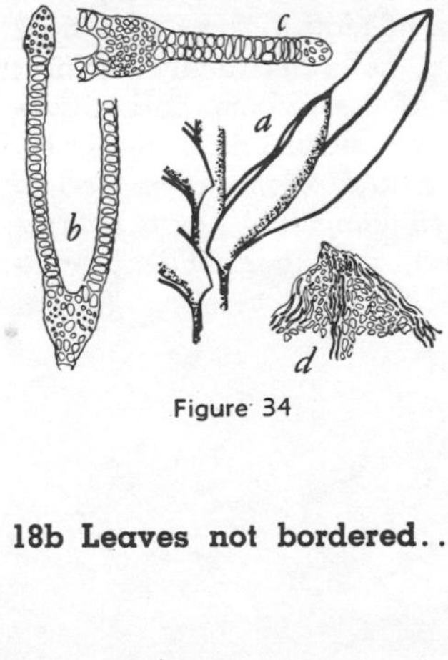

Figure 34

Fig. 34. *Fissidens rufulus*. a, leaf; b, section of leaf below middle; c, section of dorsal lamina; d, apex of leaf. A large (1-3 cm.) coarse aquatic plant on rocks in streams. California, Oregon, Washington, Idaho. Central Europe. Rare.

18b Leaves not bordered...19

19a **Main portion of leaf cartilaginous, of 4 or more layers of cells. Stems in dense tufts. Fig. 35............... *Fissidens grandifrons***

Figure 35

Fig. 35. *Fissidens grandifrons.* a, plant; b, cross section of leaf; c, plant of *F. debilis* (F. *julianus* of MFNA); d, cross section of leaf. The first of these is a stiff, dark green plant, 1 to 5 in. long, in swiftly flowing calcareous water; found widely in Europe and North America. The second is limp and soft, 2 to 6 in. long. Two other aquatic species are sometimes found.

19b **Leaves thin, slender and soft. Stems much branched, 5 to 15 cm. long. Fig. 35................................ *Fissidens debilis***

20a **Leaves bordered at least in part with long, narrow cells.......21**

20b **Leaves not bordered with long cells...........................26**

21a **Leaves obscurely finely papillose (2 dots per cell); midrib reaching apex of leaf. Fig. 36..................... *Fissidens ravenelii***

21b **Leaves not papillose; cells often bulging........................22**

22a **Leaves smoothly rounded at apex. Minute glaucous mosses covering moist, shaded rocks. Fig. 36............ *Fissidens obtusifolius***

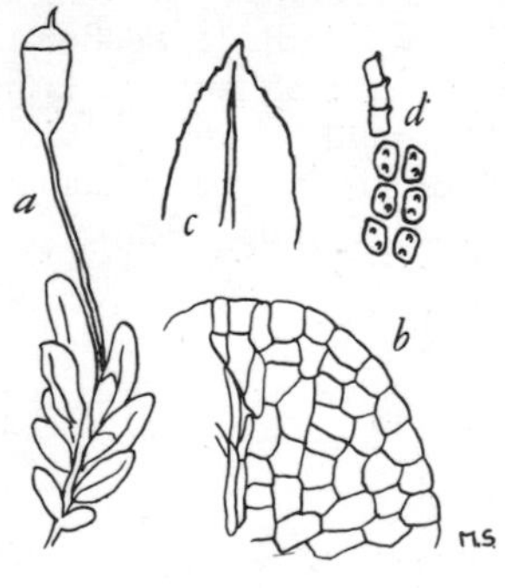

Figure 36

Fig. 36. *Fissidens obtusifolius.* a, plant; b, apex of leaf; c, apex of leaf of *F. ravenelii;* d, cells of same. The first is found east of the 96th meridian. The second grows on moist bricks or stones, North Carolina to Florida. *F. garberi* is similar to *F. ravenelii* but has a shorter midrib; s. Florida. *F. donnellii* has one large papilla on each cell; s. Florida.

22b Leaves pointed at apex....................................23

23a Midrib usually joining with borders in apex of leaf; antheridia conspicuous in axils of leaves. Fig. 37............*Fissidens bryoides*

23b Border not reaching apex of leaf..............................24

24a Lower inner margin of leaf bordered with small quadrate cells outside of the long narrow cells. Western. Fig. 37..*Fissidens limbatus*

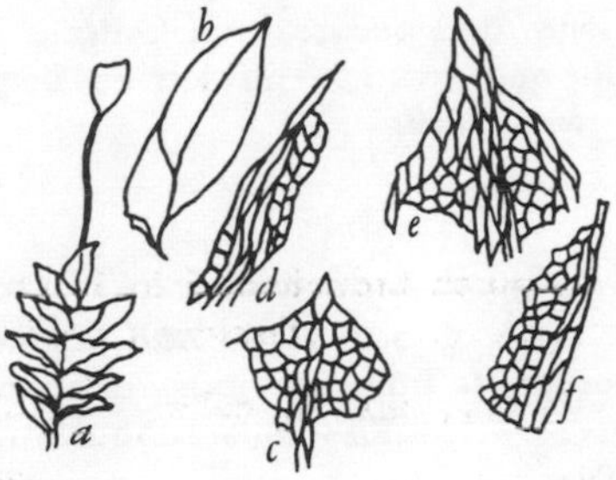

Figure 37

Fig. 37. *Fissidens limbatus.* a, plant; b, leaf; c, apex of leaf; d, margin of vaginant lamina; e, apex of leaf of *F. bryoides;* f, margin of vaginant lamina of *F. minutulus.* The first and second are 5 to 20 mm. tall; the third 1 to 3 mm. *F. limbatus* belongs on the west coast; *F. minutulus* is common on moist rocks in e. United States. *F. bryoides,* e. United States, Europe.

24b Leaves not so bordered. Eastern, rarely western..............25

25a Leafy shoots 3 mm. tall or less; on moist rocks or rarely on soil. Spores Aug.-Sept. Fig. 37..................*Fissidens minutulus*

25b Shoots 5 to 15 mm. tall. Spores Oct.-Nov......*Fissidens viridulus*

26a (b, c, d) Margins of leaf coarsely and irregularly (doubly) toothed near apex. Seta axillary. Fig. 38............................27

26b Margins finely and evenly serrulate. Fig. 39..................28

26c Margins entire or slightly wavy. Seta axillary. Stems 2 to 5 cm. long...................................*Fissidens polypodioides*

26d Margins entire; seta terminal; stems 2-3 mm. tall. (See Fig. 36).. ....*Fissidens obtusifolius*

27a Marginal 2 rows of cells usually paler than the others; midrib reaching apex of leaf. Sporophyte from middle of shoot. Fig. 38 .... *Fissidens cristatus*

Figure 38

Fig. 38. *Fissidens cristatus.* a, plant; b, apex of leaf; c, capsule; d, section of dorsal lamina; e, apex of leaf of *F. subbasilaris. F. cristatus* is 1 to 3 cm. long, and is found in all of the moist temperate United States and Europe. *F. adiantoides* is very similar, taller, smooth in section, with cells about .015 mm. in diameter (.006-.010 in *F cristatus*). *F. subbasilaris* is 5 to 10 mm. long, and occurs from Ontario to Florida and Iowa. The leaves bend down when dry.

27b Midrib ending several cells below apex of leaf; distal half of midrib covered by cells of lamina. Sporophyte from near base of shoot. On bases of trees. Fig. 38 .... *Fissidens subbasilaris*

28a Seta from tip of stem. Midrib ending several cells below apex of leaf. Cells .012-.020 mm. Fig. 39 .... *Fissidens osmundioides*

28b Seta from near base of shoot or from a basal short-shoot. Midrib stout, typically forming a cylindrical projection at tip of leaf. Cells .007-.010 mm. Fig. 39 .... *Fissidens taxifolius*

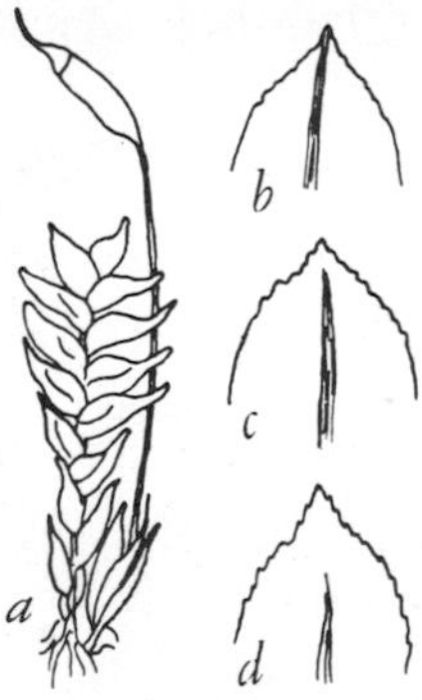

Figure 39

Fig. 39. *Fissidens taxifolius.* a, plant; b, apex of leaf; c, apex of *F. bushii;* d, of *F. osmundioides.* In the absence of sporophytes the apex and crenulation of the leaf, and length of midrib will help to distinguish the species. *F. taxifolius* has cells on the outside of the vaginant lamina prominently bulging, as seen in cross sections; the other species are relatively smooth. Typically *F. taxifolius* has the midrib excurrent as a cylindrical mucro. *F. bushii* has the upper margin (typically) slightly unequally toothed, suggesting *F. cristatus,* and the midrib ending 5 or 6 cells below the apex of the leaf. Many plants, especially young ones, cannot be identified with certainty. *F. taxifolius,* Ontario and e. United States. *F. osmundioides:* northern and eastern North America, Europe.

29a Without stem or seta. Capsule spherical, in a rosette of leaves. Entire plant barely visible to the naked eye....................30

29b With demonstrable stem, short or long........................33

30a Leaves broadly ovate, keeled. Spores .04-.05 mm. in diameter, smooth. Plant reddish. (See Fig. 75)..........*Acaulon rufescens*

30b Leaves lanceolate, flat. Plants surrounded by branching, velvety protonema. Fig. 40............Genus *Ephemerum*.............31

31a Leaves without midrib.......................*Ephemerum serratum*

31b Leaves with a midrib.......................................32

32a Leaves and calyptra smooth. Fig. 40......*Ephemerum cohaerens*

32b Leaves, and sometimes the calyptra, papillose. Fig. 40........... ....*Ephemerum spinulosum*

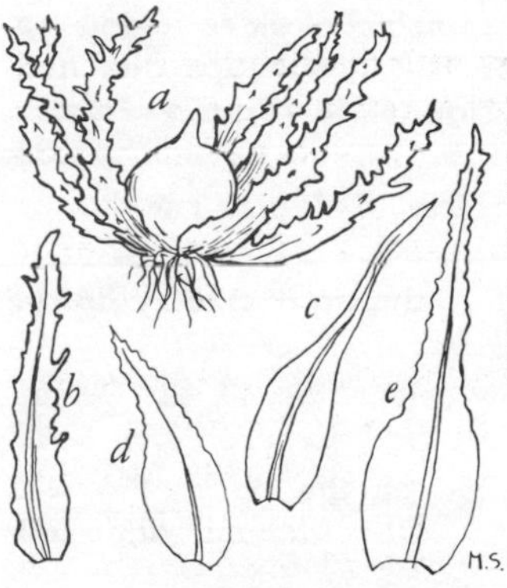

Figure 40

Fig. 40. *Ephemerum spinulosum.* a, plant; b, leaf; c, leaf of *E. sessile;* d, leaf of *E. cohaerens;* e, leaf of *E. crassinervium.* These minute mosses grow in crowds on silty banks and in gardens. They are detected by the olive green patches of protonema which they form. Only recognizable in autumn.

33a (b, c) Leaves with filiform green photosynthetic outgrowths on the upper surface. Fig. 41. Peristome of 32 twisted threads. Stems .5-2 mm. tall 34

33b Leaves with lamina-like vertical lamellae on the upper surface, at least on the midrib...35

33c Leaves without such outgrowths: sometimes with deciduous gemmae 49

34a Filaments from the midrib only. Fig. 41..*Crossidium squamigerum*

34b Filaments from upper surface of leaf. Fig. 41........*Aloina rigida*

35a Leaves entire, oval, thin, with lamellae only on distal half of midrib. Midrib prolonged into a hair (awn). Without peristome. Fig. 41 .... *Pterigoneurum subsessile*

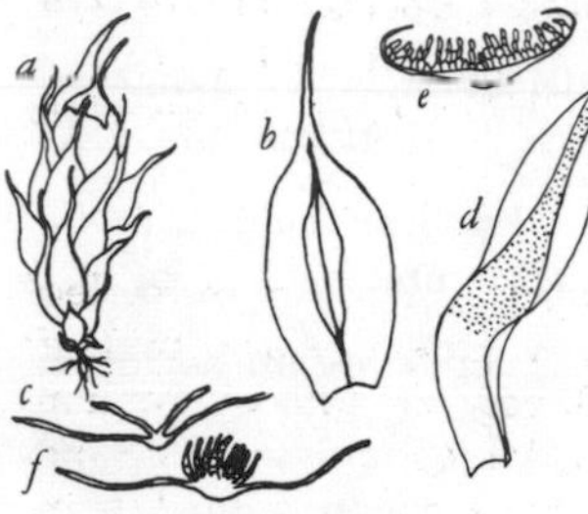

Figure 41

Fig. 41. *Pterigoneurum subsessile.* a, plant; b, leaf; c, section of leaf; d, leaf of *Aloina rigida;* e, section of same; f, section of leaf of *Crossidium squamigerum.* These pygmy mosses inhabit dry ground, especially in our arid southwest. *Aloina* has filamentous growths arising from the upper surface of the leaf. *Crossidium* has them only from the narrow midrib.

35b Leaves toothed on the margin, or with translucent sides folded up over the upper surface. Peristome teeth 32-64, with tips attached to a transverse membrane. Dioicous. Figs. 42-50. Family *Polytrichaceae* 36

36a Lamellae 1-12, mostly on the narrow midrib. Calyptra smooth, or with a few hairs 37

36b Lamellae 10-70, nearly covering the leaf. Calyptra decidedly hairy. 40

37a Margin of leaf bordered with long narrow cells. Figs. 43, 44. Genus *Atrichum* 38

37b Leaves not bordered; often with lamellae on the back. Fig. 42. .... *Oligotrichum aligerum*

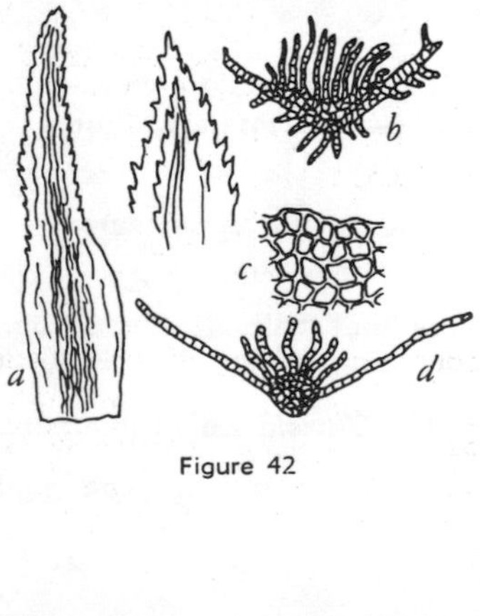

Figure 42

Fig. 42. *Oligotrichum aligerum.* a, leaf; b, cross section of leaf; c, margin of lamella. Stems 2.5-4 cm. tall; leaves curly when dry. Calyptra split on one side, with a very few hairs; peristome teeth 32; d, section of leaf of *O. parallelum.* Both (and two others) are northwestern: Oregon to Alaska.

38a **Midrib and lamina without teeth on back near apex. Lamellae 0 to 3 cells high. Median cells of leaf .020-.045 mm. in longest diameter. (See Fig. 44.)........................*Atrichum crispum***

38b **Midrib and lamina with teeth on back near apex. Lamellae 3 to 12, 2 to 14 cells high...39**

39a **Lamellae 4 to 7, tall enough to cover more than half of the leaf. Cells of leaf .010-.015 mm. in longest diameter. Fig. 43...*Atrichum angustatum***

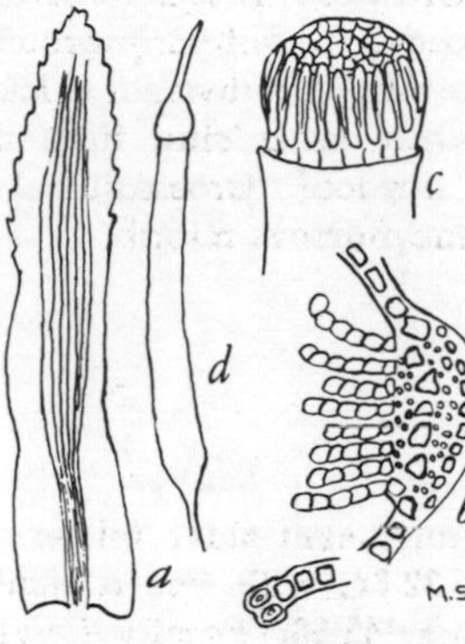

Figure 43

Fig. 43. *Atrichum angustatum*. a, leaf with lamellae; b, cross section of leaf; c, peristome; d, capsule with operculum. Leaves and/or lamellae have fine papillae, visible on sections with 1/6 in. objective. When papillae are large and prominent it has been called *A. macmillani*. Stems ½ to 2 in. tall, often in wide sods. Very common and variable.

39b **Lamellae 2 to 6, very low, 2 to 6 cells high. Cells of leaf .018-.040 mm. in longest diameter. Fig. 44............*Atrichum undulatum***

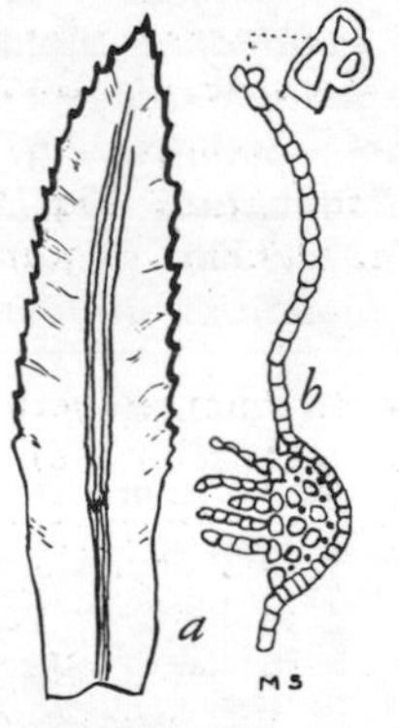

Figure 44

Fig. 44. *Atrichum undulatum*. a, leaf with lamellae; b, cross section of leaf. Very common east of the Great Plains, in moist, shady places. Capsules mature in autumn, open in spring. Stems 1-2 in. tall, seta 1-1½ in., capsule ¼ in. long, purple-red. When the lamellae are 6 or more cells high it is var. *altecristatum*. A similar plant in the Rocky Mountains and westward is var. *selwynii*. *A. crispum*, Vermont to New Jersey and Tennessee and British Columbia to Oregon, grows on wet peaty soil in shade.

40a **Capsule cylindrical. Calyptra densely hairy. Figs. 45, 46. Genus *Pogonatum*...41**

40b **Capsule 4-6-angled. End cells of lamellae in cross section of leaf not papillose; peristome teeth 64..............................44**

41a Stem obsolete. Seta ½-1 in. tall, from a tiny tuft of leaves on a green bed of filamentous protonema. Fig. 45 .... *Pogonatum pensilvanicum*

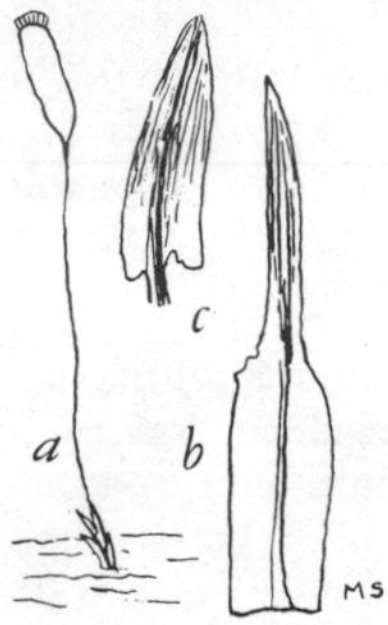

Figure 45

Fig. 45. *Pogonatum pensilvanicum.* a, plant natural size; b, leaf enlarged; c, leaf of *P. brachyphyllum.* The former species covers clayey banks with its green perennial protonema, from Newfoundland to Georgia and s.e. Iowa. The latter is more southern: New Jersey to s. Ohio, Texas and Florida. Only with care does one find the leaves at the base of the seta. The antheridial plants are very small.

41b Stems 1-8 (av. 2-4) in. tall, sometimes branched. Leaves ¼-½ in. long 42

42a Leaves thin, curly when dry, toothed half way down on the sheathing base. Teeth of peristome 32. Calif.-Alaska .... *Pogonatum contortum*

42b Leaves thick; sheaths entire. End cells of lamellae as seen in cross section of leaf papillose 43

43a (b, c) Cavity of end cell of lamellae in cross section of leaf pear-shaped, as high or higher than wide. Teeth of peristome 40-64. Fig. 46 .... *Pogonatum alpinum*

43b Cavity of end cell wider than high, often appearing transversely rectangular, the cell flat on top. Papillae large. Teeth 32. Fig. 46. .... *Pogonatum capillare*

43c Cavity of end cell vertically elliptical. Teeth 32. Fig. 46 .... *Pogonatum urnigerum*

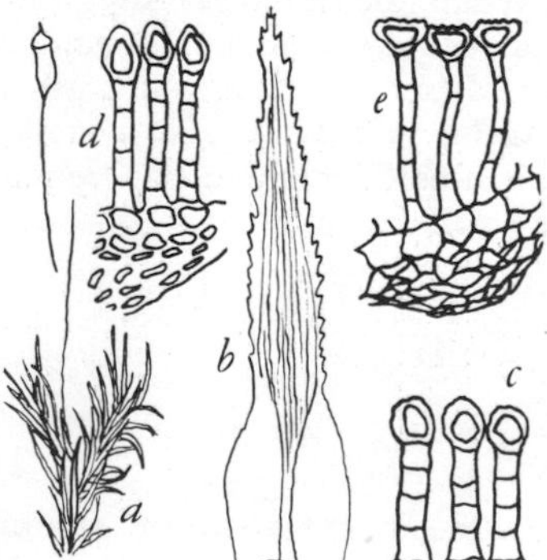

Figure 46

Fig. 46. *Pogonatum urnigerum.* a, plant; b, leaf; c, cross section of lamellae; d, lamellae of *P. alpinum;* e, lamellae of *P. capillare.* Three other species occur in North America. They are found in mountains in New England and Wyoming, but quite generally from Washington to Alaska, and n.w. Europe.

44a End cells of lamellae with outer wall thickened, roughened with shallow, elongate pits. Calyptra only slightly hairy. Fig. 47.... ....*Polytrichadelphus lyallii*

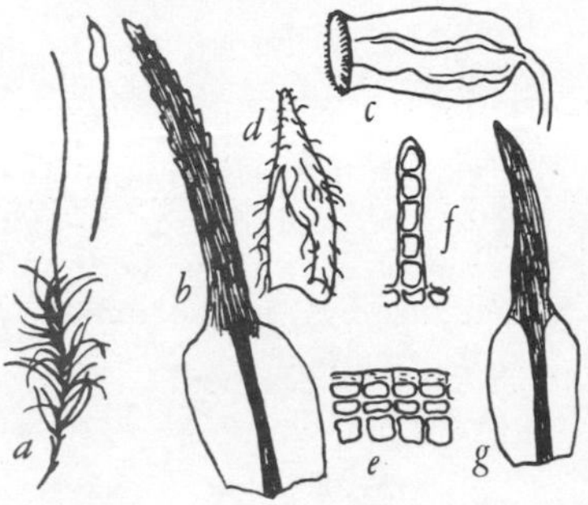

Figure 47

Fig. 47. *Polytrichadelphus lyallii.* a, plant; b, leaf; c, capsule; d, calyptra; e, side view of lamella; f, section of lamella; g, leaf of *Polytrichum norvegicum. Polytrichadelphus* has stems 1-5 cm. tall; leaves 1 cm. long; seta 4-6 cm. long; capsule inclined to horizontal, widest near the base. British Columbia to Colorado, Arizona and California. On damp ground above 3000 ft.

44b End cells of lamellae smooth. Calyptra densely hairy. Figs. 48-50. Genus *Polytrichum*..45

45a Leaves blunt at tip, entire. Capsule 6-angled. Fig. 47........... ....*Polytrichum norvegicum*

45b Leaves ending in an awn......................................46

46a Margins of leaf translucent, rolled up over upper surface of leaf completely covering the lamellae. Fig. 48..*Polytrichum juniperinum*

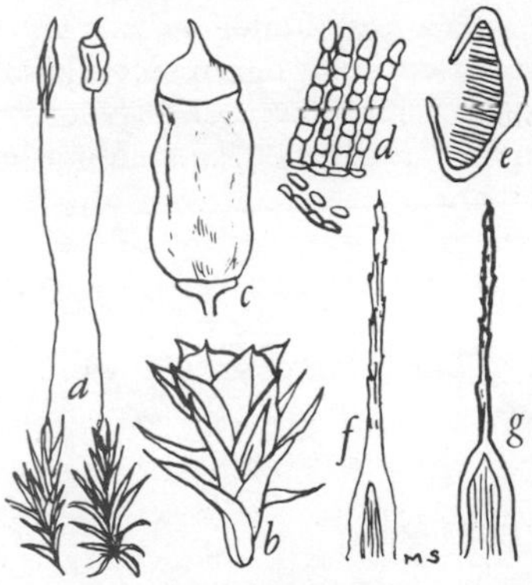

Figure 48

Fig. 48. *Polytrichum juniperinum.* a, fruiting plant; b, antheridial head; c, capsule; d, cross section of lamellae; e, cross section of leaf; f, apex of leaf; g, apex of leaf of *P. piliferum* with its abrupt narrowing to a long white hair; the leaf is otherwise similar to that of *P. juniperinum. P. juniperinum* is very common all over the Northern Hemisphere. *P. piliferum* requires silicious sand or rocks, and full sunshine; found at sea level on Long Island and at 12,500 ft. in Colorado. Europe.

46b Margin of leaf scarcely taller than lamellae, toothed from apex to middle of leaf, at least...47

47a End cells of lamellae in cross section similar to the cells below. Margins 4-9 cells wide. Fig. 49.............. *Polytrichum gracile*

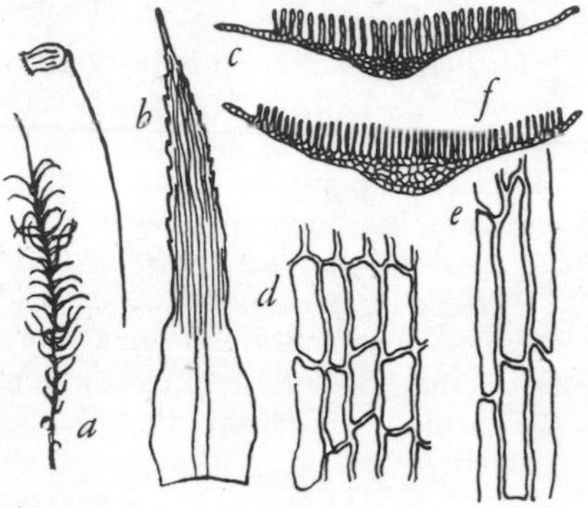

Figure 49

Fig. 49. *Polytrichum gracile.* a, plant; b, leaf; c, section of leaf; d, cells of sheath; e, cells of sheath of *P. formosum;* f, section of leaf of same. Both species are world-wide in distribution, but not common in North America.

47b End cells peculiar in shape and thickening of walls...........48

48a End cells notched, with thickened walls. Fig. 50.............. ....*Polytrichum commune*

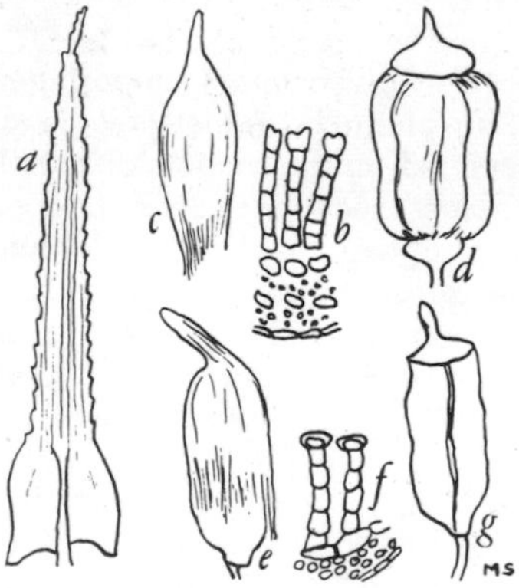

Figure 50

Fig. 50. *Polytrichum commune.* a, leaf; b, section of lamellae; c, calyptra enclosing a capsule; d, capsule alone; e, capsule and calyptra of *P. ohioense;* f, section of lamellae; g, capsule alone, with tapering base. The Haircap or Pigeonwheat Mosses grow in beds often 100 ft. across, and up to 6 in. tall. Leaves ½ in. long. Common. *P. commune* is found all over the world. *P. ohioense* s.e. United States, Alaska, Europe.

48b End cells wider than high, the upper wall thickened. Fig. 50.... ....*Polytrichum ohioense*

49a Some stems ending in a cup containing gemmae (not antheridia), others bearing a seta with a cylindrical erect capsule. Peristome of 4 stiff, many-celled teeth. Fig. 51..........*Tetraphis pellucida*

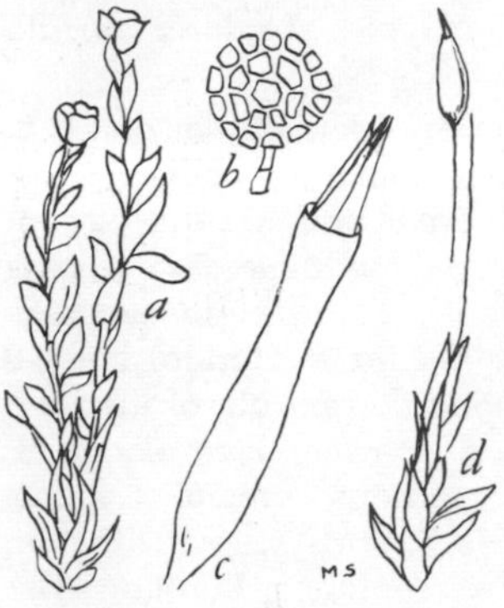

Figure 51

Fig. 51. *Tetraphis pellucida*. a, plant with gemma cups; b, gemma; c, capsule with peristome; d, capsule with seta and perichaetial leaves. This genus has the smallest number of teeth in the peristome. The plants grow in tufts and sods in deep shade on wet rotten wood or humus or porous sandstone. The protonema is a green scale, not filamentous. Common from e. New Jersey to California and northward. *T. geniculata*, a more northern form, has a crooked seta.

49b Without gemma cups. Teeth of peristome various, or none....50

50a (b, c) Peristome teeth 2 or 3 cells thick, the outer cells quadrate, forming 32 curly threads, or 16 teeth 2 cells wide, or 8 teeth 4 cells wide. Hypophysis often larger than urn. Cells of leaf large (.03-.09 mm. long). Figs. 52, 53. Family SPLACHNACEAE.........51

50b Peristome is a pleated cone, open at the top. Capsule without seta, oblique, pointed, green. Perichaetial leaves tipped with a long black bristle. Leaves minute, blackish, strap-shaped, papillose. Fig. 30...................................*Diphyscium foliosum*

50c Not having either of the above combinations of characters. Peristome teeth, when present, are strips of cell-wall split apart through the cell cavities.......................................52

51a (b, c) Hypophysis wider than urn and darker in color. Teeth of peristome 3-layered. Fig. 52............*Splachnum ampullaceum*

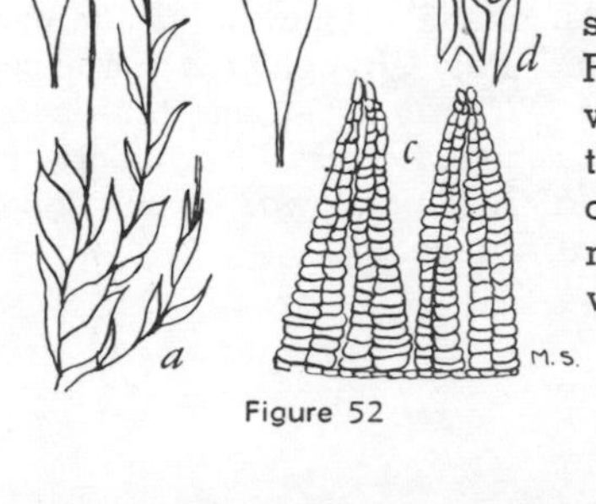

Figure 52

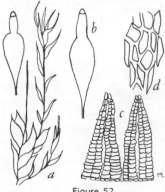

Fig. 52. *Splachnum ampullaceum*. a, plant; b, capsule; c, peristome; d, cells of leaf. On cow dung in swamps: Newfoundland to Pennsylvania and Wisconsin. *S. luteum*, on the same substrate, in Rocky Mountains and northwestward, wears a yellow, bell-shaped skirt below the small red capsule. There are 3 other species. They are said to emit a manurial odor and thus to attract flies which carry the spores.

51b Hypophysis wider than urn and lighter in color. Teeth of peristome 2-layered. Fig. 53.......................... *Tetraplodon mnioides*

51c Hypophysis narrower than urn and of the same color. Teeth of peristome 2-layered. Fig. 53..................... *Tayloria serrata*

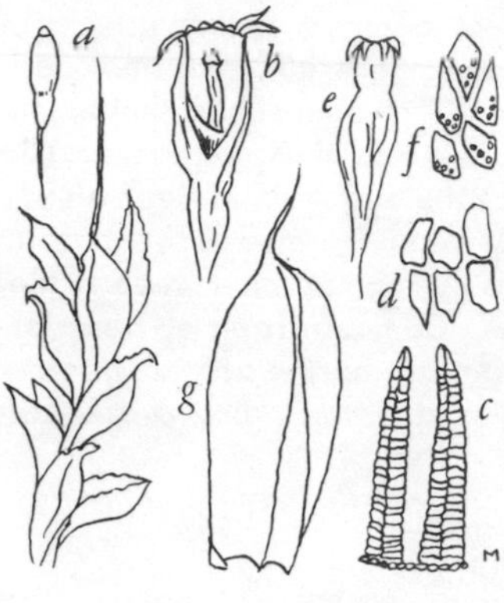

Figure 53

Fig. 53. *Tayloria serrata*. a, plant; b, capsule; c, peristome; d, cells of leaf, Vermont to Oregon and Alaska; e, capsule of *Tetraplodon mnioides;* f, cells of leaf; g, leaf. *Tetraplodon pennsylvanicus* (Nova Scotia to Florida) has 3-6 large teeth along the margin of the leaf. *Tayloria* has 5 species, *Tetraplodon* 4, on dung of various animals, hides, bones, etc., New York to Washington, Alaska and Greenland; Europe. The columella of *Tayloria* often extends prominently above the mouth of the capsule.

52a (b, c) Leaf cells conspicuously bulging-mamillose, at least on the upper (ventral) side. Figs. 54-57.............................53

52b Leaf cells papillose, the papillae not, or scarcely, including the cell cavity. Figs. 58-97.................................59

52c Leaf cells smooth. Figs. 98-164..............................124

53a Leaves 2 cells thick, the upper (ventral) cells mamillose, the lower (dorsal) smooth. Fig. 54...................... *Timmiella anomala*

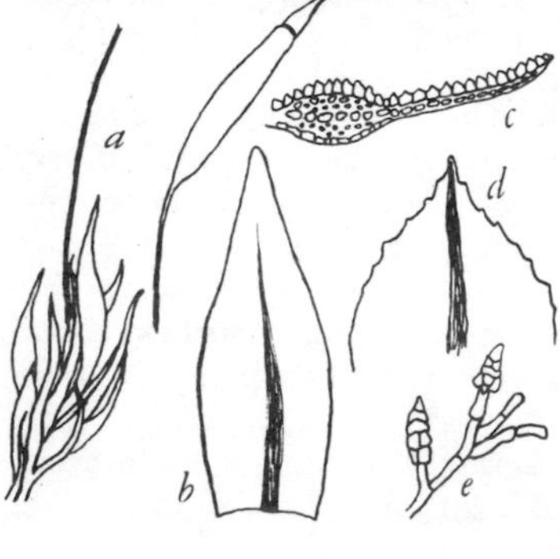

Figure 54

Fig. 54. *Timmiella anomala*. a, plant; b, leaf; c, section of leaf; d, leaf of *Hyophila tortula;* e, gemmae. *Timmiella* is up to 2 cm. tall, with seta 1.5-2.5 cm. long; peristome of 32 threads slightly twisted. Plants of mediterranean climates: California, Arizona, Italy. *Hyophila* is a tropical genus. *H. tortula* (1-3 cm. tall) is on moist, shaded rocks, New York to Florida, Arizona, Iowa, Brazil, Cuba, central Europe.

53b Leaf cells in one layer (except sometimes at margin)...........54

54a Leaves mamillose above but not beneath; slightly papillose....55

54b Leaves mamillose on both sides..............................56

55a Leaves slightly sheathing at base, with clustered, stalked gemmae among the upper leaves. Never fruiting. Fig. 54...*Hyophila tortula*

55b Leaves distinctly sheathing, with abrupt change from sheath to lamina cells. Capsules regularly produced, horizontal, on a tall seta. Without gemmae. Fig. 55............*Timmia megapolitana*

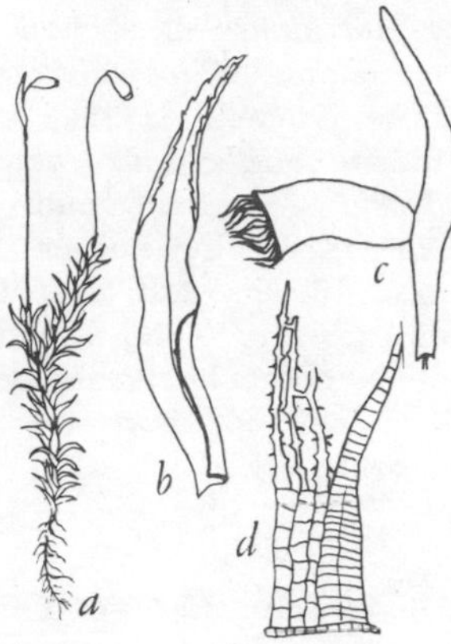

Figure 55

Fig. 55. *Timmia megapolitana.* a. plant; b, leaf; c, calyptra and capsule; d, peristome. Two to 4 in. tall, often in dense clumps. *T. austriaca* of the Rocky Mountains and northward has the sheathing base of the leaf orange color, and cilia of the inner peristome not prickly. Out of doors *Timmia* is easily recognized by the calyptra standing erect at the bend of the seta.

56a Leaves much twisted and contorted when dry, often papillose as well as mamillose. Fig. 56..............................57

56b Leaves merely wrinkled or folded when dry, on earth or rocks. Fig. 57..58

57a Leafy shoots 3-5 mm. tall, from creeping stems. Leaves not bordered. Seta 3-5 mm. long. Fig. 56....*Macromitrium mucronifolium*

57b Leafy shoots branching, 1-3 cm. tall. Leaves bordered with peculiar cells. Fig. 56..........................*Syrrhopodon texanus*

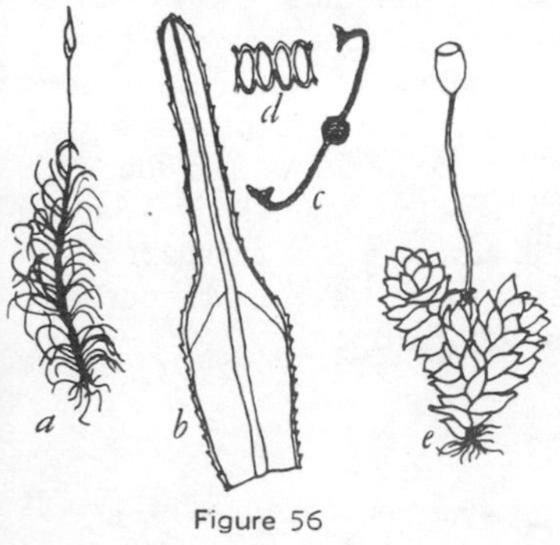

Figure 56

Fig. 56. *Syrrhopodon texanus.* a, plant; b, leaf; c, cross section of leaf of *S. floridanus;* d, cells of same; e, plant of *Macromitrium mucronifolium,* wet. These species grow in dense mats on trunks and bases of trees, Florida to Louisiana. *S. texanus* to Ohio and Texas. *Syrrhopodon* leaves often bear clusters of gemmae at the tips.

58a Leaves 1 mm. long, serrulate. Midrib with stereid bundles on lower side only. Fig. 57..........................*Oreoweisia serrulata*

58b Leaves 1-5 mm. long, extremely variable. Midrib with stereid bundles both above and below at middle of leaf. Fig. 57..*Dichodontium pellucidum*

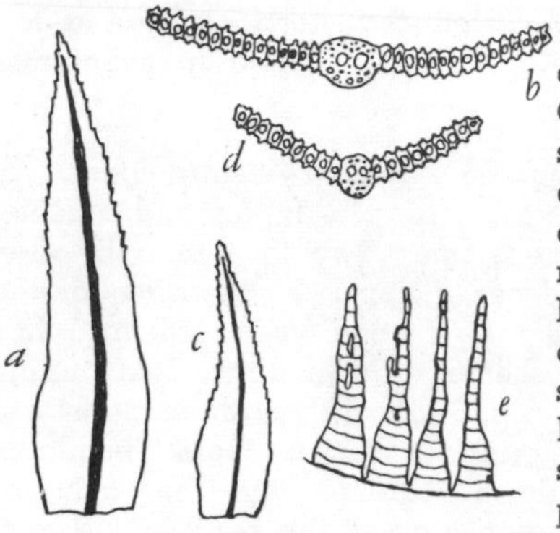

Figure 57

Fig. 57. *Dichodontium pellucidum.* a, leaf; b, section of leaf; c, leaf of *Oreoweisia serrulata;* d, section of same; e, peristome. *Oreoweisia* occurs in dense patches, ½ to 3 cm. deep, on moist, shaded rocks across northern North America, south to Maryland and Kentucky; Europe. *Dichodontium,* 1-10 cm. tall, has the same range, growing along streams; leaves entire to coarsely serrate; capsules erect or inclined, short or long; peristome teeth forked.

59a Leaves 4-9 mm. long, papillose on the back only. Cells at basal angles of leaves enlarged, with brown walls..................60

59b Leaves papillose on both sides..............................64

60a Midrib occupying 1/3 of leaf near base. Leaves dark green, curly when dry. In patches on rocks. Fig. 58........*Dicranum fulvum*

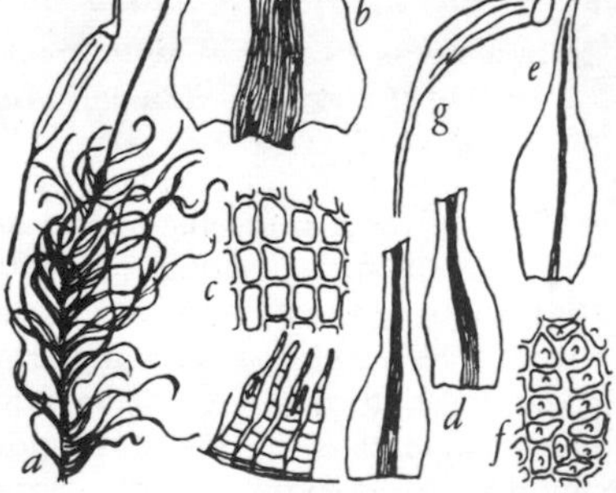

Figure 58

Fig. 58. *Dicranum fulvum.* a, plant, dry; b, base of leaf; c, median cells; d, leaves of var. *viride;* e, leaf of *D. spurium;* f, cells of leaf with papillae; g, capsule; h, teeth of peristome. *D. fulvum* occurs from Nova Scotia to Georgia, Missouri and Minnesota. The var. *viride* grows on trees and, as seen in collections, has the ends of the leaves broken off. *D. spurium* occurs in sandy soil or on rocks, Newfoundland to Minnesota, Missouri and Tennessee. Europe.

60b Midrib narrower 61

61a Leaves widest near middle. Fig. 58..........*Dicranum spurium*

61b Leaves widest near base, finely tapering....................62

62a Leaves more or less bent to one side, curly when dry. Clumps loose or dense. Fig. 59.....................*Dicranum fuscescens*

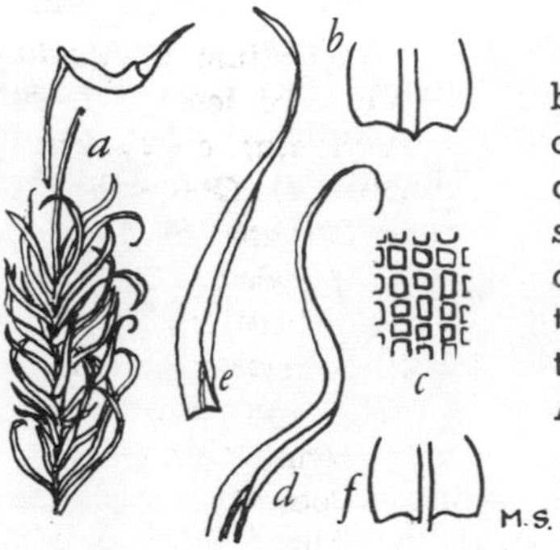

Figure 59

Fig. 59. *Dicranum fuscescens.* a, plant; b, base of leaf showing relative width of midrib; c, upper cells of leaf; d, the dry curly leaf; e, dry leaf of *D. condensatum;* f, base of leaf of same. *D. fuscescens* occurs in New England and in the northwest. *D. condensatum* is in the southeast, from New Jersey and Arkansas, southward.

62b Leaves bent and curled in all directions when dry. Plants in dense matted clumps..63

63a Stems 2-4 cm. tall. Midrib 1/8 width of leaf at base. On dry sandy soil in lowlands. Fig. 59................*Dicranum condensatum*

63b Stems 4-10 cm. tall. Papillae large, near upper ends of cells. In moist woods, Maine, to Montana, Colorado and New Jersey. Fig. 60....................................*Dicranum drummondii*

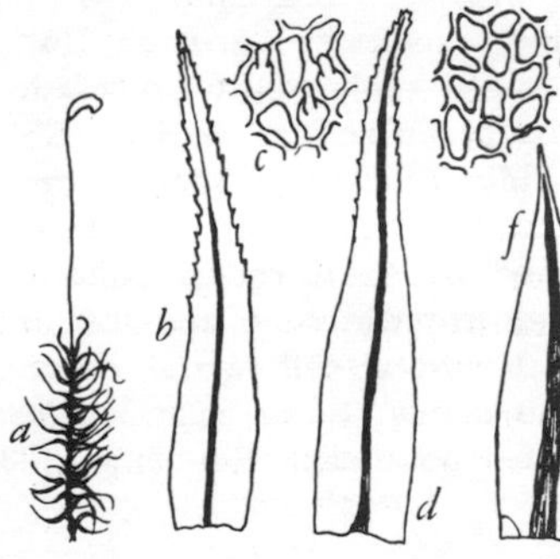

Figure 60

Fig. 60. *Dicranum drummondii.* a, plant; b, leaf; c, upper cells with papillae; d, leaf of *D. bergeri;* e, cells of same; f, leaf of *D. muhlenbeckii.* Northern and arctic plants, in dense deep cushions (to 10 cm.). The first has clustered sporophytes and large papillae. *D. bergeri* leaves are nearly straight when dry. *D. muhlenbeckii* has the lower cells .012-.016 mm. wide, with thin walls. The cells of the others are .008-.010 mm. wide, with thickened, pitted walls.

64a Small, very slender, curly patches on bark or rocks. Cells at basal angles of leaves enlarged, with brown walls. Fig. 61 .... *Dicranum montanum*

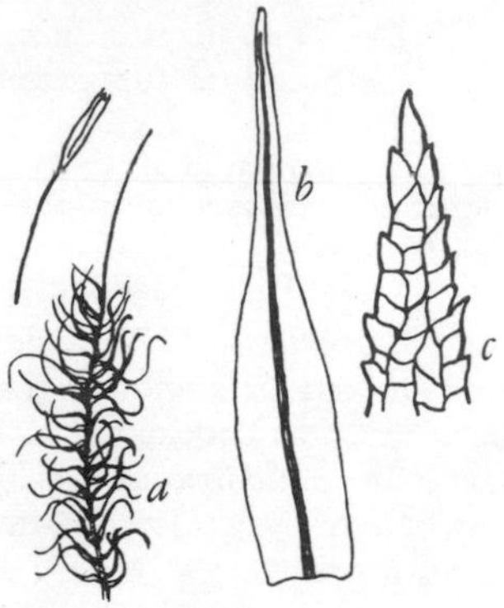

Figure 61

Fig. 61. *Dicranum montanum*. a, plant; b, leaf; c, apex of leaf. Little (to 1 cm.) very curly tufts on bases of trees, and on logs or stones. Capsules straight, erect. Common northeast, but rarely fruiting. Newfoundland to Manitoba, Arizona and Tennessee. Europe.

64b Without the specialized alar cells of 64a 65

65a Stems branching, bearing sporophytes at intervals 66

65b Stems strictly upright, or obsolete. Sporophytes terminal 85

66a Cells of leaf narrow, with extremely wavy walls. Leaves lanceolate, ending in a serrate, white hair, or the hair obsolete. Fig. 62. .... *Rhacomitrium canescens*

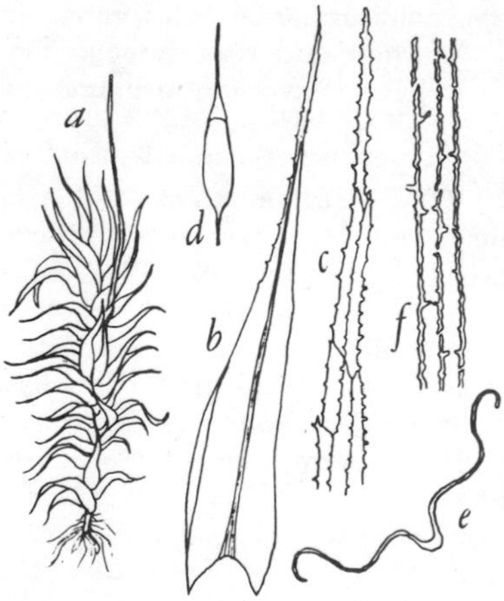

Figure 62

Fig. 62. *Rhacomitrium canescens*. a, shoot; b, leaf; c, apex of leaf; d, capsule; e, section of leaf; f, median cells. Stems 2-10 cm. long, erect or spreading, in loose grayish tufts, among rocks and stones above timber line, Greenland to Alaska, California, Montana and New Hampshire; Europe, Asia, Africa. Easily recognized by the large papillae on every cell, from base to apex of leaf. The thick wavy cell walls characterize the genus. Some other species are faintly papillose. See Figs. 133, 134.

66b Cell walls not wavy 67

67a Leaves without midrib, colorless at apex, often awned.........68

67b Leaves with midrib; lanceolate to ovate-lanceolate. Capsules abundant, with broad peristome teeth. Tufted blackish mosses on trees or rocks. Hopeless without capsules. Family ORTHOTRICHACEAE 69

68a Papillae forked. Seta shorter than leaves. Fig. 63..*Hedwigia ciliata*

Figure 63

Fig. 63. *Hedwigia ciliata.* a, plant; b, leaf of perichaetium; c, leaves with and without awn point. Common dark green or blackish moss on rocks, Arctic to Mexico; Europe. The typical form of this moss has a distinct white awn at the tip of the leaf. When this is lacking we have forma *viridis.* The branching, spreading habit of this moss makes it look like a Pleurocarp.

68b Papillae simple. Seta much longer than leaves. Fig. 64.......... ....*Braunia californica*

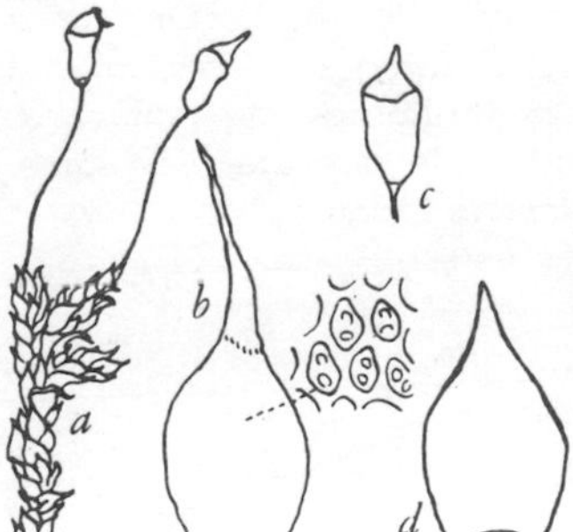

Figure 64

Fig. 64. *Braunia californica.* a, plant; b, leaf; c, capsule; d, leaf of *B. secunda.* The first grows on dry rocks, California to British Columbia. The second is found in Arizona, Texas (Davis Mountains), Mexico, South America, Africa. 21 tropical species are related to *B. secunda.* Brotherus proposed a special genus for *B. californica: Pseudobraunia.*

69a Stomata superficial, on the neck of the capsule. Seta longer than the leaves. Figs. 65, 66. Genus *Ulota*.........................70

69b Stomata on the body (urn) of the capsule, superficial or immersed (in a pit). Seta long or short. Figs. 67-73. Genus *Orthotrichum*...74

70a Leaves nearly straight and erect when dry. Fig. 65.............
...*Ulota americana*

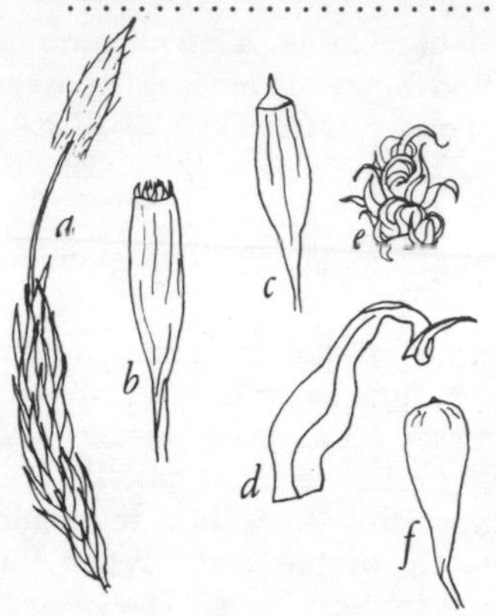

Fig. 65. *Ulota americana.* a, plant; b, capsule; c, mature capsule of *U. crispa;* d, dry leaf; e, a dry shoot; f, capsule of *U. ludwigii.* Rev. W. R. Megaw of Belfast, Ireland, has written a novel entitled "Ulota"; it tells of the loves, human and vegetal, of a bryologist.

Figure 65

70b Leaves very curly when dry...71

71a Leaves with clusters of gemmae at tips. Dioicous and only rarely fruiting. Fig. 66................................*Ulota phyllantha*

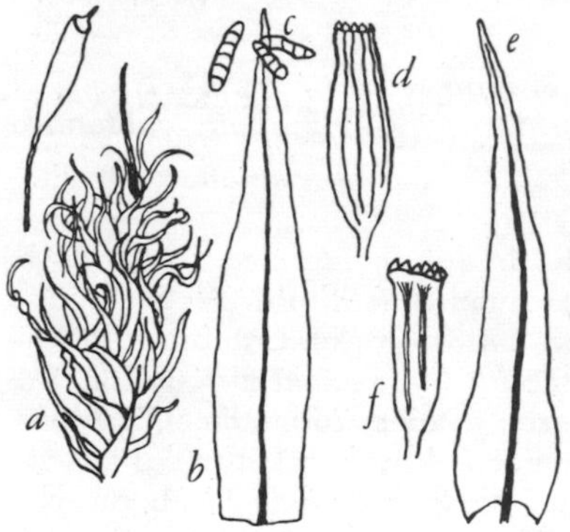

Fig. 66. *Ulota phyllantha.* a, plant; b, leaf; c, gemma; d, capsule. Oregon to Alaska; Europe. On rocks and trees. Fruiting in America, but very rarely in Europe. e, leaf of *U. obtusiuscula;* f, capsule of same. Washington to Alaska.

Figure 66

71b Without gemmae. Monoicous...................................72

72a Capsule club-shaped, smooth, rounded to the mouth. Fig. 65....
...*Ulota ludwigii*

72b Capsule 8-ribbed 73

73a Capsule widest at mouth, evenly tapering to base. Northwest coast. Fig. 66.......................................*Ulota obtusiuscula*

73b Capsule contracted below the mouth. Quebec to North Carolina and Minnesota; Alaska. Fig. 65....................*Ulota crispa*

74a Leaf margins plane or incurved; apex broadly rounded; usually with scattered gemmae. Fig. 67........*Orthotrichum obtusifolium*

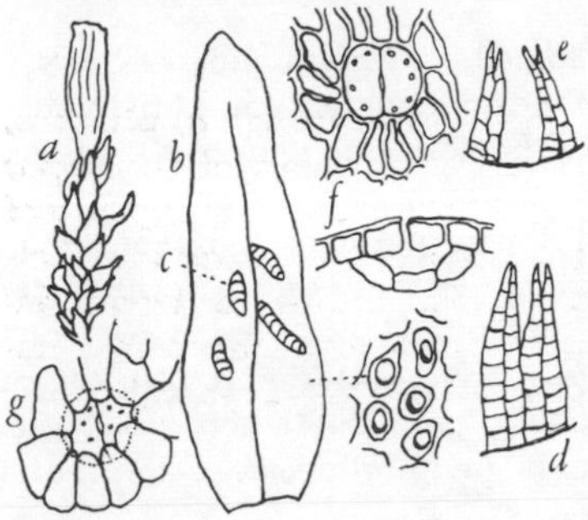

Figure 67

Fig. 67. *Orthotrichum obtusifolium.* a, plant; b, leaf; c, gemma; d, tooth; e, segments. On trees, northern North America to Maryland, Minnesota, Arizona and California; Europe. f. superficial stoma, face view and section; g, immersed stoma.

74b Leaf margins revolute..75

75a Stomata even with surface of capsule (superficial, phaneropore). Fig. 67f..76

75b Stomata set in pits, below the surface of the capsule and more or less covered by surrounding cells (immersed, cryptopore). Fig. 67g 80

76a Dioicous. Leaves slenderly acute, to 4 mm. long. Seta shorter than leaves. Capsules to 2 mm. long, 8-ribbed. On trees; western. Fig. 68..................................*Orthotrichum lyellii*

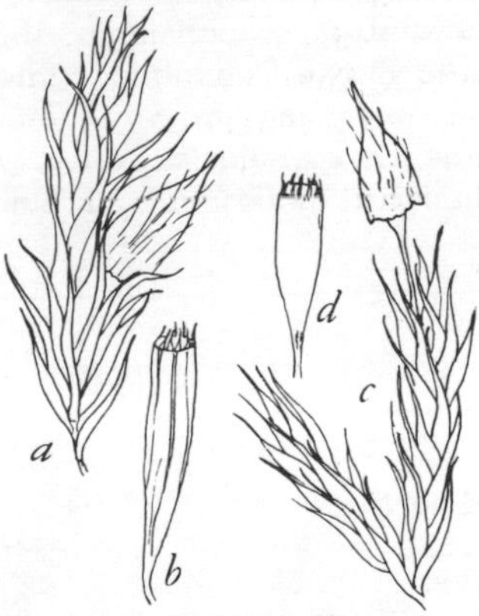

Figure 68

Fig. 68. *Orthotrichum lyellii.* a, plant; b, 8-ribbed capsule and seta; c, plant of *O. speciosum;* d, smooth capsule of same. Rocky Mountains and westward. *O. lyellii* is our largest species; leaves strongly papillose. *O. speciosum* has an antheridial bud just below the sporophyte. These big branching species are from 2 to 6 cm. tall.

76b Monoicous. Antheridial buds axillary along the stem..........77

77a On bark of trees..78

77b On rocks 79

78a Seta as long as or longer than leaves. Fig. 69..*Orthotrichum elegans*

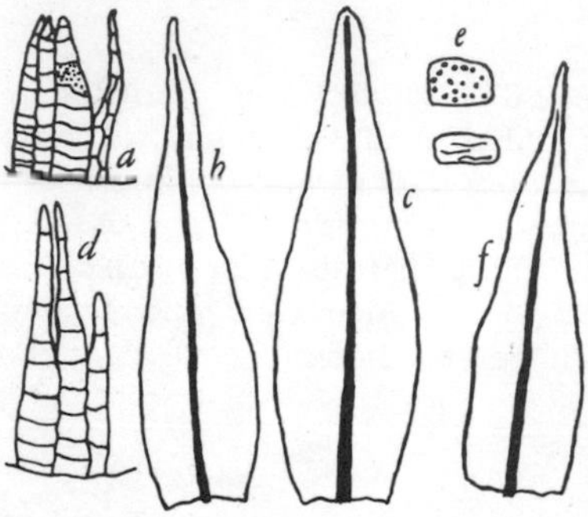

Figure 69

Fig. 69. *Orthotrichum elegans.* a, tooth and segment of peristome; b, leaf. Eastern. c, leaf of *O. laevigatum;* d, tooth and segment; e, upper and lower parts of tooth of *O. macounii;* f, leaf of same. Northwestern. *O. macounii* has slenderly acute leaves, long exserted capsules, and coarsely papillose teeth. *O. speciosum* is the northwestern form of *O. elegans.*

78b Seta distinctly shorter than leaves. *Orthotrichum affine,* western; *O. sordidum,* eastern.

79a Seta shorter than leaves. Fig. 70...........*Orthotrichum rupestre*

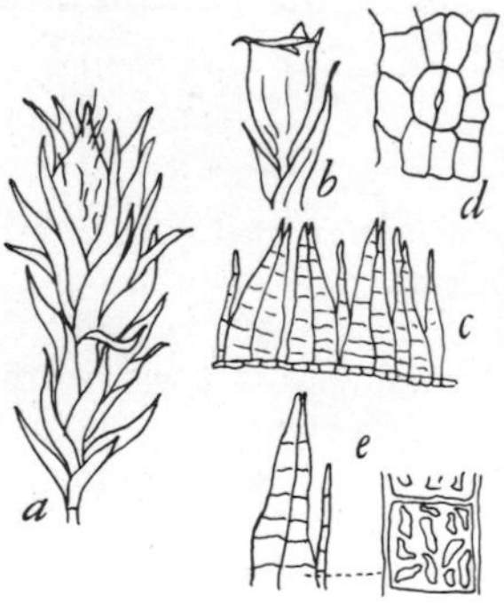

Figure 70

Fig. 70. *Orthotrichum rupestre.* a, plant; b, capsule and seta; c, peristome; d, stoma; Texas to British Columbia; e, peristome of *O. texanum.* Texas to British Columbia, common in Colorado. A specimen from Yosemite, California, with nearly globular capsules, was called *O. texanum* var. *globosum* by Lesquereux.

79b Seta as long as, or shorter than, leaves. Fig. 69..*Orthotrichum laevigatum*

80a Growing on rocks..81

80b Growing on trees..82

81a (b, c) Seta longer than leaves. Teeth with a few faint wavy lines. Fig. 71.................................*Orthotrichum anomalum*

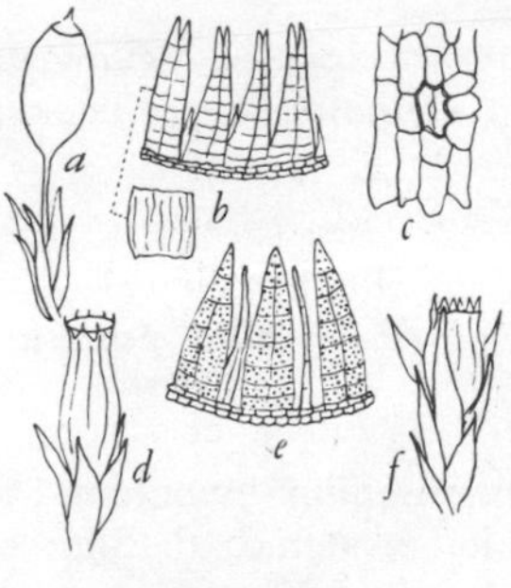

Fig. 71. *Orthotrichum anomalum.* a, capsule and seta; b, peristome; c, stoma; d, capsule and seta of O. *strangulatum;* e, peristome of same; f, capsule and seta of O. *cupulatum.* The first is common northeast and across the continent. The second is common in the central states (eastern Iowa). The third is rare, in the northwest. They are easily confused with *Grimmia* unless capsules are present.

Figure 71

81b Seta shorter than leaves. Teeth finely papillose. Fig. 71........ ....*Orthotrichum strangulatum*

81c Seta shorter than leaves. Teeth covered with fine wavy lines. Cells in 2 layers in upper half of leaf. Fig. 72......*Orthotrichum hallii*

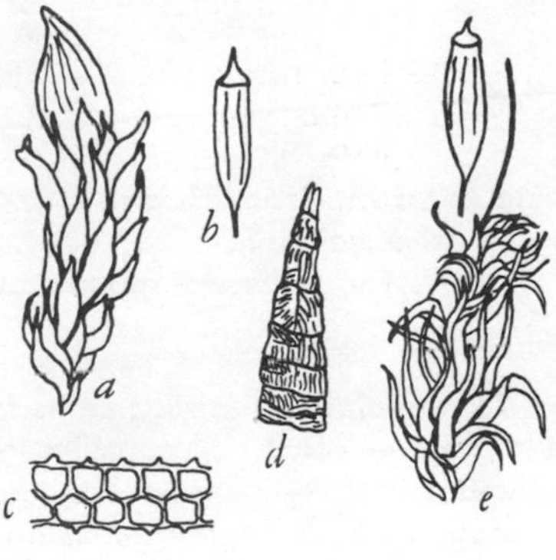

Fig. 72. *Orthotrichum hallii.* a, plant; b, capsule; c, section of leaf; d, peristome. Rocky Mountains. e, plant of O. *consimile,* dry; northwest coast. O. *pulchellum* has curly leaves like those of O. *consimile,* and "dark orange red" teeth; Washington to Alaska.

Figure 72

82a Leaves curly when dry. Northwest coast. Fig. 72............... ....*Orthotrichum consimile*

82b Leaves erect, nearly straight when dry......................83

83a Capsules smooth, or irregularly wrinkled when old, never 8-ribbed. Fig. 73................................*Orthotrichum pusillum*

83b Capsule strongly 8-ribbed when old........................84

84a Leaves tapering to a blunt, rounded apex. Capsules yellowish. Fig. 73..................................*Orthotrichum ohioense*

84b Leaves acute, often with a colorless cell at the tip with 1 to 3 papillae. Fig. 73........................*Orthotrichum pumilum*

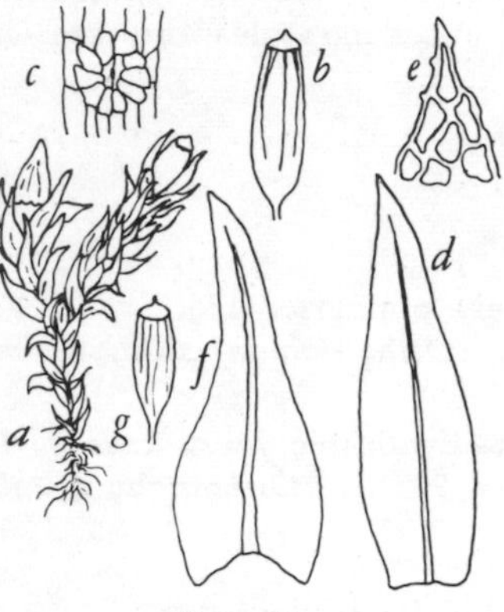

Figure 73

Fig. 73. *Orthotrichum pumilum.* a, plant; b, capsule; c, stoma; d, leaf; e, apex of leaf; f, leaf of *O. ohioense;* g, capsule of same. *O. pumilum* is abundant in the central Mississippi Valley (Iowa). *O. ohioense* is common from Canada to Florida, from Ohio eastward. *O. pusillum* resembles *O. pumilum,* but often has a few teeth at tip of leaf.

85a (b, c) Capsules 8-ribbed, ovoid; seta 1-7 mm. long. Leaves 1.7-3 mm. long. Tufted mosses on rocks or trees. Fig. 74..*Amphidium lapponicum*

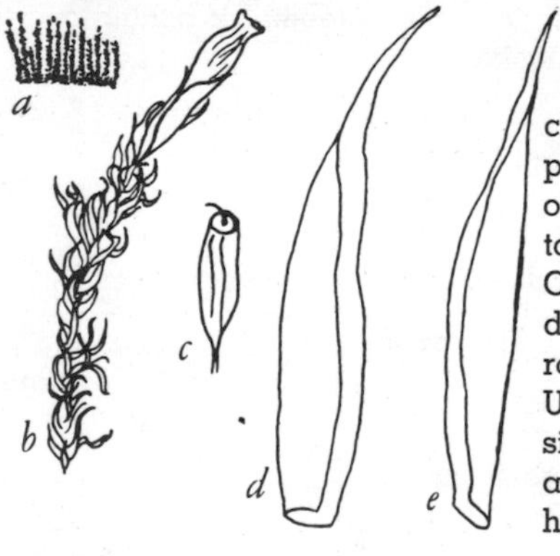

Figure 74

Fig. 74. *Amphidium lapponicum.* a, cluster; b, one plant; c, capsule; d, perichaetial leaf; e, perichaetial leaf of *A. mougeotii. A. californicum* has toothed leaves: California to British Columbia, rare. The others grow in dense clumps, to 6 cm. tall, on shaded rocks: Arctic America to northern United States; Europe. *Zygodon* is similar, but the perichaetial leaves are like the other leaves. Similar habit and range.

85b Capsules without seta. On soil. Almost stemless. Fig. 75......86

85c Capsules cylindrical or spherical or cup-shaped; seta much longer than leaves 87

86a Leaves narrowly lanceolate, the margins rolled up and in when dry. Fig. 75........................*Astomum muhlenbergianum*

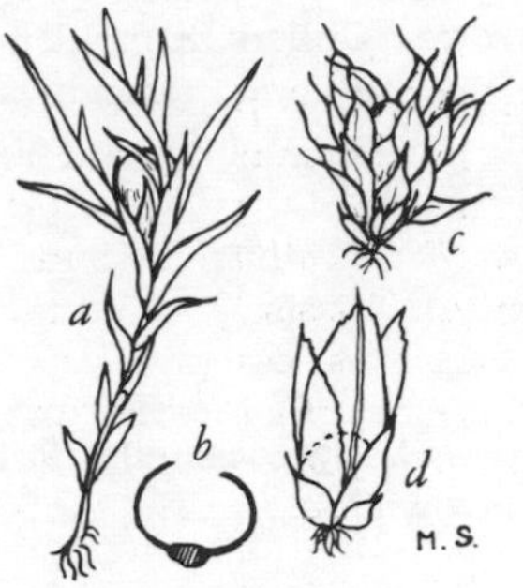

Figure 75

Fig. 75. *Astomum muhlenbergianum.* a, plant; b, cross section of leaf; c, plant of *Phascum cuspidatum* var. *americanum;* d, plant of *Acaulon rufescens.* These pygmy mosses grow in dense clusters (or scattered for *Acaulon*) on clods or bare bits of earth among grasses, fruiting in April and May. To find them tests your skill as a collector.

86b Leaves ovate to oblong-lanceolate, with an awn at tip. Fig. 75... ....*Phascum cuspidatum* var. *americanum*

87a Leaves broad, widest at middle or above. Midrib with dorsal stereids or none; often ending in an awn. Cells of lower ¼ of leaf colorless 88

87b Leaves lanceolate to linear-lanceolate, widest below the middle, long-tapering to the apex. Cells various....................102

88a Leaves opaque in upper half with densely crowded coarse rounded papillae. Lower cells transparent, large, with thick transverse walls (usually brown). Calyptra cylindrical, beaked, persistent, covering the capsule. Figs. 76, 77. Genus *Encalypta*..................89

88b Papillae dot-like or columnar or c-shaped, o-shaped, or forked. Clear cells at base of leaf thin walled. Calyptra smaller, split on one side, deciduous...92

89a Midrib not reaching the somewhat cucullate apex of the leaf, rough on the back. Calyptra fringed at mouth. Capsule with 8 spiral furrows. Fig. 76.......................... *Encalypta streptocarpa*

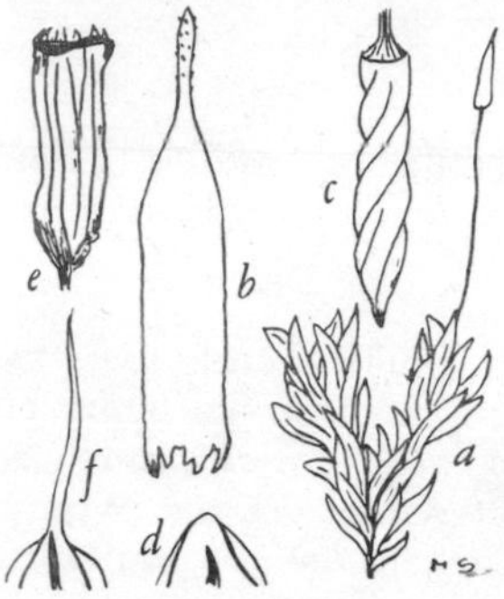

Figure 76

Fig. 76. *Encalypta streptocarpa.* a, plant; b, calyptra; c, capsule; d, apex of leaf; e, capsule of *E. rhabdocarpa;* f, tip of leaf of same. The latter species is northwestern, the former northeastern, on rocks or soil, above 1000 ft. elevation. Only mature capsules show the characteristic furrows. Called Extinguisher Mosses because the calyptra resembles a candle-extinguisher. When it falls it carries the operculum with it.

89b Midrib percurrent or excurrent as an awn. Leaves usually flat at apex. Capsule smooth or vertically furrowed..............90

90a Colorless cells at base of leaf extending up along margins... *Encalypta procera*

90b Not as in 90a...91

91a Margins of leaf plane, or incurved at base. Capsule smooth, with peristome. Fig. 76........................ *Encalypta rhabdocarpa*

91b Margins often recurved. Leaves apiculate but mostly awnless. Fig. 77.. *Encalypta ciliata*

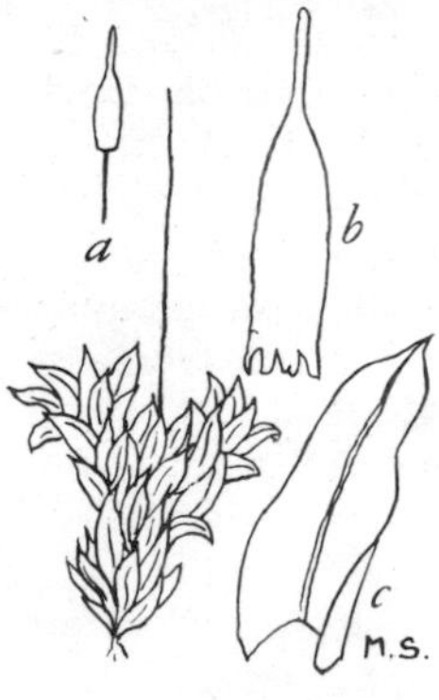

Figure 77

Fig. 77. *Encalypta ciliata.* a, plant; b, calyptra; c, leaf. On or among rocks, northern States and Canada, Atlantic to Pacific. In dense tufts, with stems 1-3 cm. tall and seta 1 cm. *E. vulgaris* is similar but has no peristome. *E. ciliata* has 16 teeth.

92a (b, c) Margin of leaf thicker than median part, due to deeper cells or more than one layer. Fig. 78................*Merceya latifolia*

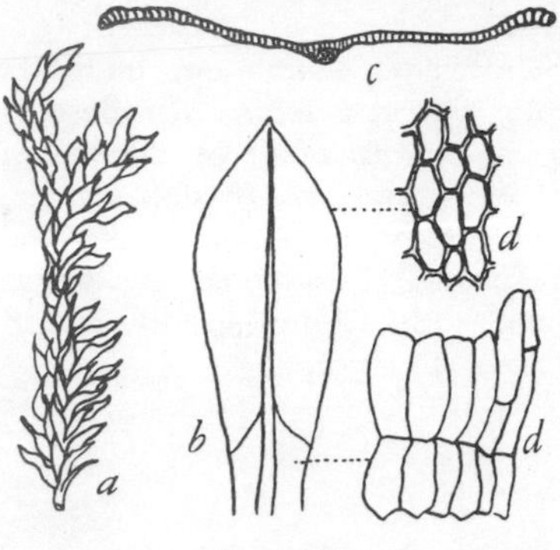

Figure 78

Fig. 78. *Merceya latifolia*. a, plant; b, leaf; c, section of leaf; d, cells of leaf. Dark green tufts, reddish below, on rocks at borders of streams, submerged at high water; British Columbia to Montana, Colorado and California. *M. ligulata*, a smaller species, has been found in the Great Smoky Mountains, Tennessee, and in Arizona.

92b Margin composed of greatly elongated cells. Fig. 80...*Tortula subulata*

92c Margins not differentiated, composed of one layer of ordinary cells 93

93a (b, c) Plants with definite gemmae............................94

93b Plants with leaves much broken, the fragments serving as gemmae. Fig. 79...*Tortula fragilis*

93c Plants without gemmae..95

94a Gemmae club-shaped, in axils of leaves. On soil, south. Fig. 79. ....*Barbula cruegeri*

94b Gemmae resemble small serrate leaves, clustered near apex of shoots. On bark of living trees. Fig. 79..........*Tortula pagorum*

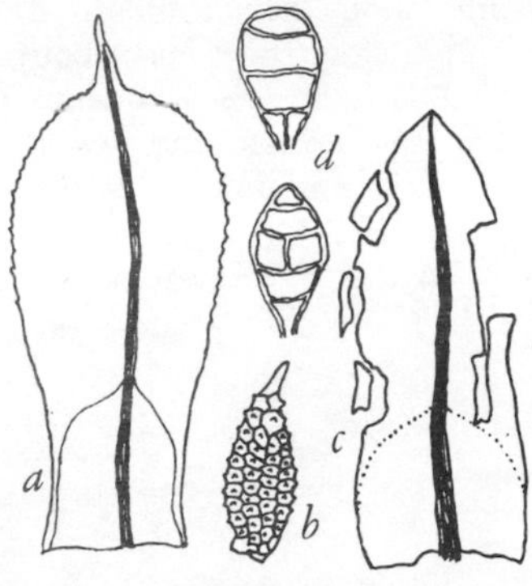

Figure 79

Fig. 79. *Tortula pagorum*. a, leaf; b, gemma. In dense thin patches, to 5 mm. tall, in or near settlements! Never fruiting. South central United States; Europe. Three similar species occur in the southeast. c, leaf of *Tortula fragilis;* on rocks and trees, Texas, Arizona, Mexico; d, gemmae of *Barbula cruegeri*, common from North Carolina to southern Missouri and southward. Distinguished from *B. unguiculata* by reddish stems and midribs, and the gemmae.

95a (b, c) Without peristome. Fig. 80.................... *Pottia heimii*

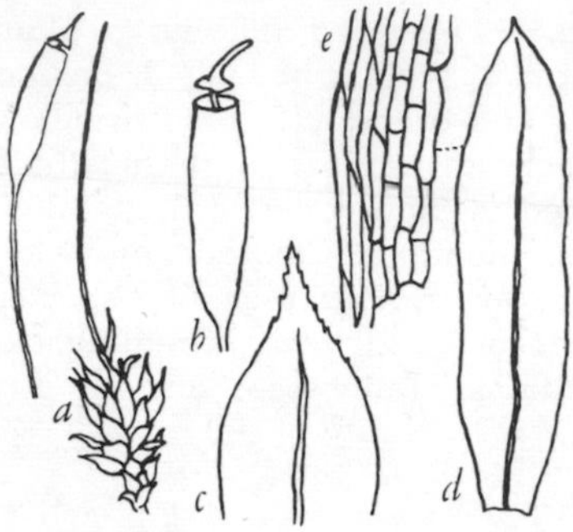

Figure 80

Fig. 80. *Pottia heimii.* a, plant, b, capsule; c, leaf; d, leaf of *Tortula subulata;* e, margin of same. Stems of *Pottia* to 8 mm. tall, in dense sods; very variable; common in Saskatchewan; Europe. *T. subulata* has stems 1-2 cm. tall; California to British Columbia; Europe.

95b Peristome of 16 teeth, slender and acute, or blunt, split, and broken off. Genus *Desmatodon.* Figs. 81, 82........................96

95c Peristome of 32 spirally twisted threads from a basal membrane. Colorless cells at base of leaf extending up along the midrib. Genus *Tortula.* Fig. 83..97

**96a Midrib ending in a colorless hair or awn. Fig. 81...............
...................................*Desmatodon plinthobius***

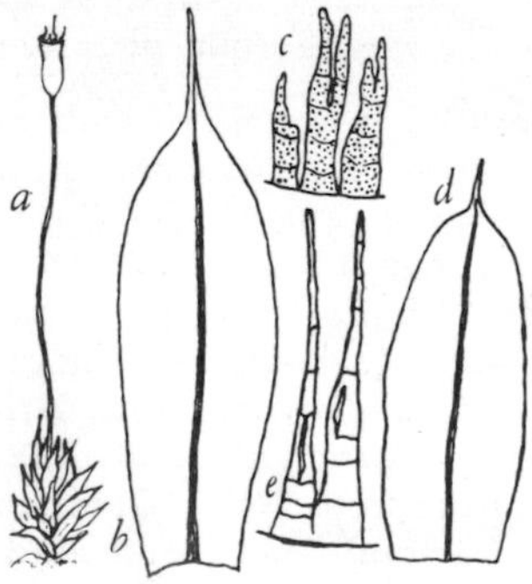

Figure 81

Fig. 81. *Desmatodon plinthobius.* a, plant; b, leaf; c, peristome. Stems about 4 mm. tall; seta 6-12 mm. Southeastern United States, on dry stones and walls. d, leaf of *D. latifolius;* e, peristome of same; similar in size and habitat; high in the Rocky Mountains to Arctic America.

96b Midrib percurrent or forming an apiculus. Fig. 82................ ....*Desmatodon obtusifolius*

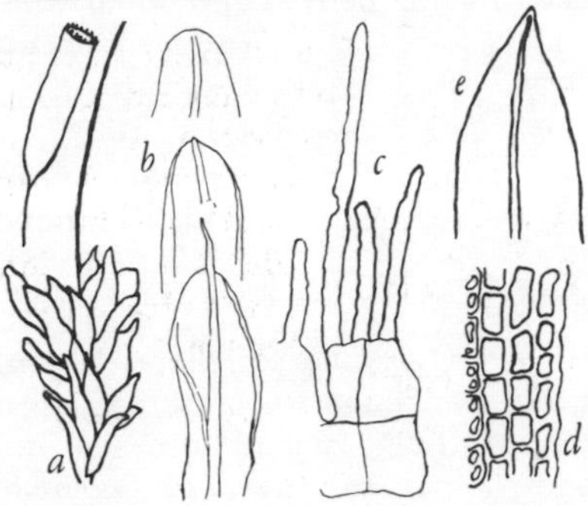

Figure 82

Fig. 82. *Desmatodon obtusifolius.* a, plant; b, tips of leaves; c, peristome. Northern United States and southern Canada, gregarious, on calcareous rocks (often sandstone). *D. coloradensis* (d, marginal cells) is scarcely different. e, apex of leaf of *D. porteri;* on calcareous rocks, Quebec to Pennsylvania, Missouri and Iowa.

97a Leaves made of 2 layers of cells (Utah)........*Tortula bistratosa*

97b Leaf cells in one layer.....................................98

98a Midrib extending out as an awn or hair. Fig. 83..............99

98b Not awned. Margin of leaf yellowish. Fig. 83. Compare *Barbula unguiculata*.................................*Tortula bolanderi*

99a Leaves small, 2-4 mm. long...............................100

99b Larger. Leaves 4-7 mm. long. Tube of peristome about as long as teeth 101

100a Awn smooth. Tube of peristome very short, hardly visible. Fig. 83...*Tortula muralis*

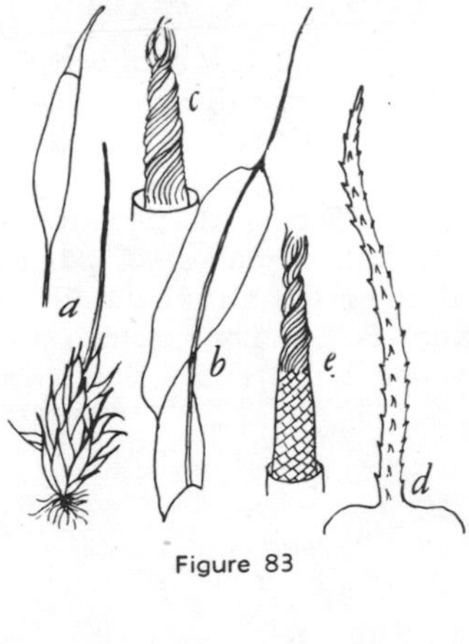

Figure 83

Fig. 83. *Tortula muralis.* a, plant; b, leaf; c, peristome. On stones and walls, northeastern to Florida and westward. *T. bolanderi* of California is similar as to peristome. d, apex of leaf of *T. ruralis;* e, peristome of same. Common northward on dry rocks and soil. On the west coast *T. princeps* resembles this, but has a tuft of antheridia just below the seta. Twenty-three species of *Tortula* are known in North America.

100b Awn prickly. Tube of peristome about as long as teeth........ .... *Tortula obtusissima*

101a Monoicous. Antheridia near base of seta. Leaves spreading when wet. Fig. 83................................ *Tortula princeps*

101b Dioicous. Leaves recurved when wet. Fig. 83...... *Tortula ruralis*

102a Margins of leaves distinctly involute from base to apex. Fig. 84. .... *Weisia viridula*

Figure 84

Fig. 84. *Weisia viridula*. a, plant; b, leaf; c, capsule and peristome; d, cross section of leaf. In dense tufts among grasses and weeds; about 1 cm. tall over all; common and widely distributed. Without sporophytes this cannot be distinguished from *Astomum*. Six other species of *Weisia* are reported for North America.

102b Margins of leaves revolute or plane........................103

103a Stems matted together with brown, branching rhizoids.......104

103b Stems free and separate.....................................111

104a Many stems ending in a naked stalk bearing a cluster of gemmae. Capsule cylindrical, curved, ribbed. Peristome double. Papillae single, near middle of cell. Fig. 85..*Aulacomnium palustre*

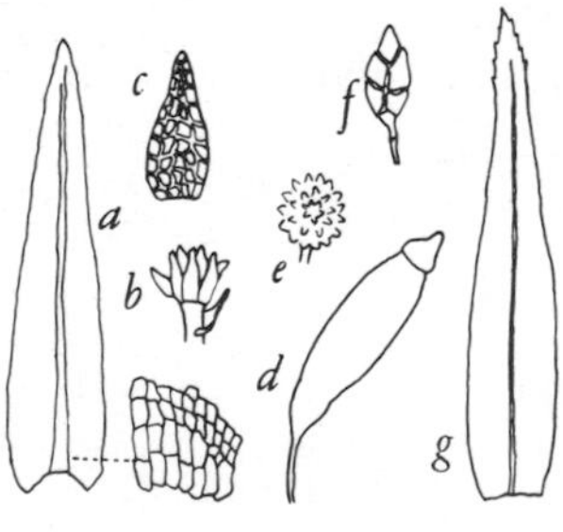

Figure 85

Figure 85. *Aulacomnium palustre*. a, leaf with swollen basal cells; b, cluster of gemmae; c, gemma; d, capsule; e, cluster of gemmae of *A. androgynum;* f, one gemma; g, leaf. Up to 7 cm. tall, in very wet, neutral or acid boggy places. *A palustre* is common east of the Grassland States. *A. androgynum* is common northwest. It lacks the swollen basal cells. Both occur also in Europe.

104b Without gemmae. Papillae much smaller. Peristome double or single 105

105a With one low broad papilla over the cell cavity. Capsule inclined, curved, cylindric. Peristome of 16 red, forked teeth. Fig. 115 .... *Oncophorus polycarpus*

105b With one papilla at upper or lower end of cell. Capsule globular when wet; peristome double or reduced 106

106a Leaves lanceolate or broader. Capsule ribbed and furrowed. In wet places. Figs. 86, 87. Genus *Philonotis* 107

106b Leaves linear to acicular, at least in upper half. On shaded rocks or banks 108

107a Leaves papillose at upper ends of cells. Fig. 86 .... *Philonotis longiseta*

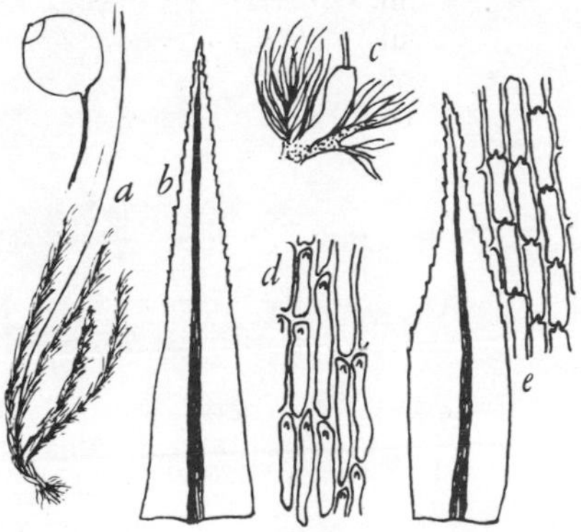

Figure 86

Fig. 86. *Philonotis longiseta.* a, plant; b, leaf; c, antheridial bud; d, median cells. Florida to Louisiana, Tennessee and Pennsylvania. In Iowa on shaded sandstone cliffs. e, leaf and cells of *P. sphaericarpa;* dioicous; North Carolina to Florida.

107b Leaves papillose at lower ends of cells. Fig. 87 .... *Philonotis fontana*

Figure 87

Fig. 87. *Philonotis fontana.* a, plant; b, capsule; c, antheridial head; d, leaf. Three to 8 cm. tall, in dense tufts, in very wet places, over United States, Canada and Europe; very variable. When dry the leaves lie close to the stem from the base upward. In *P. americana* the dry leaves come out at a large angle from the stem, then bend upward (e). Nova Scotia to Vermont, Wyoming, British Columbia and Alaska.

108a Leaves 4-7 mm. long, curly or straight. Capsule ribbed and furrowed. Fig. 89. Genus *Bartramia*............................109

108b Leaves 2.5-3.5 mm. long, erect, appressed, very stiff and slender. Capsule smooth, not furrowed. Fig. 88.........*Anacolia menziesii*

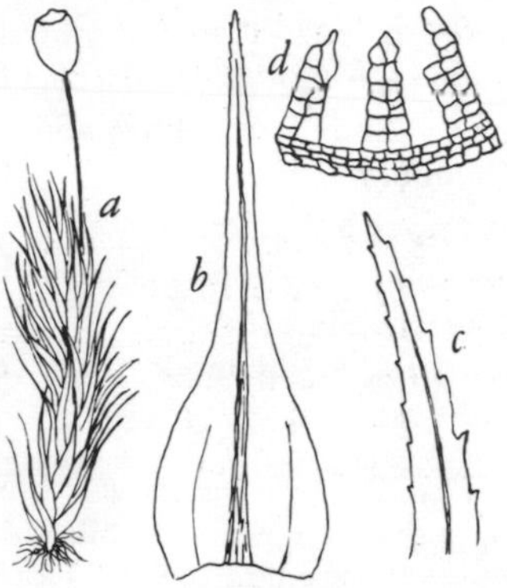

Figure 88

Fig. 88. *Anacolia menziesii.* a, plant; b, leaf; c, apex of leaf; d, peristome. In dense stiff tufts 3-5 cm. tall, on shaded rocks. Wyoming to California and Alaska. Other species in Mexico to Peru; North Africa.

109a Leaves evenly tapering from base to apex................110

109b Leaves broad and clasping at base, abruptly narrowed to the slender body. Fig. 89......................*Bartramia ithyphylla*

110a Leaves curly when dry, spreading. Fig. 89... *Bartramia pomiformis*

Figure 89

Fig. 89. *Bartramia pomiformis.* a, plant; b, capsule; c, leaf. Two to 8 in. tall, in dense clumps; common on shaded hillsides, Nova Scotia to Florida, Oregon and British Columbia. d, leaf of *B. ithyphylla;* Greenland to Pennsylvania, Alaska and California. The leaf of *B. stricta* is shaped like c; 1-3 cm. tall; Colorado and Montana to California. All three occur also in Europe.

110b Leaves erect, slender, brittle. Fig. 89..........*Bartramia stricta*

111a Margins of leaf revolute...................................112

111b Margins plane...117

112a Peristome of 32 spirally twisted, papillose threads, or entirely lacking. Fig. 92, 93. Genus *Barbula* 114

112b Peristome of 16 erect, slenderly triangular teeth, cleft or perforated. Figs. 90, 91. Genus *Didymodon* 113

113a Leaves rounded at apex, strongly decurrent at base. Fig. 90 .... *Didymodon tophaceus*

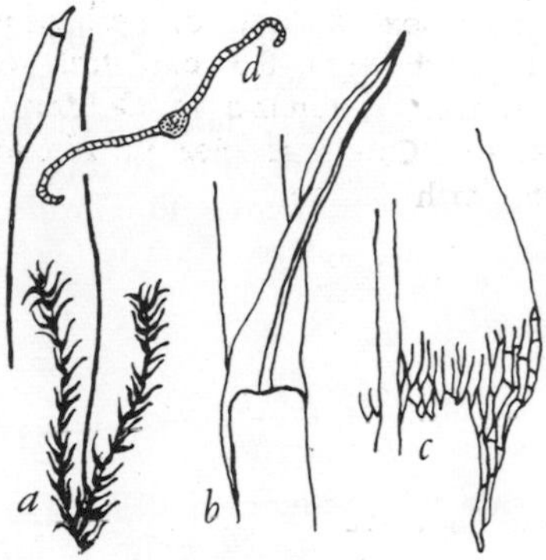

Figure 90

Fig. 90. *Didymodon tophaceus.* a, plant; b, leaf; c, decurrent base; d, section of leaf. In seepage of calcareous water, incrusted with deposits of lime (tufa). New York to British Columbia, California and Arkansas.

113b Leaves acute to narrowly acuminate. Fig. 91 .... *Didymodon recurvirostris*

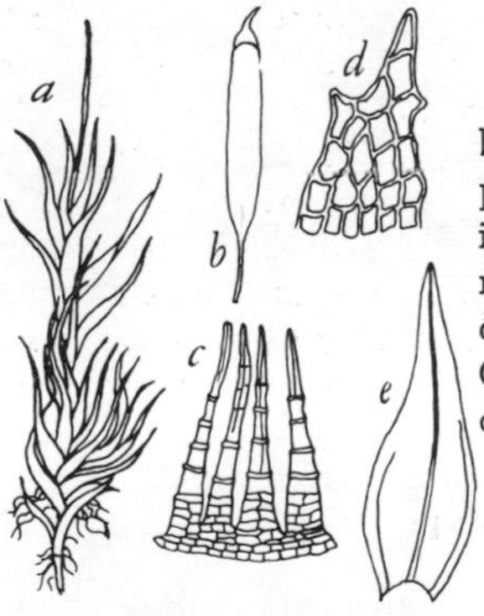

Figure 91

Fig. 91. *Didymodon recurvirostris.* a, plant; b, capsule; c, peristome; d, tip of leaf. Lower parts of plant reddish; sharp cell at tip of leaf is colorless. e, leaf of *D. trifarius,* which has no papillae on the leaves, and is rare; in the absence of capsules it has been mistaken for *Ceratodon.* The first is common northward, on limestone rocks.

114a Leaves long (3-5 mm.), slender, decurrent, curly when dry, reddish brown. Fig. 93 .... *Barbula cylindrica*

114b Leaves less slender, more or less appressed when dry 115

115a Leaves broadly rounded at apex, with a stout, colorless apiculus. Fig. 92. .... ***Barbula unguiculata***

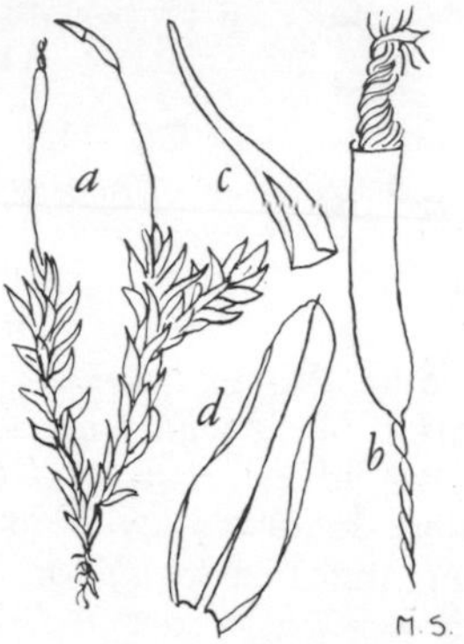

Figure 92

Fig. 92. *Barbula unguiculata.* a, plant; b, capsule and peristome; c, calyptra; d, leaf. Very common in eastern half of United States, on rocks or newly exposed soil. *B. cruegeri* is distinguished by reddish stems and abundant club-shaped gemmae: North Carolina to Missouri, Texas and Florida. *B. convoluta* is similar, but the inner perichaetial leaves are wrapped around the seta; Nova Scotia to Florida; British Columbia to Mexico; Europe.

115b Leaves acute, tapering to apex **116**

116a Midrib covered on ventral (upper) side with elongated cells. Fig. 93 .... ***Barbula fallax***

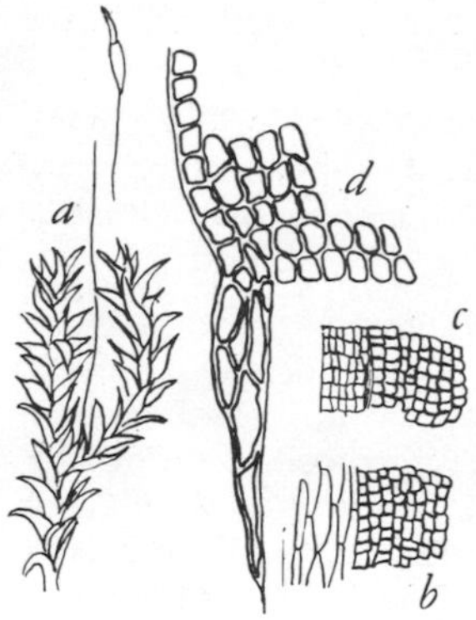

Figure 93

Fig. 93. *Barbula fallax.* a, plant in wet condition; b, cells of midrib and lamina; c, cells of midrib and lamina of *B. vinealis;* d, decurrent leaf base of *B. cylindrica;* Alaska to California, Montana and Mexico. *B. fallax* is common on moist banks northeast, to Iowa. On the west coast *B. vinealis* takes its place; this has small square cells over the midrib. Fifteen other valid species of *Barbula* are recognized in North America.

116b Midrib covered, at least in upper half, with small square cells. Fig. 93 .... ***Barbula vinealis***

117a Colorless cells at base of leaf extending up along the margin .. **118**

117b Not as in 117a **121**

118a Leaves serrate above, with sheathing base .... ***Pleurochaete squarrosa***

118b Leaves entire. Fig. 94. Genus *Tortella* **119**

119a Leaves with nearly parallel sides to near the apex; mucronate. Fig. 94 . . . . ***Tortella humilis***

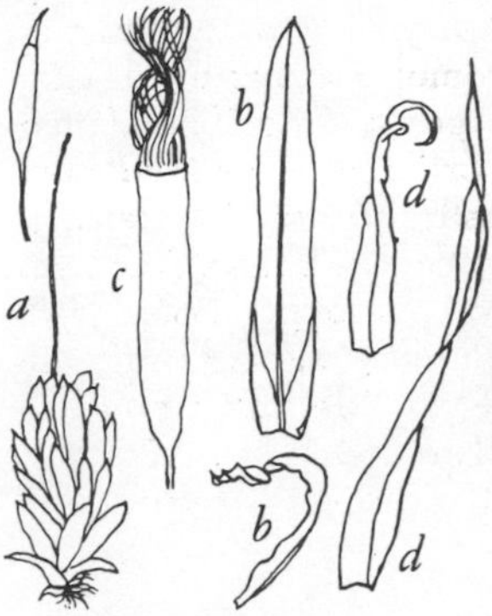

Figure 94

Fig. 94. *Tortella humilis.* a, plant; b, leaf, dry and spread out; c, capsule and peristome. A cluster of antheridia will be found just below the base of the seta. Common in the southeast, on ground, rocks or bases of trees. *Tortella tortuosa,* d, leaf, dry and spread out. *T. fragilis* resembles *T. tortuosa,* but has the tips broken off of most of the leaves. The broken pieces are able to start new plants.

119b Leaves evenly tapering from base to a very slender apex, twisted and coiled when dry **120**

120a Tips of leaves nearly all broken off. Fig. 94 . . . . . . ***Tortella fragilis***

120b Not, or but little, broken. Dry leaves coiled like a corkscrew. Fig. 94 . . . . ***Tortella tortuosa***

121a Leaves toothed on the margin where the colorless cells meet the green ones. Fig. 95 . . . . ***Eucladium verticillatum***

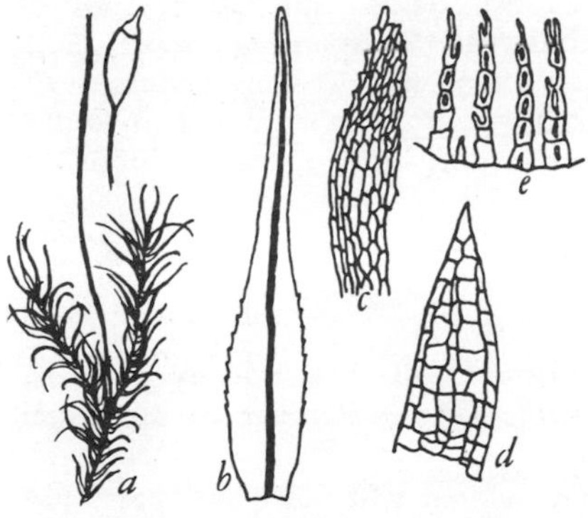

Figure 95

Fig. 95. *Eucladium verticillatum.* a, plant; b, leaf; c, margin; d, apex; e, teeth of peristome. In loose bunches 3-8 cm. tall, yellowish green; leaves curly when dry; sporophytes axillary. Newfoundland to Virginia, California and British Columbia, Europe.

121b Margins entire or wavy **122**

122a Leaves slenderly tapering to apex, to 4 mm. long. Peristome teeth short, slender, irregular. Fig. 96........................ ....*Trichostomum cylindricum*

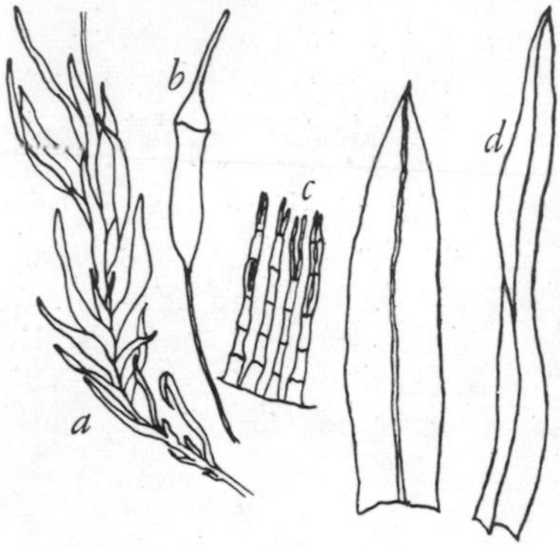

Fig. 96. *Trichostomum cylindricum.* a, plant; b, capsule; c, peristome; d, median and upper leaves. Stem 1-2 cm. tall; seta 1-1.5 cm. On rocks and bases of trees, Greenland to Manitoba, North Carolina and Arizona. Europe.

Figure 96

122b Leaves acute, 1-1.5 mm. long. Peristome lacking. Genus *Gymnostomum* 123

123a Lid of capsule raised up on the columella. Upper cells of leaf distinct. Fig. 97..................*Gymnostomum recurvirostrum*

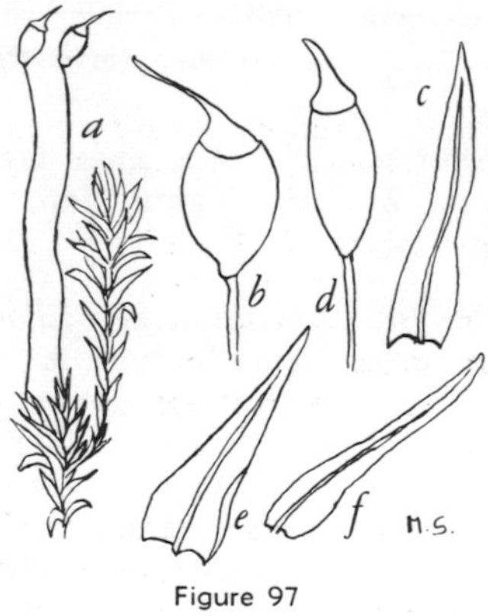

Fig. 97. *Gymnostomum recurvirostrum.* a, plant; b, capsule; c, leaf; d, capsule and e, leaf of *G. aeruginosum.* f, leaf of *G. calcareum. Gymnostomum* forms grey-green tufts or sods on shaded limestone rocks, across the northern half of the continent. *G. calcareum* is the smallest, 1-10 mm. tall. The operculum of *G. recurvirostrum* remains attached to the columella long after it loosens from the urn.

Figure 97

123b Lid falling from the columella. Upper cells obscured by papillae. Fig. 97..........................*Gymnostomum aeruginosum*

124a On bark of trees. Long creeping stems with crowded, erect (2-8 mm.) densely leafy branches on which sporophytes are borne..125

124b. On soil, rocks or bases of trees; not as in 124a.............126

125a Cells near base of leaf small, rounded. Capsule ovoid-globose. Dioicous. Northeastern uplands. Fig. 98..*Drummondia prorepens*

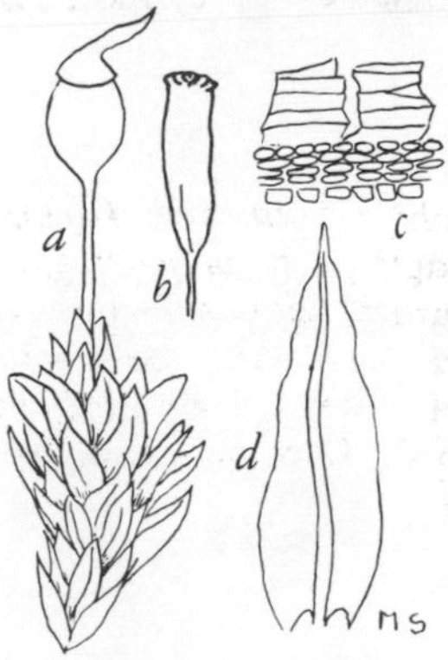

Figure 98

Fig. 98. *Drummondia prorepens.* a, plant; c, peristome; d, leaf. b, capsule of *Schlotheimia sullivantii. Drummondia* is common in southeastern states, rare northward to Vermont and Iowa. It forms broad mats 6 to 8 ft. above the ground, closely attached to bark, and freely fruiting; often on sugar maple. *Schlotheimia* occurs from Virginia and Tennessee to the Gulf. The calyptra covers the capsule, has 4 or 5 slits at the base, and is prickly at the tip.

125b Cells near base of leaf linear. Capsules oblong-cylindric. Monoicous. Southeastern coastal plain. Fig. 98 .... *Schlotheimia sullivantii*

126a Very small mosses. Stems to 4 mm. tall. Hopeless without capsules 127

126b Larger 137

127a Capsules among, or close to the leaves. Seta very short. Peristome lacking 128

127b Seta much longer than the leaves. Peristome of 16 teeth..... 134

128a (b, c) Spores very large, .15 to .25 mm. in diameter, about 24 in each spherical capsule. Calyptra very small. Fig. 99........... .... *Archidium ohioense*

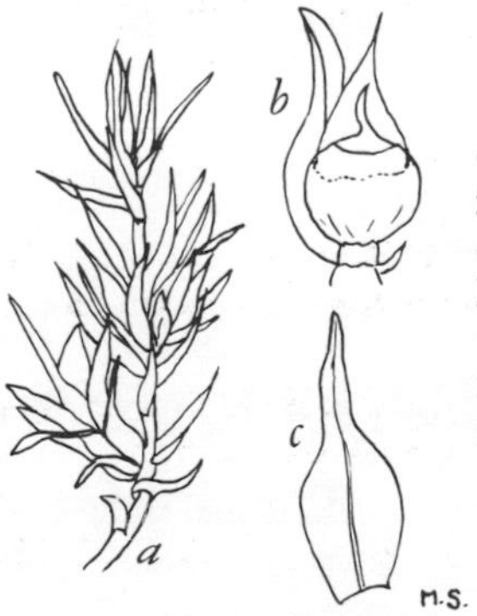

Figure 99

Fig. 99. *Archidium ohioense.* a, plant; b, capsule; c, leaf. Five other species are known in the eastern United States, mostly southeastern. The one figured ranges from Quebec to Minnesota, Texas and Florida. It entirely lacks a columella. Campbell considered it to be a unique and primitive moss. We now consider it a degenerate form.

128b Spores .045 to .070 mm. Calyptra 4-angled, completely covering the capsule. Fig. 100..........................*Pyramidula tetragona*

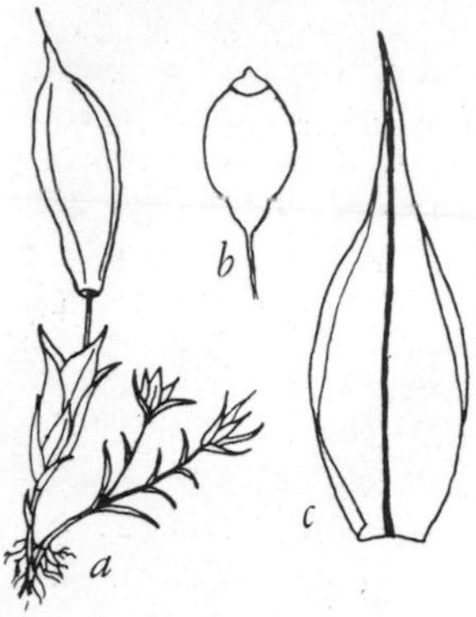

Figure 100

Fig. 100. *Pyramidula tetragona.* a, plant; b, capsule; c, leaf. On cultivated ground in spring. Indiana, Iowa, Minnesota, Colorado, Texas.

128c Spores .020 to .040 mm., numerous. Calyptra smaller, not angled. 129

129a Leaves linear-lanceolate, spreading, curly or wavy when dry. Capsule red, very minute. Whole plant hardly visible. Fig. 101. ....*Nanomitrium austinii*

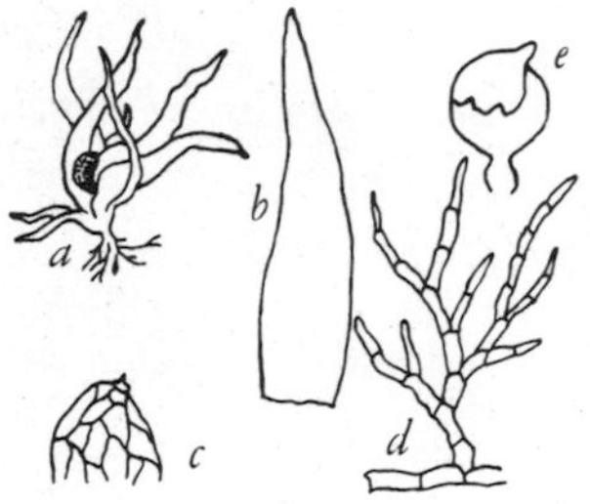

Figure 101

Fig. 101. *Nanomitrium austinii.* a, plant; b, leaf; c, calyptra on capsule; d, protonema; e, calyptra and capsule of *Ephemerum crassinervium.* Usually in extensive patches of 1 to 40 square feet, in incredible numbers, but extremely rare and local. Capsule about .2 mm. in diameter.

129b Leaves erect or bent when dry; larger........................130

130a Leaves broadly ovate or elliptic...............................133

130b Leaves ovate at base, with a filiform tip longer than the base..131

131a Capsules pear-shaped, with a conspicuous neck. Figs. 103, 104. Genus *Bruchia*..132

131b Capsules spherical (without neck). Fig. 102..*Pleuridium subulatum*

Figure 102

Fig. 102. *Pleuridium subulatum.* a, plant; b, leaf enlarged; c, cells of leaf; d, similar cells of *P. acuminatum.* These pygmies (2-5 mm. tall) occur in dense velvety clusters amongst grasses and weeds, fruiting in May. There are 7 species of *Pleuridium* in North America, from Atlantic to Pacific, and Canada to Gulf.

132a (b, c) Spores spinose. Fig. 103, 104...........*Bruchia sullivanti*

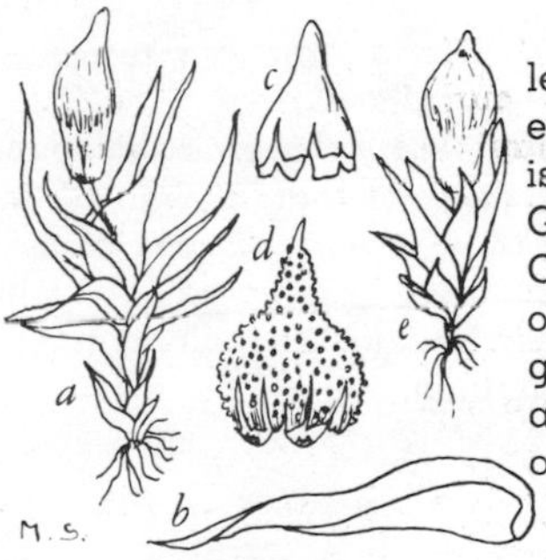

Figure 103

Fig. 103. *Bruchia sullivanti.* a, plant; b, leaf; c, calyptra; d, calyptra of *B. ravenelii;* e, plant of *B. brevifolia.* The first of these is found from Maine to Minnesota and the Gulf; the other two are southeastern, North Carolina to Texas. All are very small, not over 3 mm. in total height, mostly gregarious, fruiting in spring. Eleven species are recorded for North America; very rare on the Pacific slope.

132b Spores reticulate. Seta mostly longer than leaves. Fig. 104...... ....*Bruchia texana*

132c Spores pitted. Figs. 103, 104..................*Bruchia brevifolia*

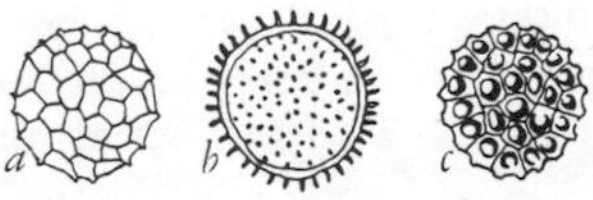

Figure 104

Fig. 104. *Bruchia texana.* a, spore; *B. ravenelii is similar;* b, spore of *B. sullivanti; B. flexuosa* is similar; c, spore of *B. brevifolia.*

133a Capsule with distinct operculum, urn-shaped when dry. Fig. 105. ....*Physcomitrium immersum*

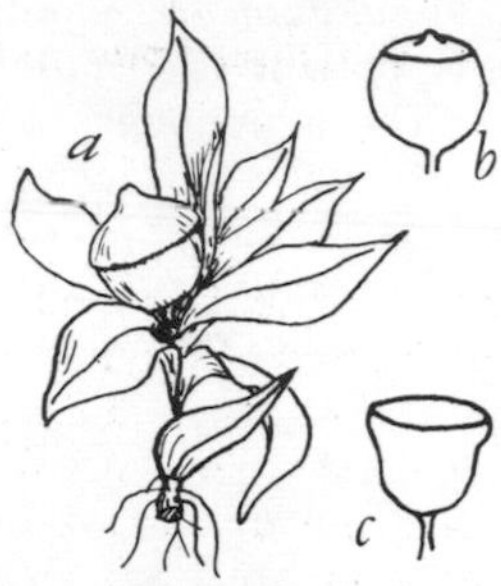

Figure 105

Fig. 105. *Physcomitrium immersum.* a, plant; b, capsule just mature; c, old capsule. Often abundant on silty banks of rivers or lakes, along with *Aphanorhegma serratum,* which has capsules globular both wet and dry.

133b Capsule opening irregularly around the middle, or breaking irregularly. Figs. 105, 106................*Aphanorhegma serratum*

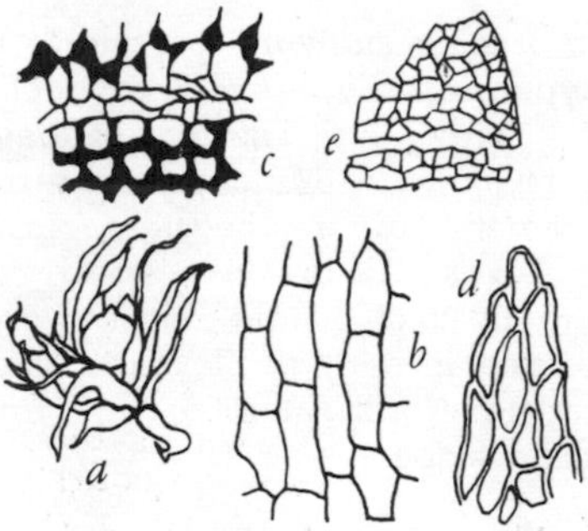

Figure 106

Fig. 106. *Aphanorhegma serratum.* a, plant; b, cells of leaf; c, cells of outer wall of capsule, with thickened walls; d, apex of leaf; e, line of dehiscence of *A. patens.* These mosses are often very abundant on silty banks and bottom land along rivers, in late autumn.

134a (b, c) Minute velvety films on limestone rocks. Peristome teeth entire (or lacking). Fig. 107..............*Seligeria campylopoda*

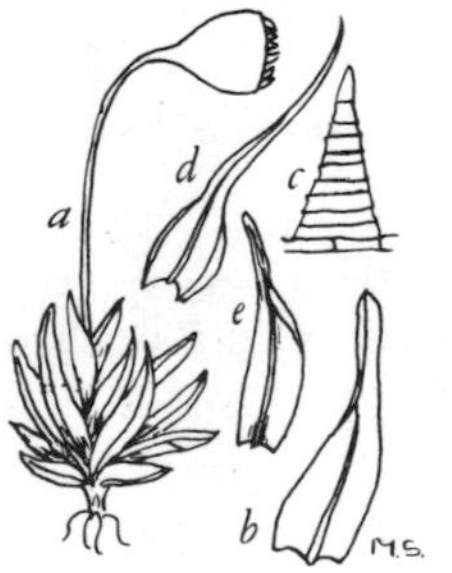

Figure 107

Fig. 107. *Seligeria campylopoda.* a, plant; b, leaf; c, peristome tooth; d, leaf of *S. pusilla;* e, leaf of *S. calcarea. S. doniana* has no peristome. These tiny mosses grow in velvety coatings on cool, shaded rocks, often in deep crevices. They are barely visible, and must be scraped off the rock with a knife blade. The seta is erect on all but *S. campylopoda.*

134b On soil. Teeth split half way down. Genus *Dicranella*.......135

134c On soil. Teeth divided into 2 threads. Fig. 108...............
..*Ditrichum pusillum*

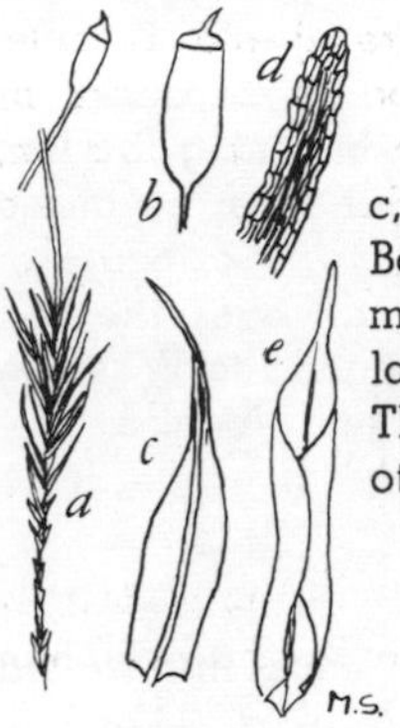

Figure 108

Fig. 108. *Ditrichum pusillum*. a, plant; b, capsule; c, leaf; d, apex of leaf; e, perichaetial leaf of *D. lineare*. Both species occur on freshly exposed clay, the former Labrador to Alaska, California and the Gulf; the latter New Brunswick to South Carolina and Missouri. They sometimes grow together and merge into each other.

135a Apex of leaf blunt, rounded, the midrib ending below it. Fig. 109.
..*Dicranella hilariana*

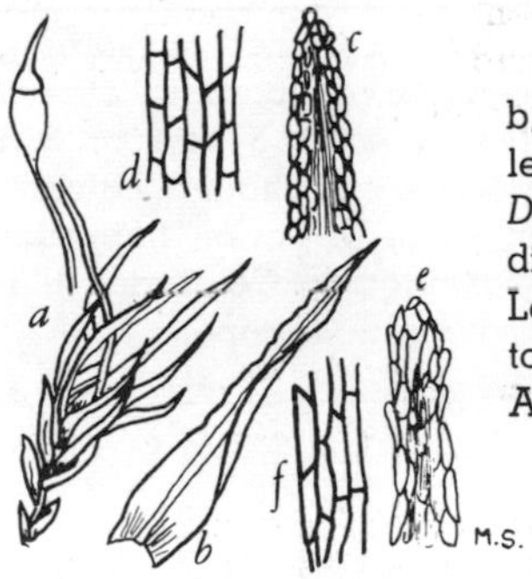

Figure 109

Fig. 109. *Dicranella hilariana*. a, plant; b, leaf; c, apex of leaf; d, median cells of leaf; e, leaf apex, and f, median cells of *D. herminieri*. Moist banks and sides of ditches, South Carolina to Florida and Louisiana, the two species often growing together. *D. hilariana* extends to South America.

135b Apex of most leaves acute, with midrib percurrent or excurrent.
..136

136a Capsules erect when dry and empty. Fig. 110...............
..*Dicranella rufescens*

136b Capsules inclined to one side, unsymmetric. Fig. 110. . . . . *Dicranella varia*

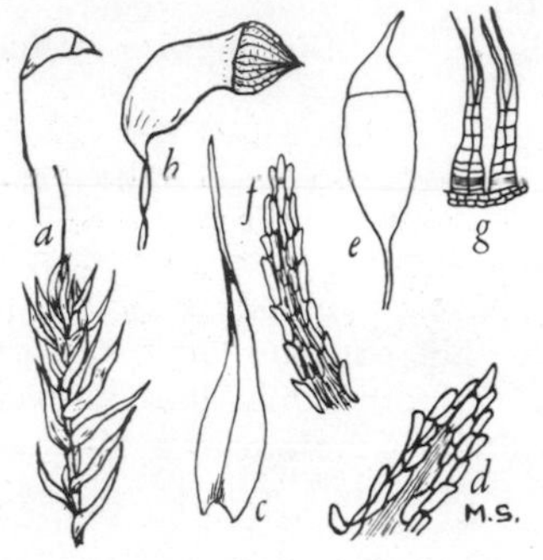

Figure 110

Fig. 110. *Dicranella varia.* a, plant; b, capsule, old; c, leaf; d, f, apex of leaf; e, capsule of *D. rufescens;* g, peristome Capsules smooth, not furrowed. D. *rufescens* has a plump erect capsule and clear (pellucid) cells composing the leaf. The cells of other *Dicranellas* are densely chlorophyllose. *D. varia* appears on freshly exposed clay all over the continent; *D. rufescens* Virginia to Washington, New Hampshire and Alaska.

137a Leaves 3-ranked. Stems triangular, the outer cells thin-walled, colorless. Capsules globular. Peristome double. Fig. 111. . . . . *Plagiopus oederi*

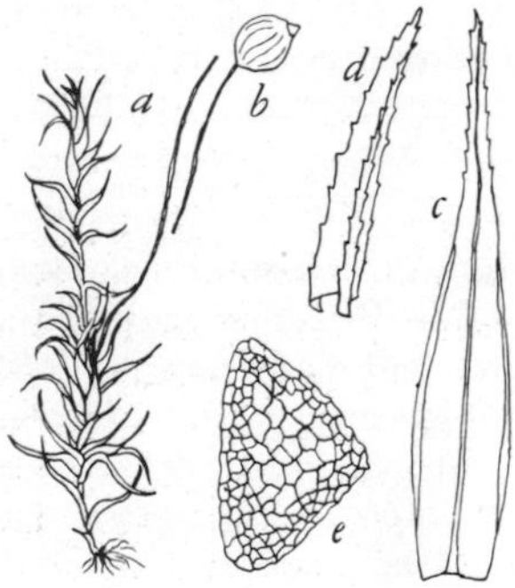

Figure 111

Fig. 111. *Plagiopus oederi.* a, shoot; b, capsule; c, leaf; d, apex of leaf; e, section of stem. In dense, often hemispheric tufts, 3-9 cm. tall; leaf margins widely recurved, toothed on the edge and on the recurved portion; otherwise not papillose. Leaves 3 to 4 or 5 mm. long. Synoicous. In shaded calcareous ravines, on earth or rocks, Labrador to Alaska, Washington, Colorado, Illinois and Pennsylvania. Europe.

137b Leaves 5—many-ranked. 138

138a Leaves 6 to 20 times as long as broad, mostly long-tapering to a slender upper half. 139

138b Leaves 1 to 5 times as long as broad. 162

139a Cells at basal angles of leaf (alar cells) enlarged, often with brown walls 140

139b Alar cells not notably enlarged. 154

140a (b, c) Peristome teeth undivided. Capsule cylindrical, erect, 1.5-2 mm. long. Leaves curly when dry. Fig. 112. .*Dicranoweisia cirrata*

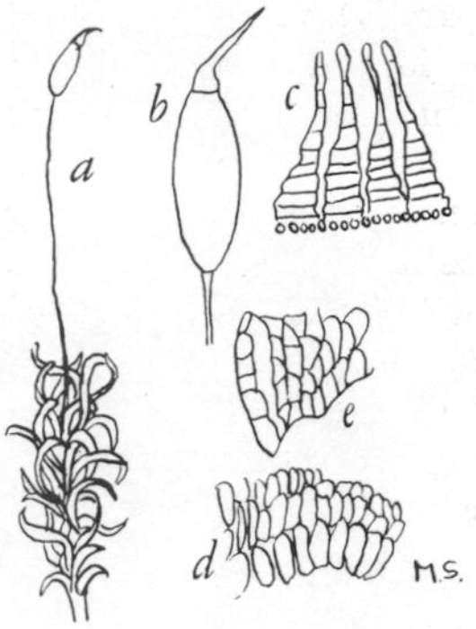

Figure 112

Fig. 112. *Dicranoweisia cirrata.* a, plant, dry; b, capsule; c, peristome; d, alar cells; e, alar cells of *D. crispula.* Small mosses in dense sods 1-2 cm. tall, common from Alaska to California and Arizona; extremely rare northeast.

140b Peristome teeth undivided or split at the tip. Capsule pear-shaped, erect, about 1 mm. long. Leaves erect or bent to one side. Fig. 113. . . . . *Blindia acuta*

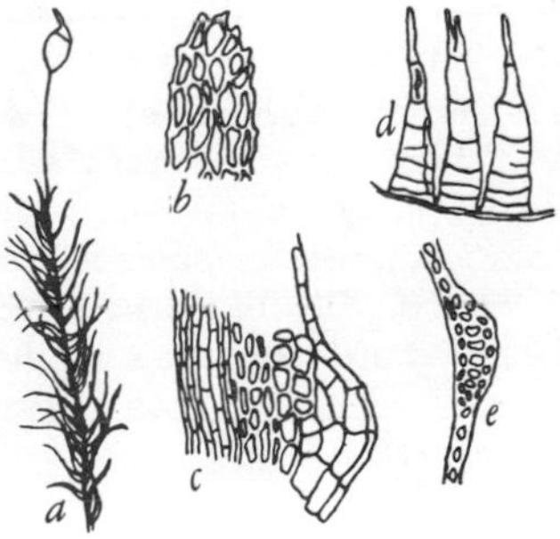

Figure 113

Fig. 113. *Blindia acuta.* a, plant; b, apex of leaf; c, base of leaf; d, teeth; e, section of midrib. In loose, glossy tufts 2-6 cm. tall, dark green to blackish. Leaves 2-3 mm. long. Wet rocks in high altitudes and latitudes: California 7500 ft.; Greenland to Alaska, California, Minnesota and New York. Europe.

140c Peristome teeth split half way down 141

141a Midrib narrow, 1/3 to 1/10 of leaf at base 142

141b Midrib wide, 1/3 to 7/8 of leaf at base 151

142a Leaves very brittle, mostly broken off. Midrib without stereids. Fig. 114 .... ***Dicranum strictum***

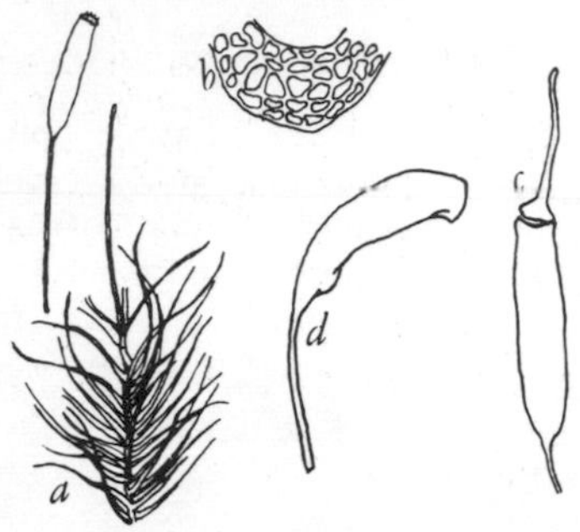

Figure 114

Fig. 114. *Dicranum strictum.* a, plant; b, section of midrib; c, capsule. On rotten wood Alaska to California and Wyoming. d, capsule of *Arctoa starkei.* Plants 1-3 cm. tall. High altitudes and latitudes, south to New Hampshire, Montana and Washington.

142b Leaves not easily broken **143**

143a Midrib without stereids. Leaves curly when dry. Fig. 114 .... ***Arctoa starkei***

143b Midrib with stereid bands **144**

144a Base of leaf broad, clasping, abruptly narrowed to the slender upper portion. Capsules strumose. Fig. 115 .... ***Oncophorus wahlenbergii***

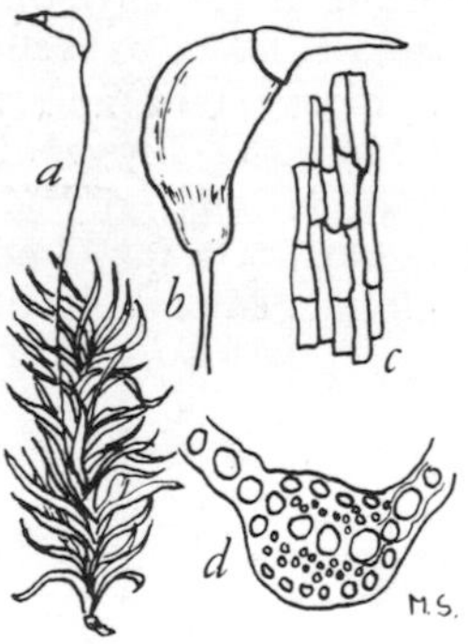

Figure 115

Fig. 115. *Oncophorus wahlenbergii.* a, plant; b, capsule; c, alar cells; d, cross section of leaf. Tufts of silky texture, in cool, mountainous regions. Nine other species are known in North America. *O. polycarpus* and *O. virens* are frequent northward and in the Rocky Mountains. *O. polycarpus* has a furrowed capsule, suberect, usually not strumose.

144b Leaves evenly tapering from base upward. Capsules not strumose. Genus *Dicranum* **145**

145a Upper cells of leaf 4 to 6 times longer than wide, with thick, pitted walls. Capsules curved **146**

145b Upper cells nearly isodiametric, not pitted **148**

146a Leaves large (to 10 mm.), crinkled (undulate). Two or 3 setae on one stem. Fig. 116............................*Dicranum rugosum*

146b Leaves not undulate, mostly all turned to one side..........147

147a Leaves to 15 mm. long. Setae 2 to 5 on one stem. Fig. 116..*Dicranum majus*

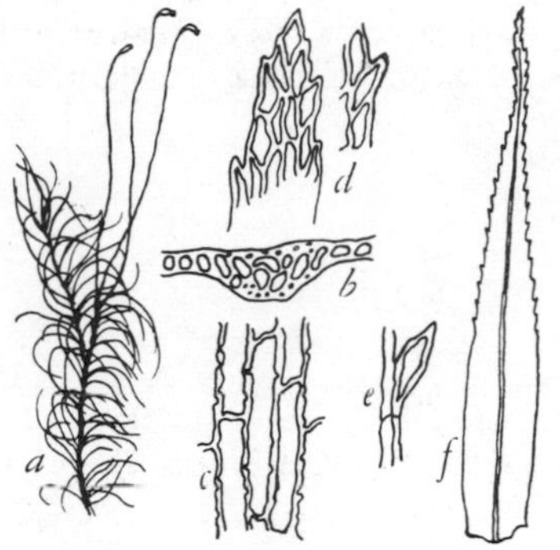

Figure 116

Fig. 116. *Dicranum majus*. a, plant; b, section of midrib; c. lower cells; d, apex and tooth of leaf; e, tooth of leaf, and f, leaf of *D. rugosum*. British Columbia to Oregon, West Virginia and Newfoundland. Europe.

147b Leaves rarely 9 mm. long, with 2 to 4 toothed ridges or wings on back of midrib. One seta to a stem. Fig. 117...*Dicranum scoparium*

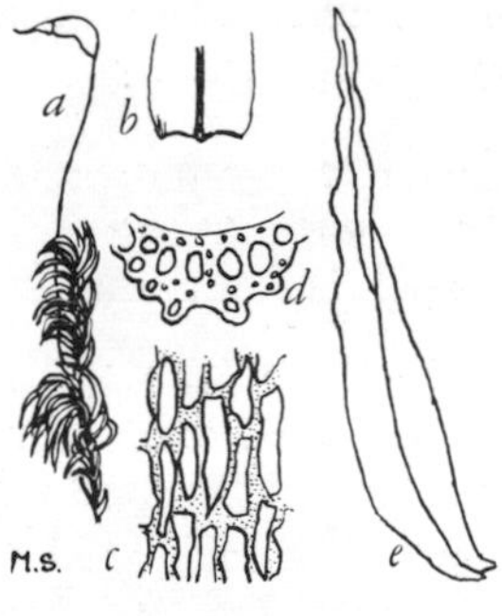

Figure 117

Fig. 117. *Dicranum scoparium*. a, plant; b, base of leaf showing width of midrib; c, upper cells of leaf; d, cross section of midrib; e, leaf of *D. bonjeani*. Large, common mosses in dense, shiny clumps, green to yellowish green, up to 3 in. tall. Almost universal in the north temperate zone. When *D. bonjeani* has wide wings on the back of the midrib it is *var. alatum*.

148a Leaves erect, nearly straight when dry. Capsule erect, straight. Fig. 118..............................*Dicranum rhabdocarpum*

148b Leaves curly when dry....................................149

149a Midrib 1/3 of leaf at base. Dark green patches on rocks. Fig. 118 .... *Dicranum fulvum*

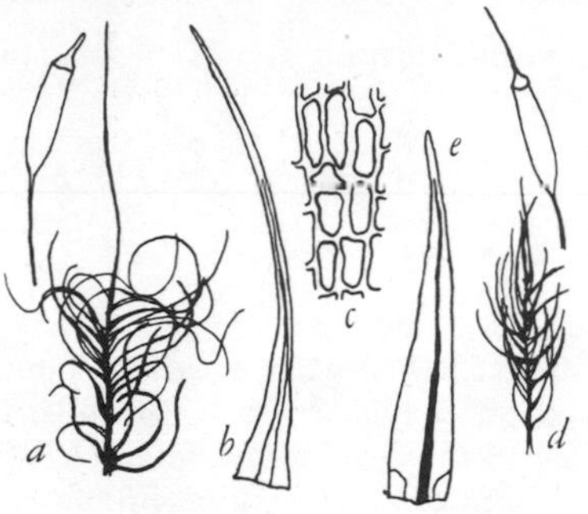

Figure 118

Fig. 118. *Dicranum fulvum.* a, plant; b, leaf; c, median cells. Stems 2 to 4 cm. long; leaves 5 mm. Nova Scotia to Georgia, Missouri and Minnesota. d, shoot of *D. rhabdocarpum;* e, leaf. Colorado, New Mexico, Arizona, Mexico; stems 2 to 4 cm. tall.

149b Midrib 1/4 to 1/9 of leaf at base 150

150a With slender, erect, scaly shoots (flagella); capsule erect. Fig. 119 .... *Dicranum flagellare*

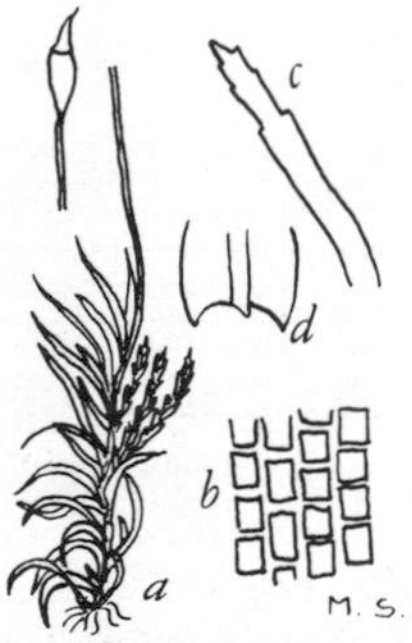

Figure 119

Fig. 119. *Dicranum flagellare.* a, plant with capsule and flagella; b, cells from upper part of leaf; c, apex of leaf; d, base of leaf showing relative width of midrib. In dense cushions and sods, to 1 in. thick, on rotten wood, in damp, shady places. In all of North America except the extreme southeast and southwest. Also in Europe.

150b Without flagella. Capsules curved. Fig. 120 .... *Dicranum fuscescens*

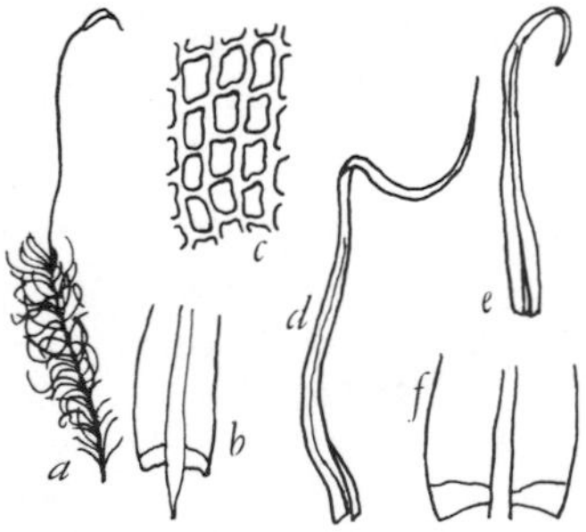

Figure 120

Fig. 120. *Dicranum fuscescens.* a, plant; b, base of leaf showing relative width of midrib; c, upper cells of leaf; d, a dry curly leaf; e, dry leaf of *D. condensatum*; f, base of leaf of same. *D. fuscescens* is common and luxuriant along the northwest coast, less so in the northeast. *D. condensatum* is southeastern, from New Jersey and Arkansas southward.

151a Midrib with stereid bands..................................152

151b Midrib without stereids or guide cells, very wide............153

152a Midrib with dorsal and ventral stereid bands, with guide cells between; surface cells large, similar on both sides. Fig. 121.... ....*Dicranodontium denudatum*

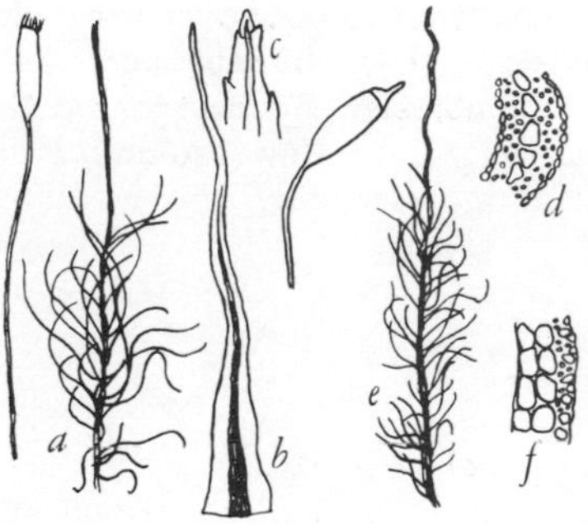

Figure 121

Fig. 121. *Dicranodontium denudatum.* a, plant; b, leaf; c, apex of leaf; d, section of midrib. Tufts on rocks, 2 to 5 cm. tall; New England to Florida and Alaska; e. plant of *Campylopus flexuosus;* f, section of midrib. One to 4 cm. tall, in dense clumps; Ohio; Europe. Eight other species of *Campylopus* occur in southeastern United States, west to Arizona.

152b Midrib with large clear cells ventrally; dorsally with strands of stereids alternating with large clear cells. Fig. 121............ ....*Campylopus flexuosus*

153a With clusters of fusiform gemmae whose surface cells are clear and empty. Fig. 122............................*Brothera leana*

153b Without gemmae. Midrib of 3 or 4 layers of uniform cells. Fig. 122.............................*Paraleucobryum longifolium*

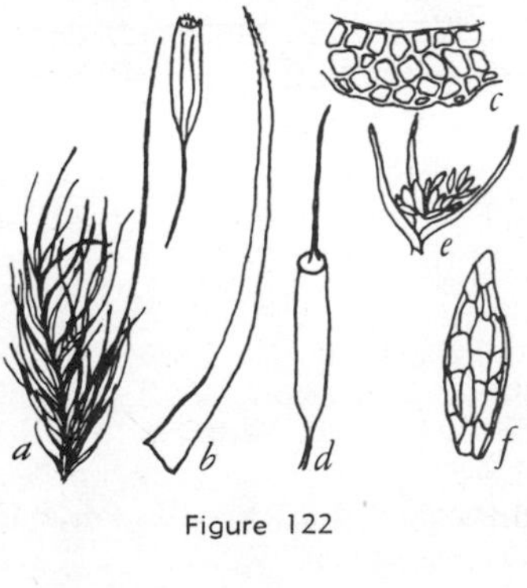

Figure 122

Fig. 122. *Paraleucobryum longifolium.* a, plant; b, leaf (4-7 mm. long); c, section of midrib; d, capsule. Newfoundland to North Carolina, Colorado and Alaska. e, gemmae of *Brothera leana;* f, one gemma. Whitish, resembling a *Leucobryum.* Pennsylvania to Iowa and Minnesota; Siberia; Japan.

154a **Cells of lamina 6 to 10 times as long as wide. Midrib occupies most of leaf. Capsule nodding, pear-shaped. Peristome double. Fig. 123................................*Leptobryum pyriforme***

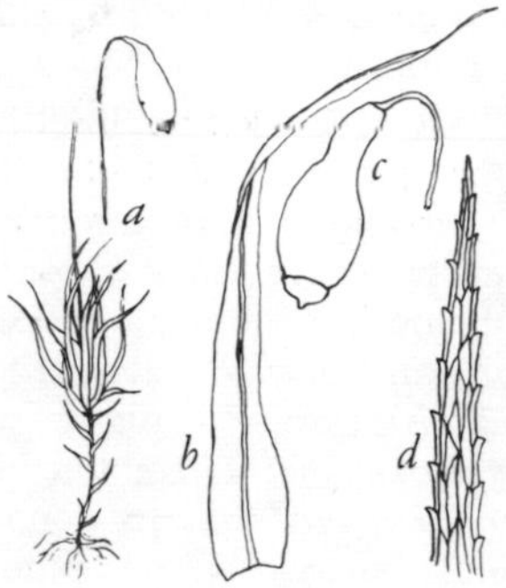

Figure 123

Fig. 123. *Leptobryum pyriforme*. a, plant; b, leaf; c, capsule; d, apex of leaf. Everywhere, especially on newly disturbed soil. The brown semi-transparent capsules with narrow, wrinkled neck are unmistakable. Up to 10,000 ft. in Colorado; Spitzbergen to the Alps and Caucasus, Asia, New Zealand; Patagonia to Brazil and Ecuador.

154b **Cells of lamina 1 to 6 times as long as wide................155**

155a **Midrib narrow, percurrent. Margin of leaves thickened, toothed. Capsules horizontal; peristome double. Fig. 124.. *Rhizogonium spiniforme***

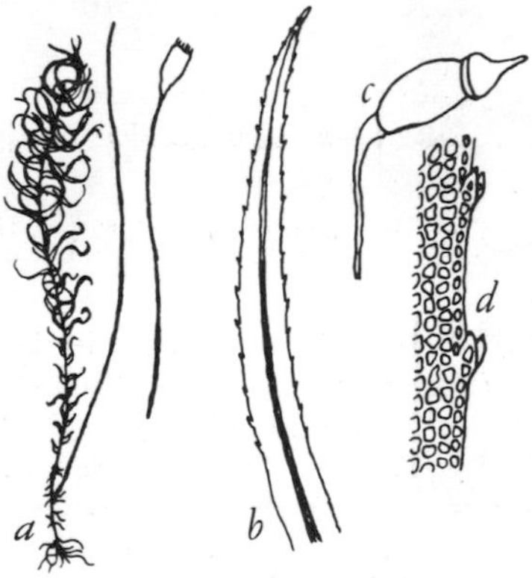

Figure 124

Fig. 124. *Rhizogonium spiniforme*. a, a twig; b, leaf, c, capsule; d, margin of leaf. In tufts 3-4 cm. tall, Georgia to Florida and Louisiana. A tropical genus and family (*Rhizogoniaceae*) related to *Mniaceae*. Teeth of leaf in pairs.

155b **Midrib slender; margins of leaf not toothed if thickened. Peristome single 156**

156a Neck of capsule about as long as urn. Autoicous. Fig. 125..... .... *Trematodon longicollis*

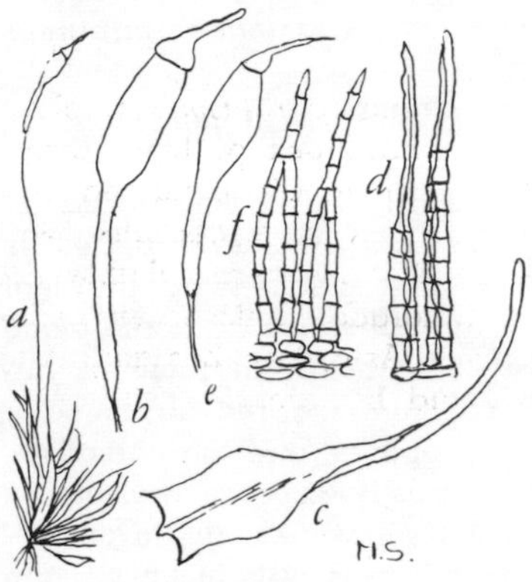

Figure 125

Fig. 125. *Trematodon longicollis.* a, plant; b, capsule; c, leaf; d, teeth of peristome; e, capsule of *T. ambiguus;* f, peristome. On moist, sandy soil, Newfoundland to Florida and Louisiana.

156b Without noticeable neck. Peristome teeth 16.................157

157a (b, c) Teeth split to base into 2 threads....................158

157b Teeth cleft half way down.................................161

157c Teeth lanceolate, not cleft at all. Leaves 2-3 mm. long, erect, not filiform; margins plane. Capsules ribbed. Fig. 126.............. .... *Rhabdoweisia denticulata*

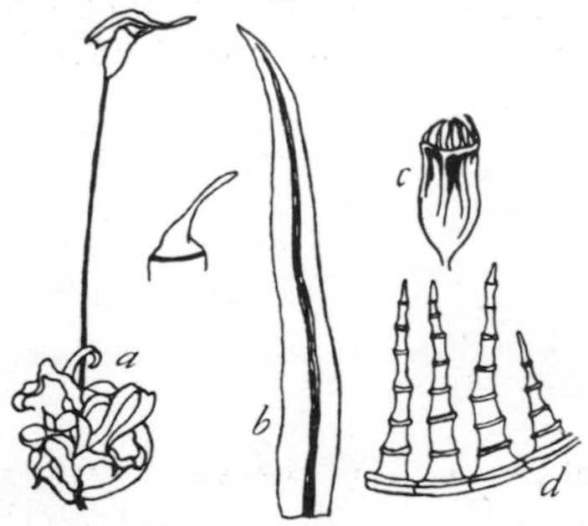

Figure 126

Fig. 126. *Rhabdoweisia denticulata.* a, plant; b, leaf; c, capsule, old; d, peristome. On shaded vertical rocks or overhangs, in wide, dense beds 5-8 mm. deep, from far north to North Carolina, Tennessee and Missouri. Europe. Typically with leaves distinctly toothed, but eastern plants have entire leaves: var. *americana.*

158a Leaves 5 to 6 times as long as broad, flat; margins revolute to near apex, then plane and toothed. Peristome of 16 pairs of threads, curved into a dome shape. Fig. 127.................. ....*Ceratodon purpureus*

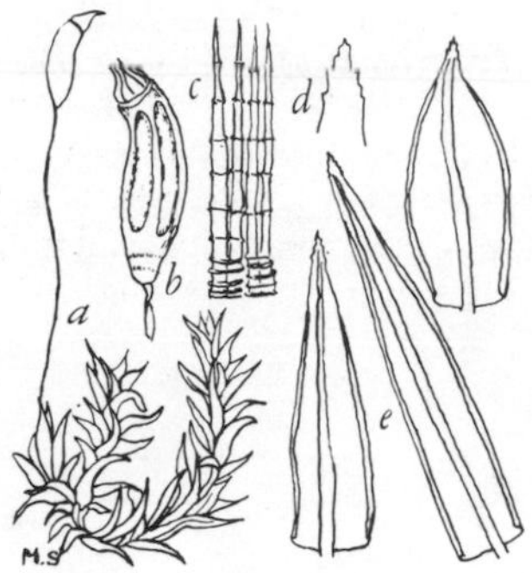

Figure 127

Fig. 127. *Ceratodon purpureus.* a, plant; b, capsule; c, peristome; d, apex of leaf; e, extreme forms of leaf. This cosmopolitan species is perfectly characterized by the leaf with margins revolute up to the plane and few-toothed tip, the inclined, furrowed capsule, the red-purple color of the sporophyte, and the peristome. It grows mostly in very dry places —on walls, sidewalks, dry ground— but also in purple tufts in lawns, and even in swamps. Extremely variable in size and shape of leaves.

158b Leaves with ovate to lanceolate base, shorter than the long, slender upper portion. Peristome of 32 separate, entire, erect or wavy threads. Plants gregarious. Figs. 128-130. Genus *Ditrichum..159**

159a Upper part of leaf concave, channeled....................160

159b Leaf is mostly a slender, rough awn. Capsules slender, cylindric. Fig. 128................................*Ditrichum cylindricum*

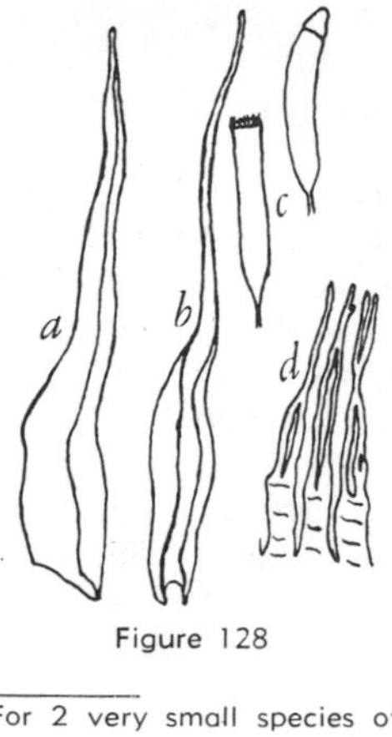

Figure 128

Fig. 128. *Ditrichum cylindricum.* a, median leaf; b, upper leaf; c, capsules; d, teeth. Stems about 5 mm. long; seta 1-1.5 cm. Montana, Nevada, Washington and northward.

*For 2 very small species of *Ditrichum* see Fig. 108.

160a Stems to 5 mm. long; in dense yellowish tufts on soil; seta yellow. Antheridia in axillary buds below the seta. Fig. 129. . . . . *Ditrichum pallidum*

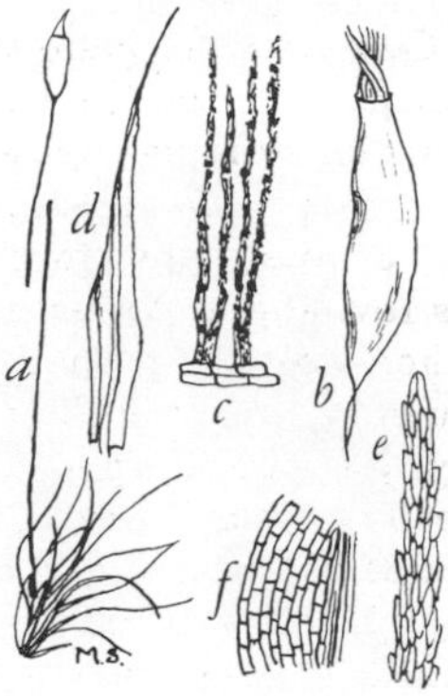

Figure 129

Fig. 129. *Ditrichum pallidum.* a, plant; b, capsule; c, peristome; d, leaf; e, apex of leaf; f, basal cells of leaf. Common in dry grassy places or in thin woods, eastern United States, making conspicuous little silky sods, with long yellow setae. Also in Europe.

160b Stems 2-10 cm. tall, brown below and matted together. Leaves usually bent to one side (secund). Fig. 130. . . . *Ditrichum flexicaule*

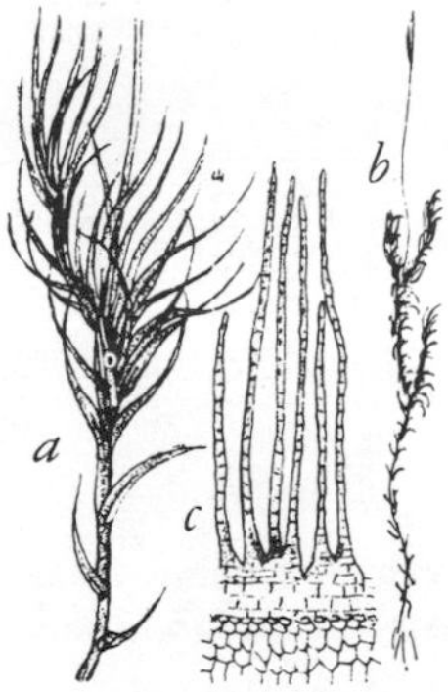

Figure 130

Fig. 130. *Ditrichum flexicaule.* a, plant, enlarged; b, plant natural size; c, peristome. Dense matted clumps 2-10 cm. tall. Greenland to Ontario, Minnesota, British Columbia and Alaska. Europe. Var. *brevifolium* Ontario, Wisconsin, Minnesota.

*For 4 very small species of *Dicranella* see Figs. 109, 110.

161a Leaves bent to one side, not sheathing at base. Midrib 1/3 of leaf at base. Fig. 131 .... *Dicranella heteromalla**

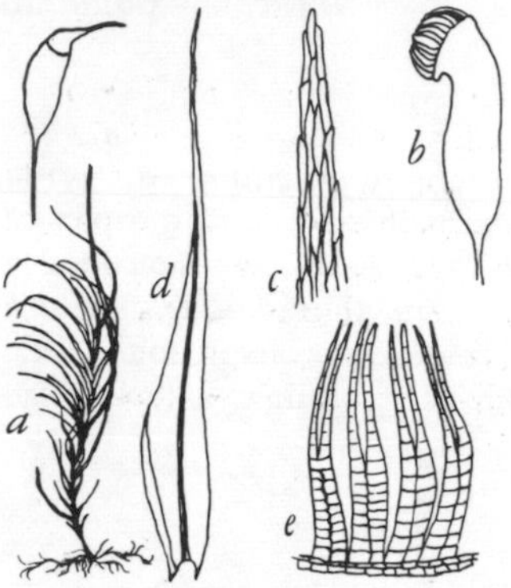

Figure 131

Fig. 131. *Dicranella heteromalla.* a, plant; b, capsule; c, apex of leaf; d, leaf; e, peristome. This moss is abundant on wooded banks in the eastern United States, often covering many square yards with a silky green carpet. The "chuck under the chin" makes the mouth of the dry capsule oblique.

161b Leaves sheathing at base, strongly squarrose, not falcate. Midrib 1/10 of leaf at base. Fig. 132 .... *Dicranella schreberi*

Figure 132

Fig. 132. *Dicranella schreberi.* a, plant; b, capsule with lid; c, base of leaf; d, apex of leaf. In silky tufts about 1 in. tall, Pennsylvania to Oregon and British Columbia. Three other species have the wide clasping base of leaf, with leaves squarrose recurved. *D. squarrosa* grows in wet ground and in bogs; northern.

162a Leaves dense and blackish; upper cells mostly isodiametric and small, thick-walled. Peristome single or lacking. Figs. 133-140. Family Grimmiaeae 163

162b Leaves bright or dark green 181

163a Walls of leaf cells closely and evenly wavy. Peristome teeth 16, split nearly to base into 2 or 3 slender prongs. Figs. 133, 134. Genus *Rhacomitrium* 164

163b Walls smooth, or irregularly wavy at middle of leaf 166

*For 4 very small species of *Dicranella* see Figs. 109, 110.

164a Leaves with a strongly papillose, scalloped hair-point. Fig. 133. .... ***Rhacomitrium lanuginosum***

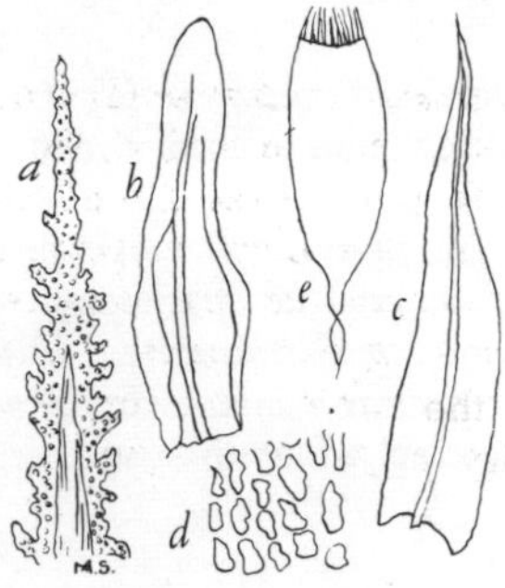

Figure 133

Fig. 133. *Rhacomitrium lanuginosum.* a, apex of leaf; b, leaf of *R. aciculare;* c, leaf of *R. heterostichum;* d, cells of lower part of leaf, and e, capsule of the last. Common on rocks, north and northwest. Seven other species occur in North America. *R. heterostichum* is extremely variable. Some species are faintly papillose.

164b Hair points smooth or absent 165

165a (b, c) Leaves rounded and toothed at apex. Fig. 133 .... ***Rhacomitrium aciculare***

165b Leaves with a colorless hair-point. Fig. 133 .... ***Rhacomitrium heterostichum***

165c Leaves acute, without a hair-point. Capsule 3-4 mm. long. Fig. 134 .... ***Rhacomitrium varium***

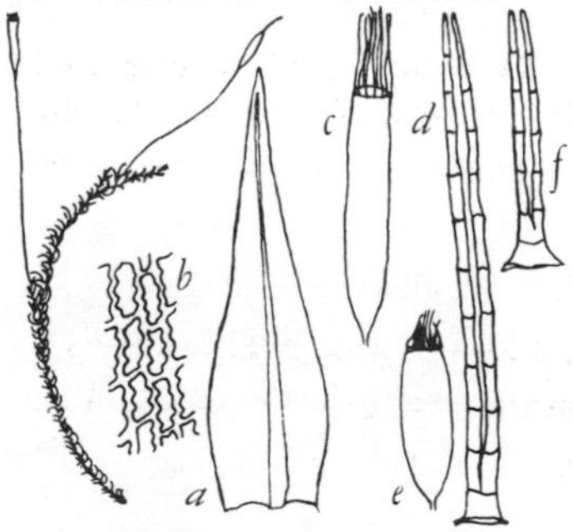

Figure 134

Fig. 134. *Rhacomitrium varium.* a, leaf; b, upper cells; c, capsule; d, peristome. Robust plants, California to Alaska; e, capsule; f, peristome of *R. fasciculare.* Stems 8-10 cm. long; California to Alaska; Europe, Asia.

166a Leaves bearing rhizoids at base. Seta shorter than leaves. On rocks in streams. Western. Fig. 135 .... *Scouleria aquatica*

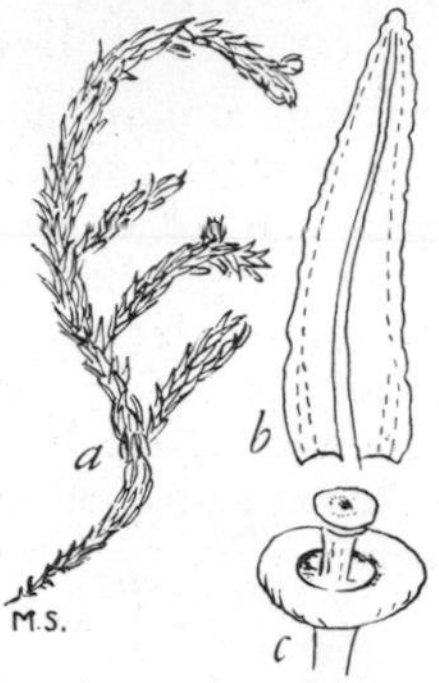

Figure 135

Fig. 135. *Scouleria aquatica.* a, plant; b, leaf; c, capsule. Large mosses on rocks in streams, Alaska to Wyoming and California. *S. marginata* has the leaves 2 cells thick along the margins; it has no peristome at all, but the peristome of *S. aquatica* often falls off with the operculum. Stems to 15 cm. long, more or less branched, with large, stiff leaves.

166b Leaves without rhizoids 167

167a Plants in blackish tufts on rocks or trees, 7-30 mm. tall. Leaves without hair-points, closely curved over each other when dry. Calyptra nearly covering capsule, slit into several linear strips. Peristome teeth split into 2 threads. Fig. 13. Genus *Ptychomitrium.* 168

167b Calyptra various. Peristome teeth narrowly triangular, often irregularly perforated or cleft, or lacking. Figs. 136-140. Genus *Grimmia* 169

168a Leaves entire. On rocks. Eastern. Fig. 13 .... *Ptychomitrium incurvum**

168b Leaves serrate on upper half. On trees. Southeastern .... *Ptychomitrium drummondii***

169a On rocks on the seashore. Leaves 2 or 3 cells thick in upper part. Seta shorter than leaves .... *Grimmia maritima*

169b On inland rocks, at all altitudes 170

*A large species, western Texas to Arizona, is *P. leibergii.*

**A large (3-4 cm.) toothed species, British Columbia to California, on rocks is *P. gardneri.*

170a Leaves ovate in the lower half, the cells nearly uniformly quadrate to the base. Margins revolute. Capsules surrounded by leaves. Columella attached to lid and falling with it. Fig. 136. .... *Grimmia apocarpa*

Figure 136

Fig. 136. *Grimmia apocarpa*. a, plant; b, sporophyte in perichaetial leaves; c, tooth of peristome; d, peristome; e, cross section of margin of leaf; f, calyptra; g, calyptra of var. *alpicola*. Very common tufted, black moss on rocks. The tufts readily break into separate stems. *G. apocarpa* is the commonest *Grimmia* in the eastern United States. The midrib projects as a ridge on the back of the leaf. Peristome red; ripe in April.

170b Lower cells of leaf colorless, longer than upper cells.......171

171a Leaves linear-lanceolate, curled and twisted when dry, yellowish, translucent (glassy)...................... *Grimmia torquata*

171b Leaves broader, opaque, ending in a colorless hair...........172

172a Leaf margins plane or bent upward. Leaves not keeled......173

172b Margins plane or revolute. Leaves sharply folded along the midrib (keeled), at least above..............................176

173a Margins curved upward; leaf concave......................174

173b Margins plane, flat..175

174a Leaves 2-2.5 mm. long; median cell cavities irregularly elliptical. Seta longer than leaves, straight. Dioicous. Western. Fig. 137. .... *Grimmia ovalis*

174b Leaves 1-2 mm. long; median cells quadrate with slightly rounded corners. Seta straight, 1.5-3 mm. long. Basal marginal cells (4-6 rows) colorless, with thick transverse walls. Fig. 137 .... *Grimmia montana*

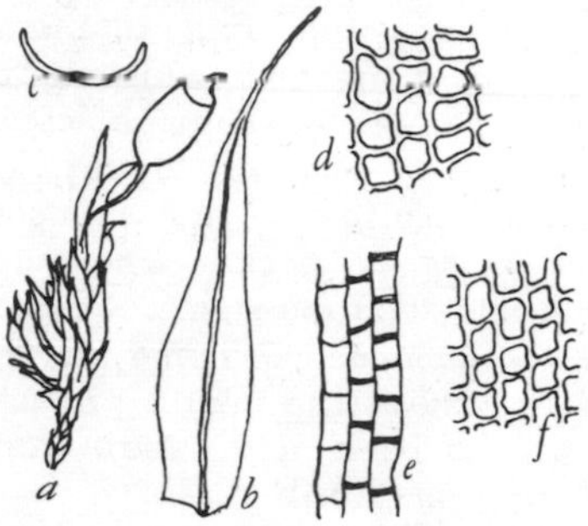

Figure 137

Fig. 137. *Grimmia montana.* a, plant; b, leaf; c, section of leaf; d, median cells; e, basal marginal cells. *G. alpestris* is a smaller form: leaves 1-1.5 mm. long. Both occur British Columbia to Montana and Arizona. f, median cells of *G. ovalis (G. commutata* of MFNA); leaves 2-2.5 mm. long. British Columbia to Minnesota and Arizona.

175a Midrib flat, even with surface on back of leaf. Hair point decurrent. Capsule partly covered by leaves. Fig. 138 .... *Grimmia laevigata*

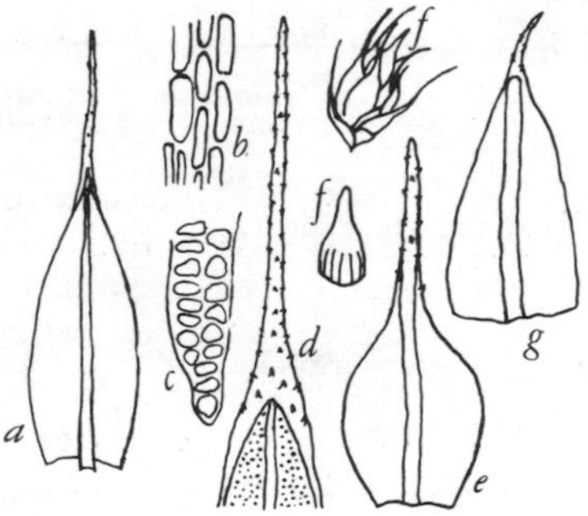

Figure 138

Fig. 138. *Grimmia laevigata.* a, leaf; b, median cells; c, section of leaf; d, decurrent awn; e, leaf of *G. wrightii;* f, plant and calyptra, g, leaf of *G. raui.* Minnesota to Texas and Arizona.

175b Midrib forms a ridge on back of leaf 176

176a Calyptra bowl-shaped, nearly covering the symmetrical capsule. Fig. 138 .... *Grimmia wrightii*

176b Calyptra conical, shorter 177

177a Leaves less than 2 mm. long. Capsule unsymmetrical at base, on a very short, crooked seta 178

177b Leaves 2 mm. long or longer. Capsules symmetrical 179

178a With peristome of 16 teeth. Fig. 139........*Grimmia plagiopodia*

178b Without peristome. Fig. 139....................*Grimmia anodon*

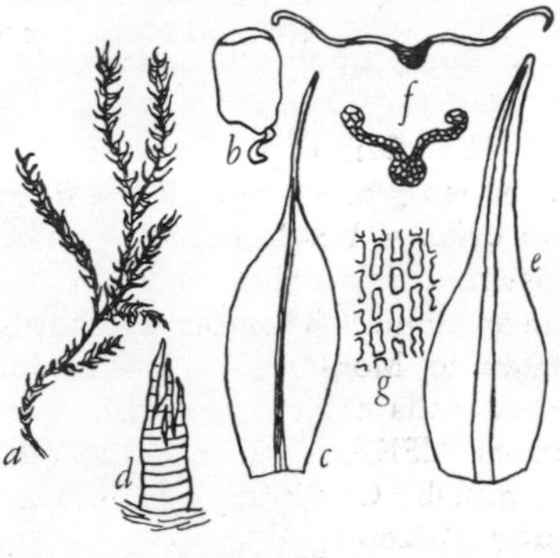

Figure 139

Fig. 139. *Grimmia anodon*. a, plant; b, capsule and seta. British Columbia to Saskatchewan and Arizona; New Brunswick — G. *plagiopodia* is similar, but has a peristome; c, leaf; d, tooth, British Columbia to Alberta, Missouri and New Mexico; e, leaf of *G. pilifera;* f, sections of leaf; g, median cells. Nova Scotia to Minnesota, Arkansas and Georgia, Mexico, Japan.

179a Both margins of leaf revolute; cells in 2 layers above. Capsule enclosed by leaves. Fig. 139..................*Grimmia pilifera*

179b Margins plane, or one or both recurved.....................180

180a (b, c) Median leaf-cell cavities rectangular, with evenly scalloped sides. Seta bent over; capsule ribbed. Fig. 140............... ....*Grimmia trichophylla*

180b Cell cavities irregularly elliptical. One margin of leaf recurved, the other plane; cells in 2 layers above; marginal basal cells with thick transverse walls. Calyptra conical. Autoicous: antheridia on a leafy branch. Fig. 140...............*Grimmia affinis*

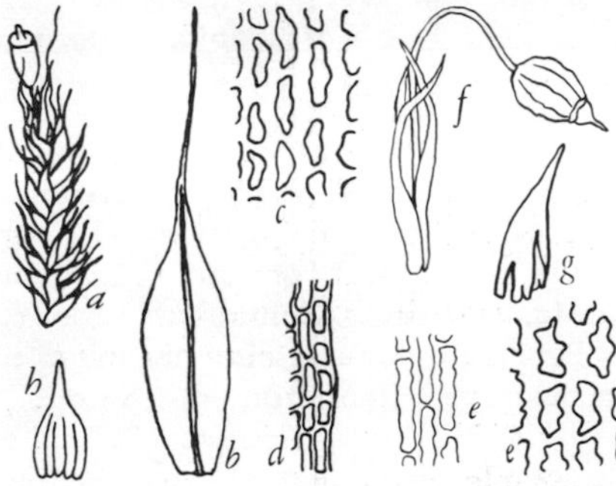

Figure 140

Fig. 140. *Grimmia affinis (G. ovalis* of MFNA). a, plant; b, leaf; c, median cells of leaf; d, basal marginal cells; North America, except southeast; Eurasia; e, median cells of G. *trichophylla;* f, seta and capsule; g, calyptra; Alaska to California and Colorado; h, calyptra of *G. calyptrata;* British Columbia to Alberta, New Mexico and California.

180c Cell cavities quadrate. Leaf cells in one layer except on margins, extending up around base of awn. Calyptra bowl-shaped, pleated, nearly covering the capsule. Fig. 140........*Grimmia calyptrata*

181a (b, c) Upper leaf cells small (to .015 mm.), quadrate or irregular. Peristome single, double or none..........................182

181b Upper leaf cells elongate rectangular to linear. Peristome double. Genus *Pohlia*..188

181c Upper leaf cells large (to 0.8 mm), hexagonal, rhombic or shortly rectangular. Peristome double, single or none..............190

182a Margins of leaves revolute..............................183

182b Margins plane..184

183a Leaves entire. Rare. Fig. 91..............*Didymodon trifarius*

183b Leaves toothed at the plane apex. Common everywhere. Fig. 127. ....*Ceratodon purpureus*

184a Leaves entire..185

184b Leaves toothed at apex..................................187

185a Leaves half sheathing at base, sharply bent back (squarrose) at middle. Fig. 132..........................*Dicranella squarrosa*

185b Leaves erect, not sheathing or squarrose...................186

186a Capsules minute, horizontal, black. Fig. 141.................. ....*Catoscopium nigritum*

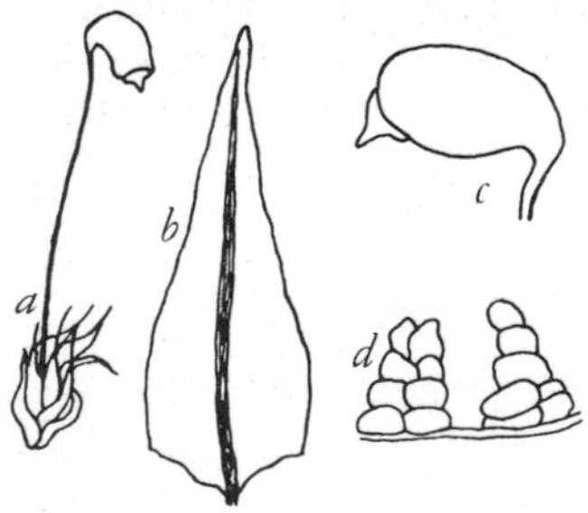

Figure 141

Fig. 141. *Catoscopium nigritum*. a, plant; b, leaf; c, capsule; d, tooth of peristome. Dense tufts 2-4 cm. deep; seta 1-1.5 cm. long. On cold, wet ground, Michigan, Minnesota, British Columbia, Alaska; Bruce Peninsula; one station in Iowa recently destroyed (fen drained). Europe.

186b Capsules erect, brown. Leaves ending in a hair. Fig. 142...... ....*Pottia truncata*

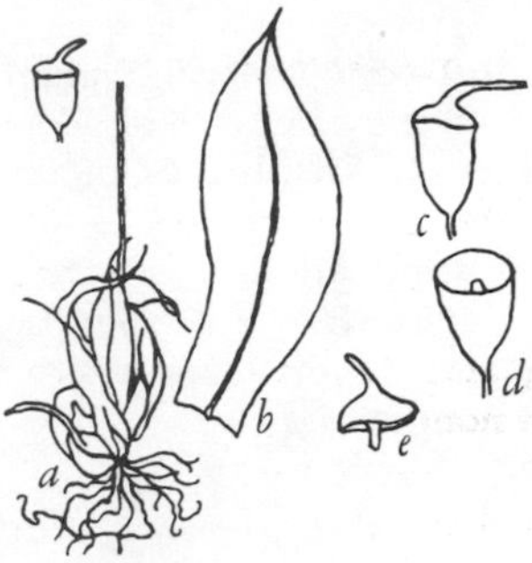

Figure 142

Fig. 142. *Pottia truncata.* a, plant; b, leaf; c, capsule with operculum; d, old capsule; e, operculum with columella. In crowded sods; stems 5 mm. tall; leaves entire or finely serrulate above. Nova Scotia to Maryland and Michigan. Rare. *Physcomitrium* has serrate leaves with large, clear cells, common in the east and easily mistaken for *Pottia*. See Figs. 105, 162.

187a Capsule erect; operculum raised up on the columella. Peristome lacking. Stems to 8 mm. tall. Fig. 80..............*Pottia heimii*

187b Capsule curved, ribbed; peristome double. Stems 1-4 cm. tall. Fig. 143...........................*Aulacomnium heterostichum*

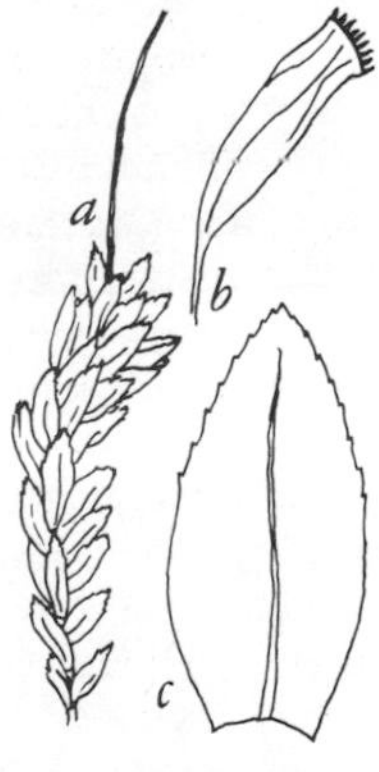

Figure 143

Fig. 143. *Aulacomnium heterostichum.* a, plant; b, capsule; c, leaf. Common on rich wooded hillsides, Ontario to Minnesota, Texas and Florida, often associated with *Bartramia pomiformis.* Upper cells have minute papillae. Naked stalks crowned with gemmae sometimes occur.

188a (b, c) Leaves glossy, with metallic luster...........*Pohlia cruda*

188b Leaves pale and watery. Capsule as broad as long. Fig. 144.... ....*Pohlia wahlenbergii*

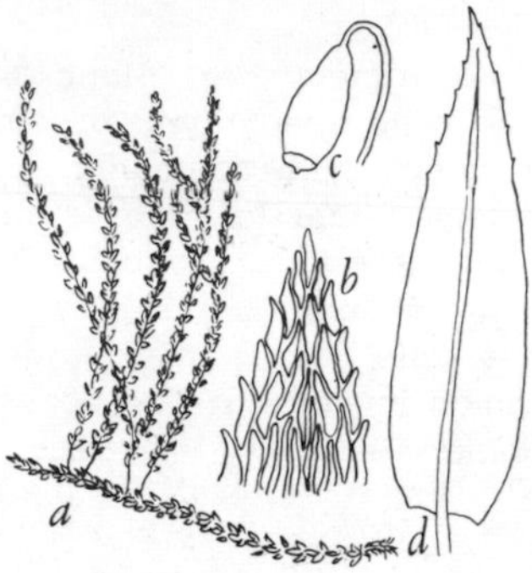

Figure 144

Fig. 144. *Pohlia wahlenbergii.* a, plant; b, apex of leaf; c, capsule; d, leaf. Common in wet places. The leaves of this water-loving moss are very slow to take up water after being dried. *P. delicatula (P. carnea* of MFNA) is similar but smaller, with very short capsules, on dry ground; rare.

188c Leaves grass-green, with dull surface. Capsule much longer than thick 189

189a With gemmae in axils of leaves. Fig. 145........*Pohlia annotina*

189b Without gemmae. Fig. 145.......................*Pohlia nutans*

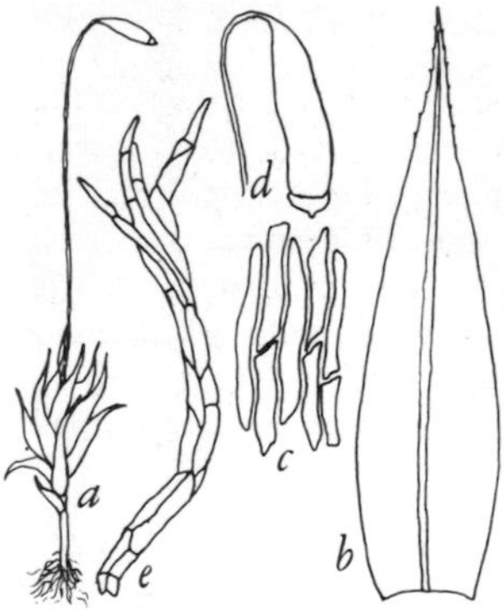

Figure 145

Fig. 145. *Pohlia nutans.* a, plant; b, leaf; c, cells of leaf; d, capsule; e, gemma of *Pohlia annotina* var. *decipiens. P. nutans* has 2 antheridia at the base of each perichaetial leaf, as have several other *Pohlias.* Common and widespread around the Northern Hemisphere. *P. elongata* lacks luster and is a similar plant, with neck as long as urn; northern; uncommon. *P. proligera* has very glossy leaves and gemmae like e, but with only one point at tip. *P. rothii* has globular gemmae.

190a Marginal cells similar to those of lamina..................211

190b Leaves bordered with slender, fusiform cells...............191

191a Capsules erect; peristome single.............................192

191b Capsules nodding; peristome double, the 16 teeth made of cell walls only, split apart through the cavity...................193

192a Peristome of 32 stout teeth attached to a transverse membrane, each tooth made of many cells. Fig. 44........*Atrichum crispum*

192b Peristome of 32 twisted threads rising from a tube about as long as the threads. Fig. 146....................*Tortula mucronifolia*

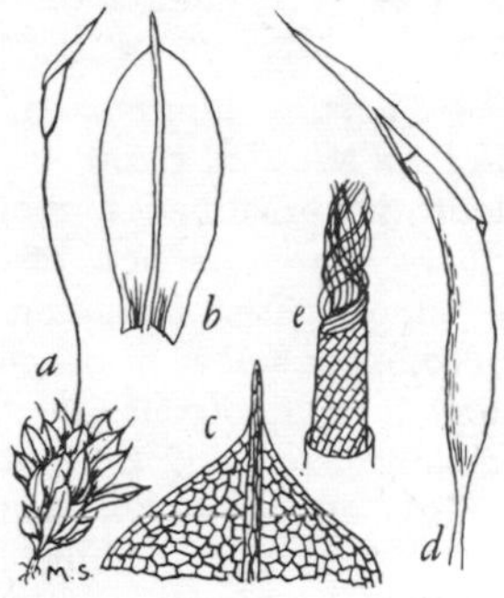

Figure 146

Fig. 146. *Tortula mucronifolia*. a, plant; b, leaf; c, apex of leaf; d, capsule with calyptra; e, peristome. In small patches on earth in woods and on banks, Greenland to Alaska, New York, Iowa, New Mexico and California Europe. Easily recognized in fruit. The shape and apex of leaf and the clear cells of the basal ¼ of the leaf, with revolute margins in this region, are unique. The peristome is a beautiful thing, the brick-red, twisted filaments shading off to the nearly white tube below.

193a Leaves to 6 mm. long, in dense terminal rosettes. Stems connected by tough rhizomes. Fig. 147................*Rhodobryum roseum*

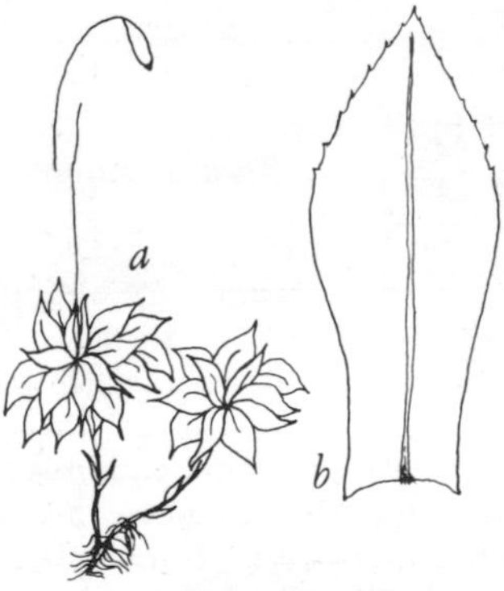

Figure 147

Fig. 147. *Rhodobryum roseum*. a, plant; b, leaf. Rosettes to 1.5 cm. across, on scaly stems. Leaves bordered by narrow cells, sharply toothed along upper half. Usually in crowded, exclusive patches, rarely fruiting. Widespread in North America, Europe, Asia.

193b Stems erect, or spreading horizontally. Not as in 193a......194

194a Margins of leaves revolute; upper leaf cells rhombic, the ends pointed. Capsules nodding, pear-shaped (broadest near mouth). Genus *Bryum*...195

194b Margins plane. Upper cells often quadrate. Capsules nodding, barrel-shaped, narrowed equally to both ends. Family MNIACEAE 203

195a Teeth with oblique bars on the inner side between the transverse bars. Fig. 148............................*Bryum pendulum*

195b Without oblique bars; all bars parallel....................196

196a Capsule with distinct neck, curved. Fig. 148...*Bryum uliginosum*

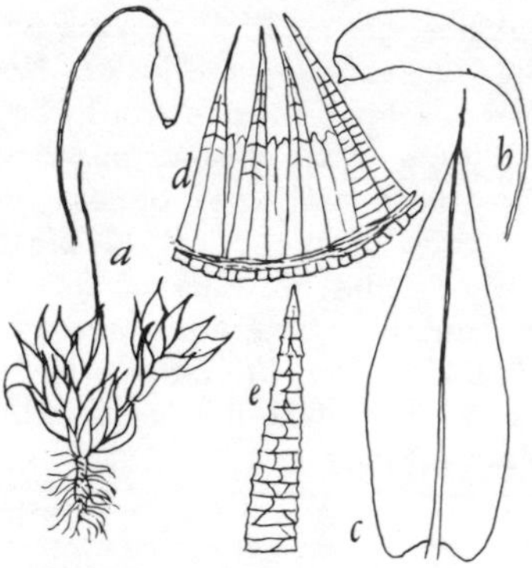

Figure 148

Fig. 148. *Bryum uliginosum. (B. cernuum* of MFNA). a, plant; b, capsule; c, leaf; d, peristome; e, tooth of *B. pendulum.* The absence of cilia from the inner peristome, and the large curved capsules characterize *B. cernuum;* it is autoicous; in damp places, mostly exposed, around the northern parts of the globe, south to Ohio, Texas, New Mexico and Oregon. *B. pallens* has similar capsules, is dioicous, and comes south to New York, Montana and Washington.

196b Capsule symmetrical 197

197a (b, c) Leaves small, silvery white at apex. Fig. 149...*Bryum argenteum*

Figure 149

Fig. 149. *Bryum argenteum.* a, plant; b, leaf; c, capsule. Common on earth, walls, stones, ashes, sidewalks, but not always fruiting; throughout the whole world. Forming sods of tiny silvery shoots; unmistakable. At times the ends of the shoots break off and are disseminated as gemmae. *B. bicolor* is a similar small moss, with entirely green leaves, percurrent or shortly excurrent midrib, and thick, pitted cell walls.

197b Leaves large, rounded-obtuse, reddish. Fig. 150..*Bryum miniatum*

197c Leaves acute to awned, not silvery........................198

198a (b, c) Leaves large, in a rosette; cells very large (to .15 mm.). Fig. 150..................................*Bryum sandbergii*

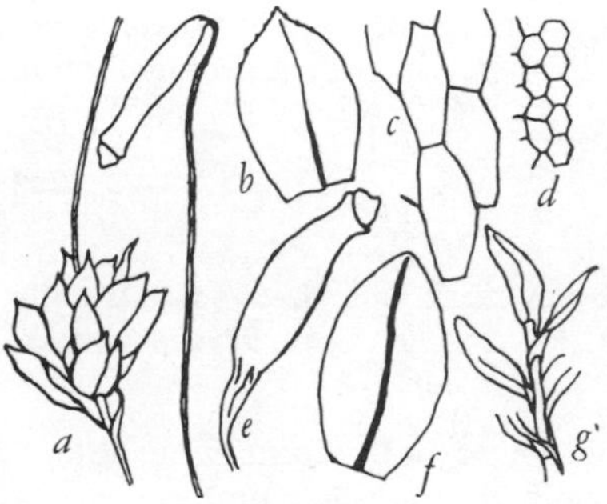

Figure 150

Fig. 150. *Bryum sandbergii.* a, plant; b, leaf; c, cells of leaf; d, cells of *Mnium cuspidatum* on same scale; e, capsule. Wyoming to California and British Columbia; f, leaf of *B. miniatum;* California to British Columbia and Montana; g, stem leaves of *B. weigelii;* New York to Colorado and northward; Europe.

198b Leaves far apart, strongly decurrent. In wet places or water. Fig. 150 ....*Bryum weigelii*

198c Leaves crowded; cell walls thin, not pitted..................199

199a (b, c) Leaf cells broad (to .07 by .035 mm.). Leaves often spirally twisted when dry. Chloroplasts large. Fig. 151...*Bryum capillare*

199b Leaf cells narrower (.07 by .03 mm.). Leaves awned. Dioicous. Fig. 151...............................*Bryum caespiticium*

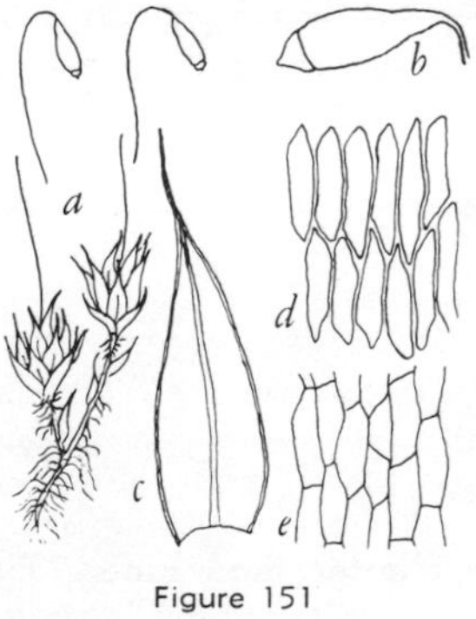

Figure 151

Fig. 151. *Bryum caespiticium.* a, plant; b, capsule; c, leaf; d, cells of leaf; e, leaf cells of *B. capillare. B. caespiticium* is the commonest typical *Bryum* in the United States, growing on earth, stones, walls, paths. *B. cuspidatum* is very similar, but is synoicous. Typical leaves of *B. capillare* resemble a *Mnium,* with large open cells and barely percurrent midrib; others are much like *B. caespiticium.*

199c Leaf cells intermediate between a and b....................200

200a Leaves awned. Synoicous. Fig. 151..........*Bryum cuspidatum*

200b Leaves not awned, or midrib very shortly excurrent.........201

201a Teeth and segments of peristome clear lemon-yellow. Leaves not decurrent..................................*Bryum turbinatum*

201b Teeth brownish......................................202

202a Capsule small (1.5-3 mm. long), oval, dark red. Leaves and cells small. Fig. 149................................*Bryum bicolor*

202b Capsule larger (to 6 or 7 mm.), brown or red. Plants with abundant brown tomentum; leaf cell walls rather thick and pitted. In wet places. Fig. 152....................*Bryum pseudotriquetrum*

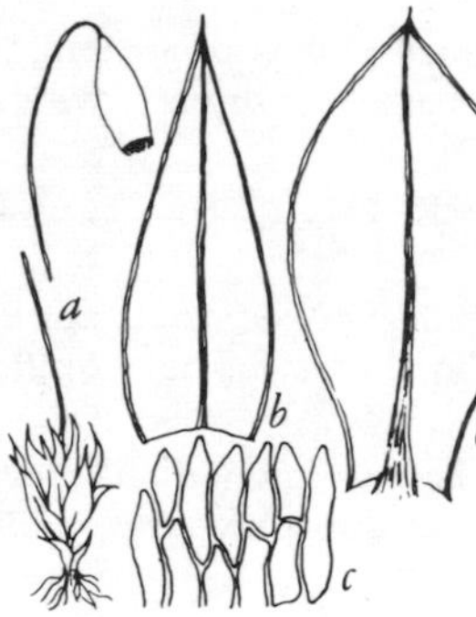

Figure 152

Fig. 152. *Bryum pseudotriquetrum (B. bimum* of MFNA). a, plant; b, leaf; c, cells of leaf; d, leaf of *B. crassirameum.* The first is common in water and wet places, the stems bound together with brown rhizoids; North America and Europe. *B. crassirameum* is a large form of our west coast.

203a (b, c) Margins of leaves entire, thickened...................204

203b Margins with teeth in a single row..........................205

203c Margins with teeth in pairs.................................209

204a Seta slender, crooked. Outer peristome shorter than inner. Fig. 153.....................................*Cinclidium stygium*

204b Seta stiff and erect. Outer peristome as long as inner. Fig. 153. .... *Mnium punctatum*

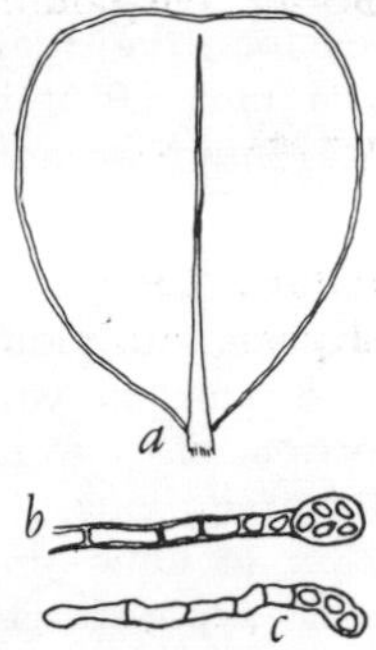

Figure 153

Fig. 153. *Mnium punctatum*. a, leaf; b, section of border. Mostly gregarious, up to 5 cm. tall (var. *elatum*); Greenland to Alaska, Colorado, Iowa and Georgia; Eurasia. A small form clings to moist, shaded rocks, Iowa etc. The form that is common on the northwest coast has been called *M. glabrescens*. c, section of border of leaf of *Cinclidium stygium;* Canada, Greenland, Europe.

205a All stems erect, without runners. Capsule with a brown, warty neck. Fig. 154 .... *Mnium venustum*

205b With erect fruiting stems and horizontal runners 206

206a Leaf cells (to .04 mm.) precisely hexagonal; walls thin. Plant glaucous .... *Mnium drummondii*

206b Leaf cells longer in one axis than another 207

207a Stems winged by the broadly decurrent leaves. Dioicous .... *Mnium insigne*

207b Leaves much less broadly decurrent, or not at all 208

208a Leaves toothed on upper half only. Cells small (to .025 mm.). Synoicous. Fig. 154 .... *Mnium cuspidatum*

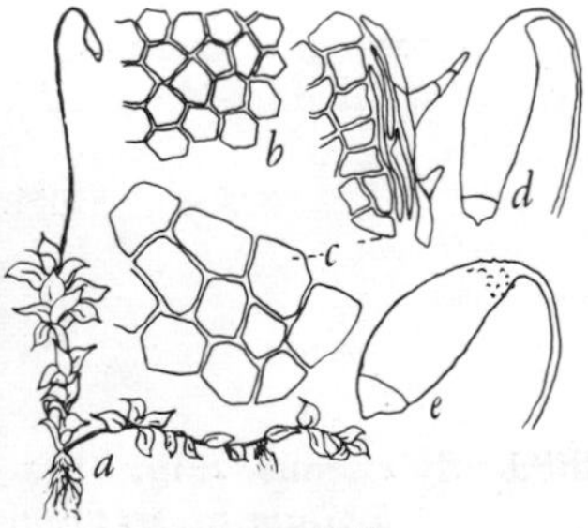

Figure 154

Fig. 154. *Mnium cuspidatum*. a, plant; b, cells of leaf, very common in central and eastern states; c, cells of *M. affine* with 3-celled tooth on border; d, capsule of same; e, capsule of *M. venustum*. M. *medium* is large-celled and synoicous; across the continent.

208b Leaves toothed nearly to base; teeth 3-celled to obsolete. Dioicous. Fig. 154 .... *Mnium affine*

209a (b, c) Leaves long and narrow, the midrib not reaching the apex. Operculum short, not beaked. Leaf cells .02-.025 mm. (.035) in diameter. Dioicous. Fig. 155 .... *Mnium hornum*

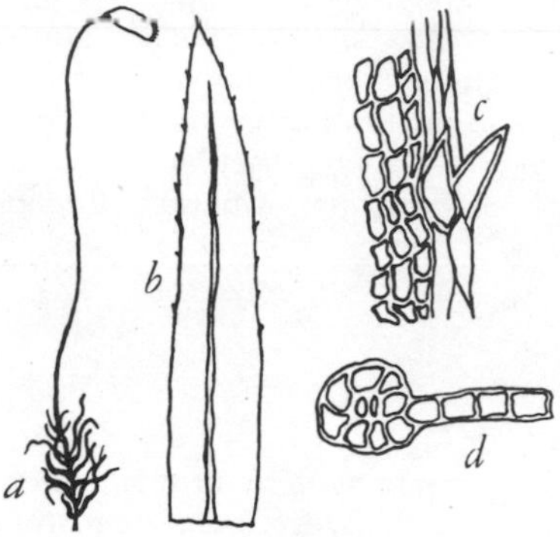

Figure 155

Fig. 155. *Mnium hornum.* a, plant; b, leaf; c, cells and margin with paired teeth; d, section of margin. Stems 2-5 cm. tall, gregarious, on moist ground, Georgia to Ohio and Labrador, Europe. The type species of the genus.

209b Leaves broader; margin cord-like, enclosing a fiber cell. Mouth of capsule red. Synoicous. Fig. 156 .... *Mnium spinulosum*

209c Leaves broader; margins without stereids 210

210a Leaf cells .02 mm. or less wide; midrib toothed on back near apex. Dioicous. Fig. 156 .... *Mnium orthorhynchum*

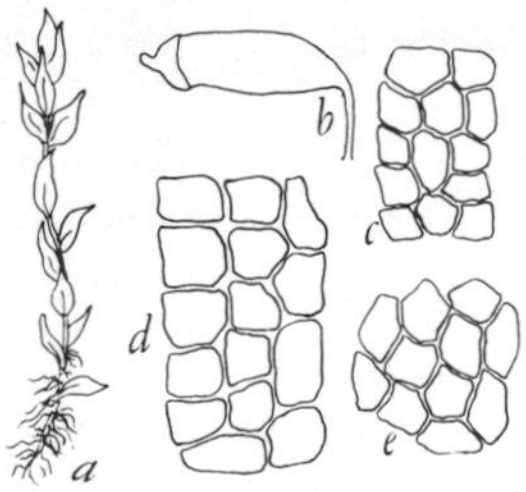

Figure 156

Fig. 156. *Mnium orthorhynchum.* a, plant; b, capsule and operculum; c, cells of leaf; d, cells of *M. serratum (M. marginatum* of MFNA); e, cells of *M. spinulosum*, the Red-mouthed *Mnium.* These three are common in woods northeast, and across the continent. *M. spinulosum* is the rarest. It and *M. serratum* are synoicous.

210b Leaf cells to .035 mm. Midrib not toothed. Synoicous. Fig. 156. .... *Mnium serratum*

211a Leaf cells mostly with flat (transverse) ends................213

211b Leaf cells with pointed ends..............................212

212a Stems unbranched. Leaves turning dark when dry. Fig. 157..... ....*Mnium stellare*

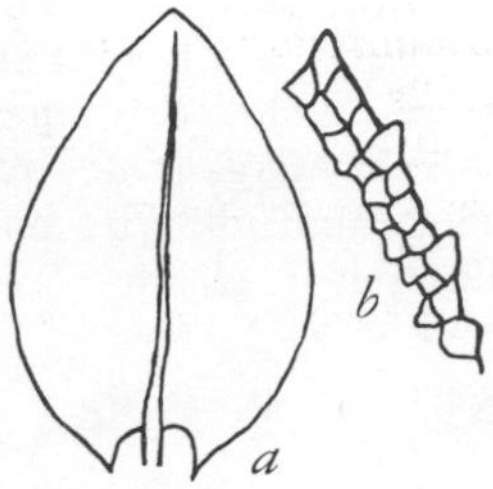

Figure 157

Fig. 157. *Mnium stellare.* a, leaf; b, apex and margin of leaf. Growing in loose clumps or sods on wooded banks, northeast to Minnesota, Iowa and Virginia. Eurasia.

212b Stems erect, much branched, to 8 cm. tall. Fig. 158............ ....*Mnium menziesii*

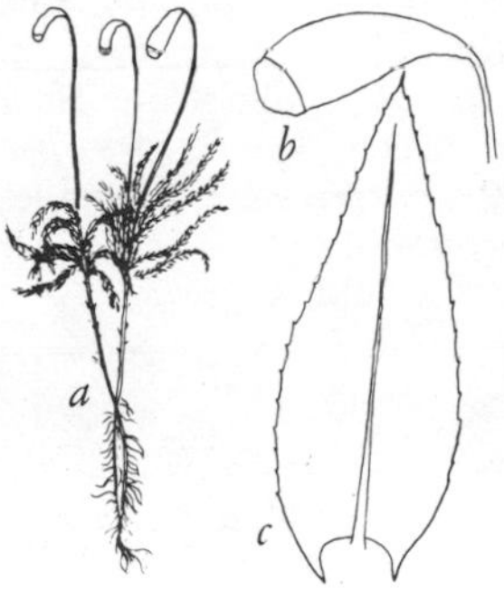

Figure 158

Fig. 158. *Mnium menziesii.* a, plant; b, capsule; c, leaf. Abundant on the Pacific Coast, California to Alaska. A stately and impressive plant, 4-8 cm. tall, in wide beds. Stem leaves wide apart colorless in upper half. Seta as much as 5 cm. tall, with the capsule up to 8 mm. long.

213a Leaf cells large. Capsules with neck nearly as long as urn, nearly erect. Inner peristome taller than outer..................214

213b Neck of capsule not noticeable. Outer peristome stronger than inner, or peristome single or lacking.......................215

214a Leaves with short, acuminate point........*Amblyodon dealbatus*

214b Leaves narrowly linear above, rounded at apex. Fig. 159........ ....*Meesia uliginosa*

Figure 159

Fig. 159. *Meesia uliginosa.* a, plant and capsule; e, peristome; f, apex of leaf; b, leaf of *M. triquetra;* c, apex of leaf; d, dry capsule. Stems tall; 3-10(15) cm. tall; seta to 8 cm. long; on wet ground, New Jersey to Ohio, Michigan, California, Alaska, Greenland. All are denizens of high altitudes and latitudes. Europe.

215a Capsule unsymmetric, horizontal. Peristome of 16 teeth, each one split from base nearly or quite to apex. Fig. 160. .*Discelium nudum*

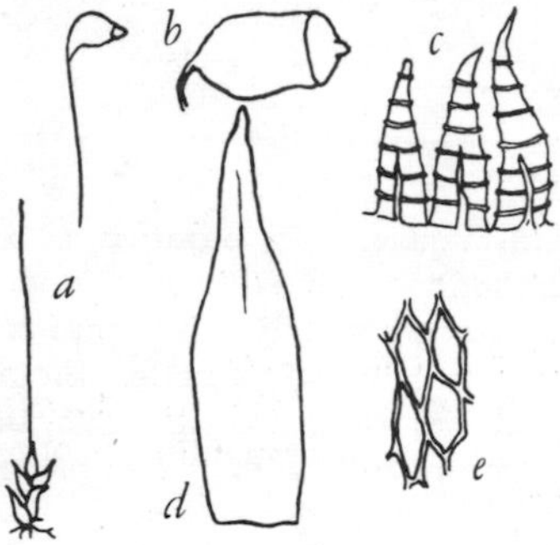

Figure 160

Fig. 160. *Discelium nudum.* a, plant; b, capsule; c, teeth of peristome; d, leaf, with faint midrib in upper part; e, cells of leaf. Rarely seen; on bare clay, in spring: March to May; Illinois to New Jersey. Europe. The leaves suggest *Funariaceae,* the capsules *Dicranella.* "A lovely wee thing" as Dr. Megaw (Belfast, Ireland) would say.

215b Capsules erect or nodding, symmetric or unsymmetric. Peristome lacking or single or double. Figs. 161-164. Family FUNARIACEAE. 216

216a Capsule symmetrical, erect...................................217

216b Capsules unsymmetrical, oblique to nodding. Peristome double. Figs. 163, 164. Genus *Funaria*............................219

217a Without peristome. Fig. 162. Genus *Physcomitrium*..........218

217b With single peristome. Fig. 161........*Entosthodon drummondii*

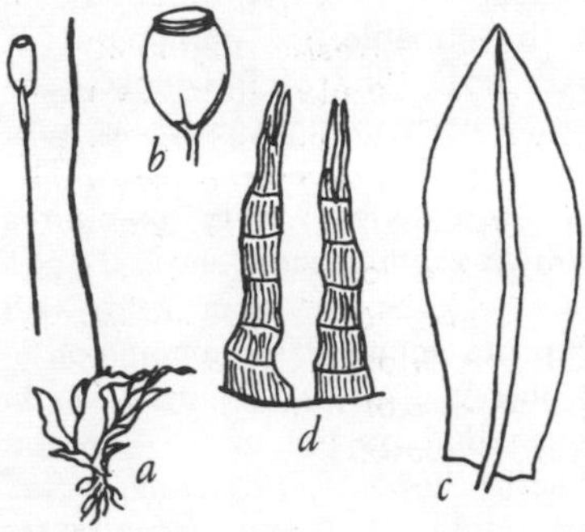

Figure 161

Fig. 161. *Entosthodon drummondii.* a, plant; b, ripe capsule; c, leaf; d, peristome. Stems 1-4 mm. tall; seta 10-15 mm. Without annulus. On clay, Georgia to Louisiana, rare. Eleven species of *Entosthodon* occur in North America. In Europe some species hybridize with *Funaria.*

218a Seta 5-15 mm. long. Mouth of capsule bordered by 8 to 10 rows of flattened cells. Fig. 162..............*Physcomitrium pyriforme*

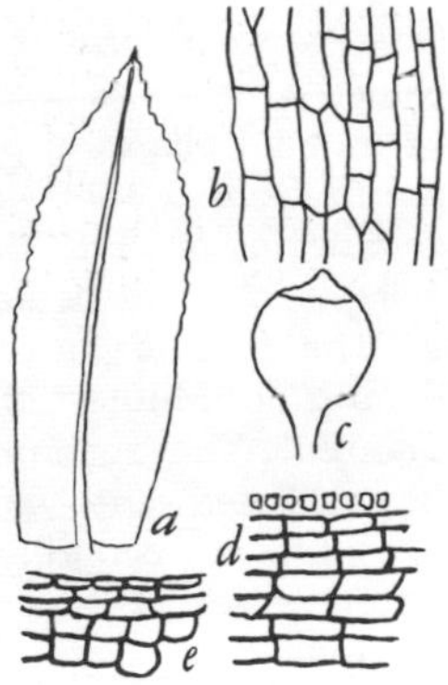

Figure 162

Fig. 162. *Physcomitrium pyriforme (P. turbinatum* of MFNA). a, leaf; b, cells of leaf; c, capsule just mature; d, cells at mouth of capsule. A very abundant moss in eastern United States, in gardens, lawns, pastures and open woods. May. e, cells at mouth of capsule of *P. hookeri;* Ontario to Ohio, Kansas and Manitoba.

218b Seta 2-4 mm. long. Mouth of capsule bordered by 3 to 5 rows of flattened cells. Annulus large, rolling back when capsule opens. Fig. 162..............................*Physcomitrium hookeri**

*For 4 very small species (*P. immersum, Aphanorhegma serratum, A. patens, Pyramidula).* See Figs. 100, 105-106.

219a Capsule with large annulus. Outer cells of capsule wall with cavity much wider than walls. Fig. 163. . . .*Funaria hygrometrica*

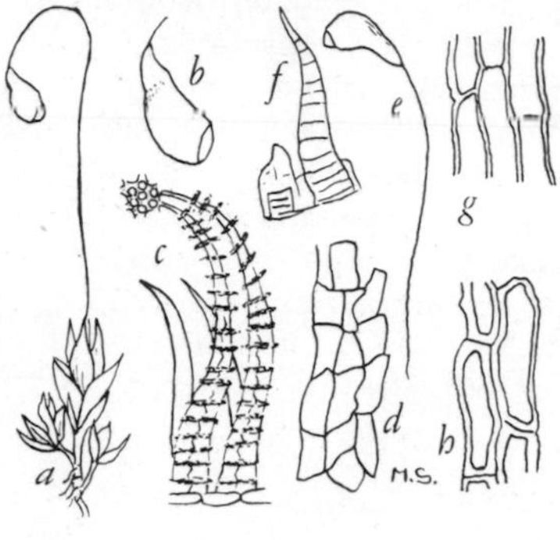

Figure 163

Fig. 163. *Funaria hygrometrica.* a, plant; b, capsule; c, peristome; d, cells of leaf. One of the most common and cosmopolitan mosses, preferring lime, limestone or ashes. The curved and twisted seta un-curves and untwists when moistened. *F. calvescens,* e, has an erect seta with the capsule inclined; common southward and into South America. *F. h.* var. *convoluta* is the usual form on the Pacific Slope. *F. flavicans,* f, has the segments short and truncate; g, cells of capsule of var. *convoluta* from a furrow; h, from a ridge.

219b Capsule without annulus. Walls of outer cells of capsule often wider than the cavities. Fig. 164. . . . .*Funaria americana*

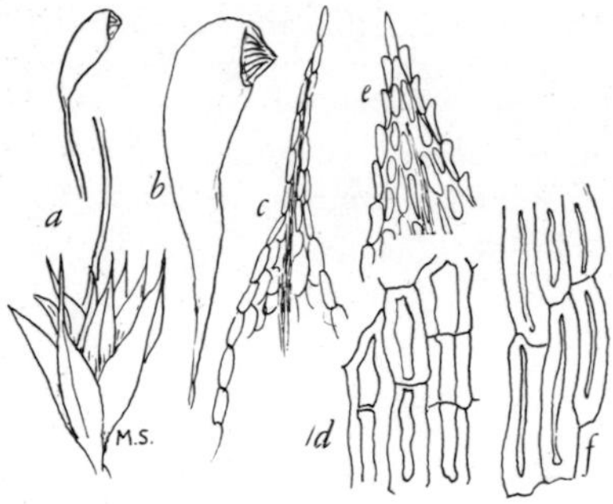

Figure 164

Fig. 164. *Funaria americana.* a, plant; b, capsule; c, apex of leaf and margin; d, upper cells of capsule of *F. serrata* from a furrow; e, apex and margin of leaf of same; f, upper cells of capsule from a ridge. The first is found from Pennsylvania to Minnesota, Texas and Georgia. The second, Georgia to Texas. Three other exannulate species are occasionally found. The peristomes of these are similar to that of *F. hygrometrica.* The narrow cells of the capsule in this group, with enormously thickened walls, d and f, contrast with the much thinner walled cells of the annulate *Funarias,* Fig. 163, g, h.

PLEUROCARPI

1a Leaves papillose, at least on posterior (under) side and on upper half of leaf. (See Fig. 15.)....................................2

1b Leaves not at all papillose; more or less glossy................34

2a Papillae consist of projecting angles of the cell wall. (See Fig. 15.) 3

2b Papillae stand out as knobs or points over the cell-cavity. Plants dull, without luster. (See Fig. 15.)..............................13

3a Leaves with a single strong midrib extending beyond middle of leaf 4

3b Leaves without midrib, or with very short or double rib.........8

4a Leaves large (to 3-5 mm.), rugose and plicate, secund (all bent to one side.) Fig. 165..............................Genus *Rhytidium*

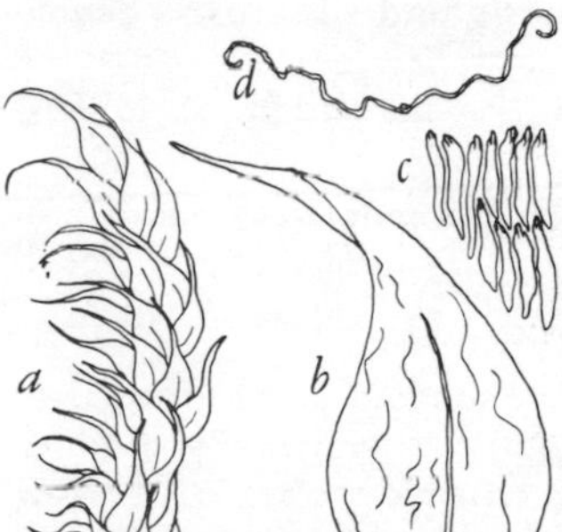

Fig. 165. *Rhytidium rugosum.* a, branch with leaves; b, leaf; c, papillae; d, cross section of leaf. A large (to 12 cm.), dull green moss forming mats on rocks, across the continent, south to North Carolina, Missouri, New Mexico and Arizona. Reaches 12,000 ft. altitude in Colorado. Margin of leaf narrowly reflexed, finely toothed above; cells 8-10:1.

Figure 165

4b Leaves .6-1.2 mm. long, not wrinkled.........................5

5a Leaves sharply serrate, translucent, decurrent; midrib not prominent; cells fusiform, 1:4-6. thin walled. On earth. Eastern. Fig. 166. Genus *Bryhnia*...6

5b Leaves entire or nearly so, mostly revolute on margin, opaque, not decurrent; midrib prominent on back of leaf; cells small, angular, rather thick walled. Paraphyllia numerous. On rocks, western. Figs. 167, 180. Genus *Pseudoleskea*...............................7

6a **Branch leaves ovate, abruptly short-acuminate, the tip twisted to the right, broadly decurrent. Fig. 166........*Bryhnia novae-angliae***

6b **Branch leaves lanceolate, distinctly acuminate, slightly decurrent. Fig. 166..................................*Bryhnia graminicolor***

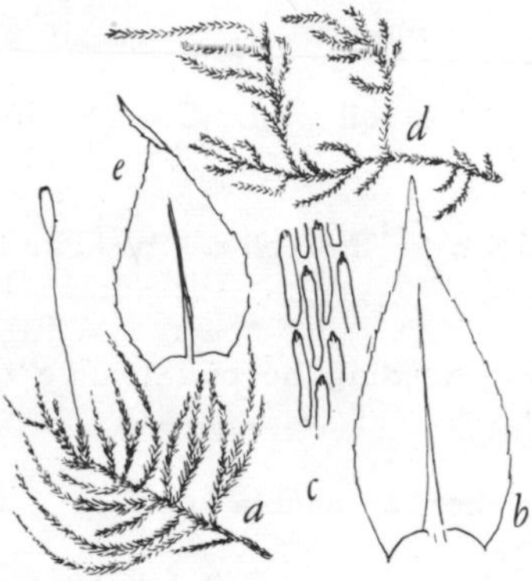

Figure 166

Fig. 166. *Bryhnia graminicolor*. a, plant; b, leaf; c, cells and papillae; d, plant, and e, leaf of *B. novae-angliae*. The former creeps on moist earth in thin yellowish green mats; the branches taper to a point. The latter species is of bushy growth, preferring very wet places. Eastern United States to Minnesota and Missouri.

7a **Cells thick-walled, opaque, variable in shape and size, rarely reaching .025 mm. Fig. 167... ....*Pseudoleskea incurvata (P. oligoclada* of MFNA)**

7b **Cells clear, with thinner walls, often .025-.045 mm. long, more uniform in shape. Fig. 167....................*Pseudoleskea radicosa***

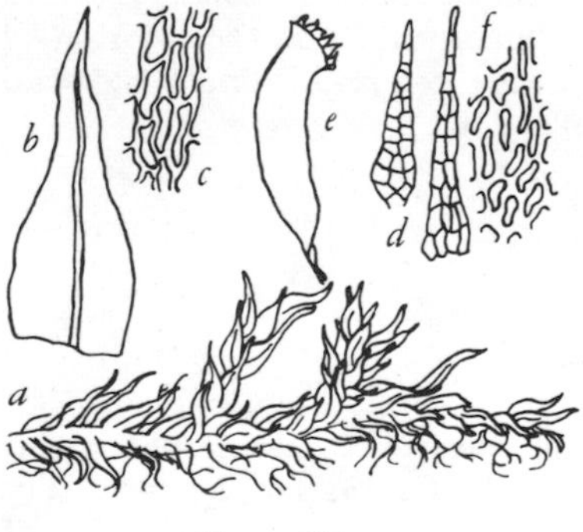

Figure 167

Fig. 167. *Pseudoleskea radicosa*. a, shoot; b, leaf; c, median cells; d, paraphyllia; e, capsule. Labrador to New Hampshire, Idaho and British Columbia, f, median cells of *P. incurvata*. On rocks in mountains, Colorado and Utah to British Columbia. These mosses occur in thin mats of brownish color from a few inches to a foot or more across. Dioicous; rarely fruiting freely.

8a **Paraphyllia lacking 9**

8b **Parayhyllia few and small to abundant and large.............11**

9a Small, creeping matted mosses. Leaves 1.5-2.5 mm. long.......10

9b Large, erect and spreading moss, to 15 cm. tall. Leaves to 5 mm. long, cordate-triangular, widely spreading, wet or dry; 2 ribs reach to middle of leaf or beyond; upper cells spinose-papillose on back. Fig. 168..............................*Rhytidiadelphus triquetrus*

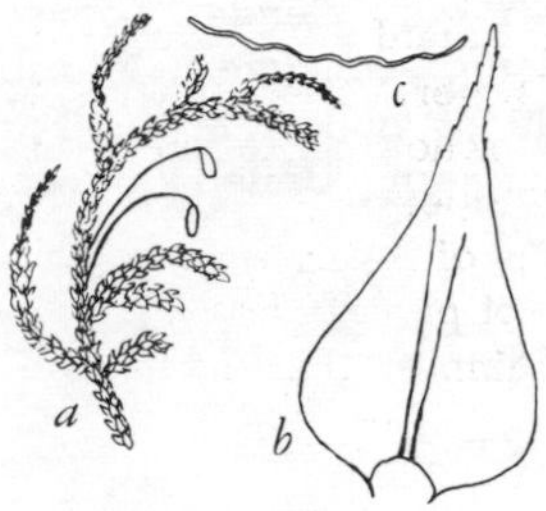

Figure 168

Fig. 168. *Rhytidiadelphus triquetrus.* a, plant; b, leaf; c, cross-section of leaf. A robust moss, very abundant in places, used for packing crockery. On the ground in coniferous woods across the continent; Europe. South to North Carolina, Missouri and California. The broad-based plicate stem leaves are very characteristic.

10a Leaves broadly cordate at base, abruptly long-acuminate, serrate, strongly falcate-secund, more or less papillose on back near apex. Fig. 280..................................*Hypnum molluscum*

10b Leaves ovate, acuminate, decurrent, julaceously imbricate when dry. Fig. 169..............................*Pterogonium gracile**

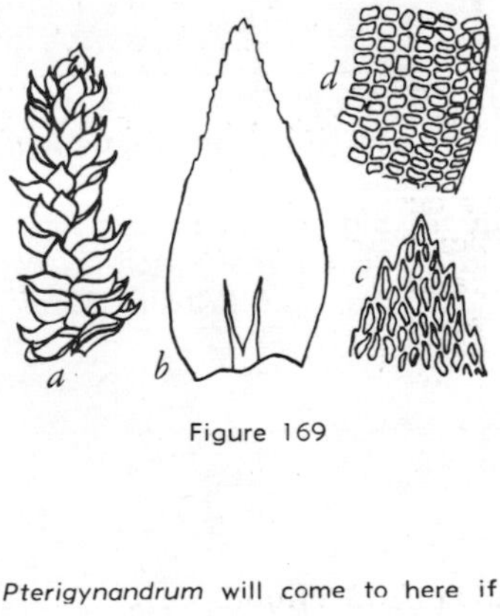

Figure 169

Fig. 169. *Pterogonium gracile.* a, shoot; b, leaf; c, apex of leaf; d, cells near basal angles. The leaf cells are characteristic of *Leucodontaceae* Loose, spreading patches on rocks or trees, Ontario to Oregon and California. Europe.

**Pterigynandrum* will come to here if you missed the paraphyllia.

11a Small, spreading, creeping moss with cylindrical shoots. Leaves to .6 mm. Paraphyllia few, small, filiform or branched. Fig. 170.. *Pterigynandrum filiforme*

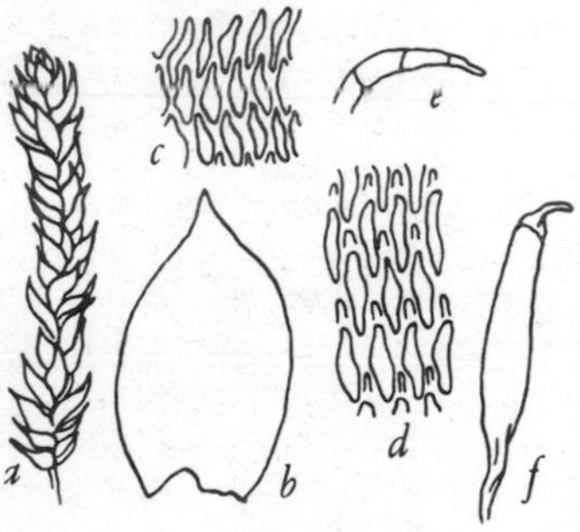

Figure 170

Fig. 170. *Pterigynandrum filiforme.* a, shoot; b, leaf; c, median cells; d, upper cells with papillae; e, paraphyllium; f, capsule. Thin mats on stones or trees, very slender. Leaves .4-.6 mm. long, concave. Midrib single, double or almost none. Far north to northern United States. Europe.

11b Larger. Leaves 2-3 mm. long, spreading, straight or curved. Paraphyllia large, abundant..12

12a Leaves rugose (transversely wrinkled), plicate, falcate-secund. Fig. 171.. *Rhytidiopsis robusta*

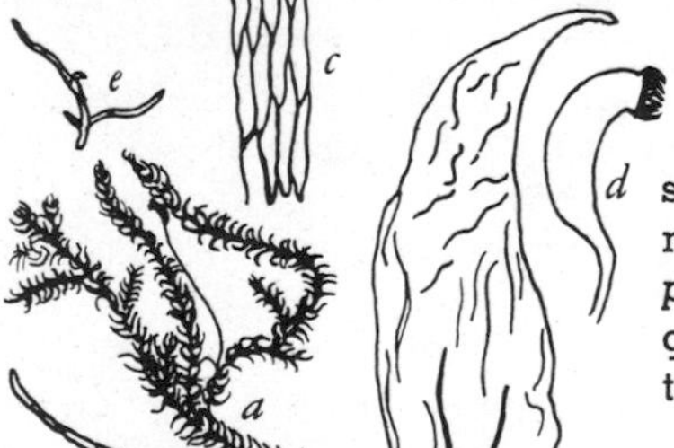

Figure 171

Fig. 171. *Rhytidiopsis robusta.* a, shoot; b, leaf with 2 unequal ribs; c, median cells; d, capsule; e, paraphyllium. Big loose masses on the ground in coniferous woods, Montana to Oregon and British Columbia.

12b Leaves not rugose or falcate. Shoots 2-3 times pinnately branched in one plane, each year's growth rising from the middle of the preceding. Fig. 172........................*Hylocomium splendens*

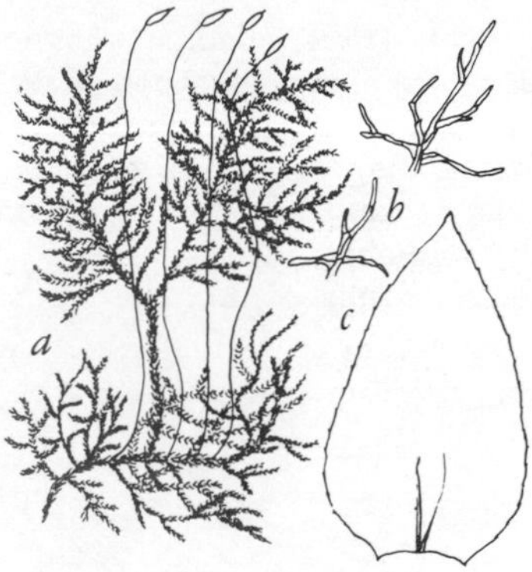

Figure 172

Fig. 172. *Hylocomium splendens.* a, plant; b, paraphyllia; c, leaf. Often carpeting rocks and soil in deep mats, across the continent, south to North Carolina (mountains), Iowa, North Dakota, Colorado and California; 3800 ft. in Catskills. A denizen of the spruce-fir forest in Europe and America. One of the most beautiful frondose (fern-like) mosses.

13a With creeping, matted rhizomes, on bark; stems erect, nearly leafless; branches densely leafy, becoming curled up when dry; paraphyllia numerous; capsule as long as seta. Fig. 173............ ....*Dendroalsia abietina*

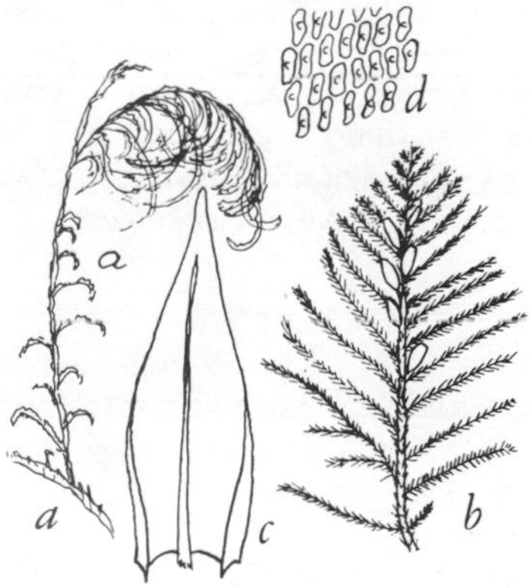

Figure 173

Fig. 173. *Dendroalsia abietina.* a, a dry plant; b, branch with capsules; c, leaf; d, cells of leaf. California to British Columbia and Idaho, often abundant. The plant curls up in a characteristic way when dry.

13b Plants not dendroid (with trunk and branches), variously creeping and branching.......................................14

14a Leaves without midrib, or with very short or double rib........15

14b Leaves with single midrib to middle or beyond................17

15a Paraphyllia present, linear or lanceolate, not branched, few and small. Fig. 174.....................*Heterocladium heteropteroides*

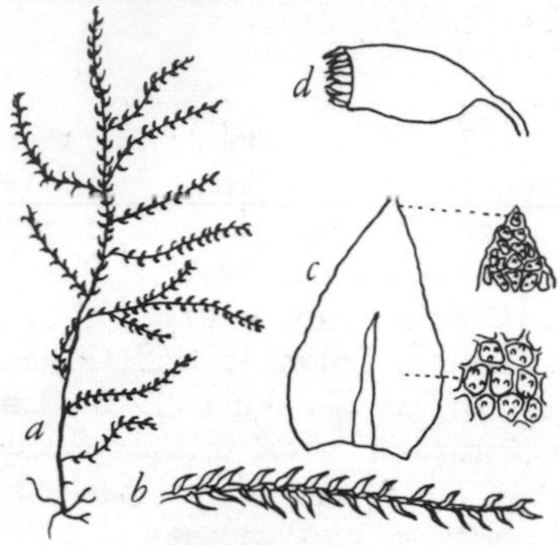

Figure 174

Fig. 174. *Heterocladium heteropteroides.* a, plant; b, shoot, wet; c, leaf; d, capsule. Thin mats of very slender shoots (leaves .4-.5 mm. long) on moist rocks, Idaho to Oregon and British Columbia. Closely related to *H. heteropterum* of Europe.

15b Without paraphyllia 16

16a Leaves erect-spreading, ovate or narrower, acuminate; serrulate all round; papillae small. Fig. 175.....*Schwetschkeopsis denticulata**

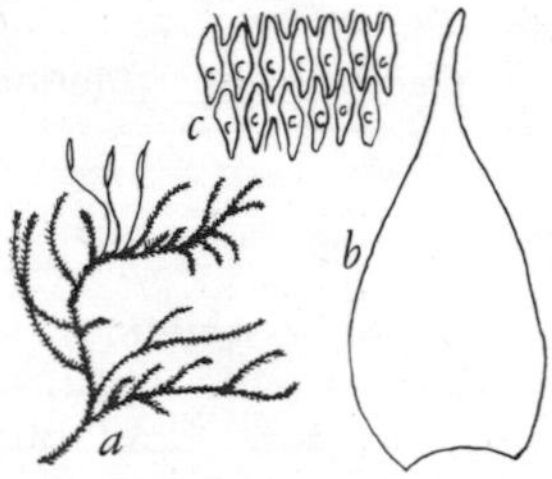

Figure 175

Fig. 175. *Schwetschkeopsis denticulata.* a, plant; b, leaf; c, cells of leaf. A tiny pale green moss on trees or rocks, Connecticut to Minnesota, Texas and Florida. Frequent southeast. Seta 4-8 mm. long. Each leaf cell has one papilla on the dorsal surface. It was formerly considered to be a *Leskea.*

16b Leaves round-ovate, deeply concave, closely packed, wet or dry. Fig. 176...Genus *Myurella*

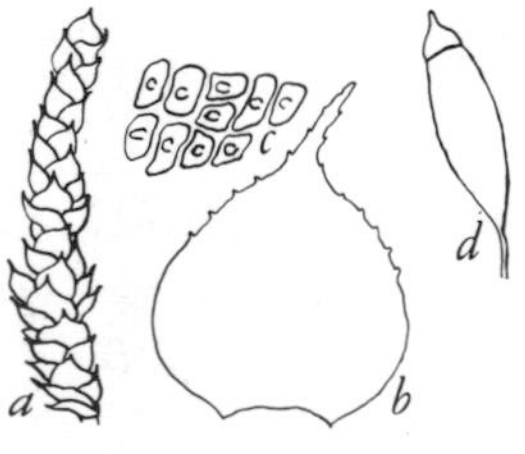

Figure 176

Fig. 176. *Myurella careyana.* a, shoot; b, leaf; c, papillae; d, capsule. *M. julacea* is papillose by projecting angles of the cells; *M. careyana* has one large papilla over the cell-cavity. Across the continent from Nova Scotia to the Yukon and south to North Carolina, Tennessee and Iowa. The little cylindrical shoots of *Myurella,* creeping over hard limestone rocks, have a peculiar charm.

**Heterocladium* will come to here if you missed the paraphyllia.

17a Leaf cells small, with narrowly oval or elliptical cavity and very thick walls; many quadrate cells at basal angles. Seta shorter than leaves. Fig. 177........................*Cryphaea glomerata*

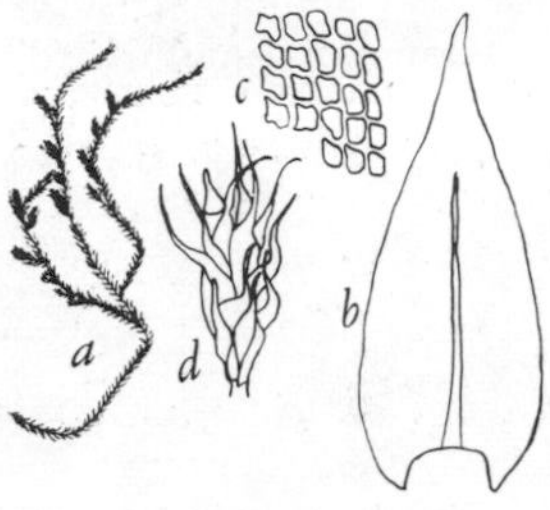

Figure 177

Fig. 177. *Cryphaea glomerata.* a, plant; b, leaf; c, cells of leaf near base; d, branch with capsule. Leaves closely packed (julaceous) when dry. Inner peristome teeth short, slender and hard to find. Thin mats on trees and shrubs, southeast, north to Connecticut, west to Texas. *C. nervosa* has the midrib ending in or near the apex of the leaf; Gulf states.

17b Cells not shaped and thickened as above. Seta much longer than leaves. Figs. 178-194. Family LESKEACEAE..................18

18a Leaf cells with a single very large papilla, as tall as the diameter of the cell, often forked into 2, 3 or 4; shoots julaceous; leaves nearly circular, deeply concave. United States east of the Plains. Figs. 178, 179. Genus *Thelia*....................................19

18b Papillae smaller, often several on one cell..................20

19a Papillae 3—(2-4)—pointed; marginal cilia of leaf long. Fig. 178. ....*Thelia asprella*

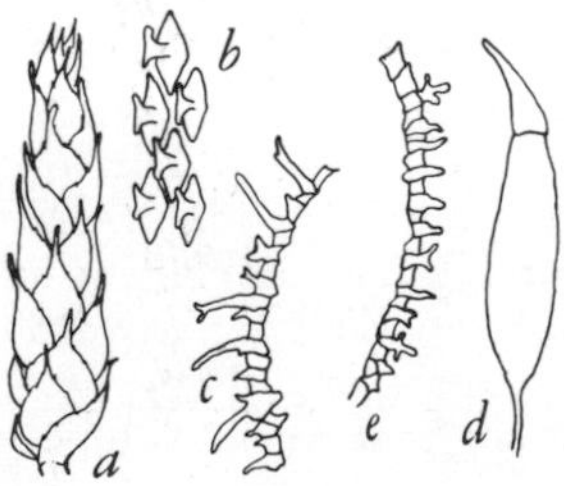

Figure 178

Fig. 178. *Thelia asprella.* a, shoot; b, papillae; c, margin of leaf; d, capsule; e, margin of leaf of *T. lescurii. T. asprella* makes dense gray-green mats 1 cm. deep on the bark of trees, preferably white oak. *T. lescurii* grows on rocks and earth, more common southward. Capsules are in perfect condition in October in southeastern Iowa.

19b Papillae unbranched, curved toward apex of leaf. Fig. 179...... ....*Thelia hirtella*

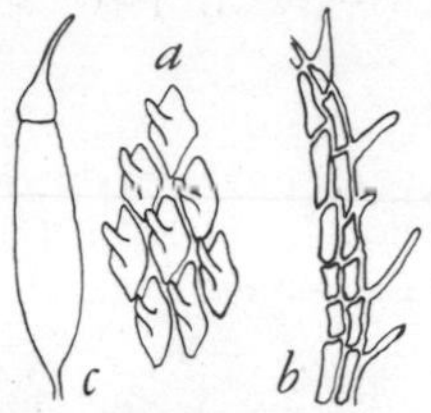

Figure 179

Fig. 179. *Thelia hirtella.* a, papillae; b, margin of leaf; c, capsule. Common southward. The simple papillae distinguish this from the preceding species.

20a (b, c) Paraphyllia absent or few, scale-like or lanceolate......22

20b Paraphyllia numerous to few, linear to lanceolate; cilia poorly developed or absent. Midrib strong, forming a ridge on back of leaf. Leaves .8-1.6 mm. long. Western. Figs. 167, 180. Genus *Pseudoleskea* 21

20c Paraphyllia numerous, filamentous, mostly branched..........29

21a Cells papillose on both sides with papillae near middle of cell cavity; cells short, 1:1-2. Fig. 180.............................. ....*Pseudoleskea patens* (*P. atrovirens* of MFNA)

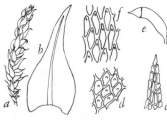

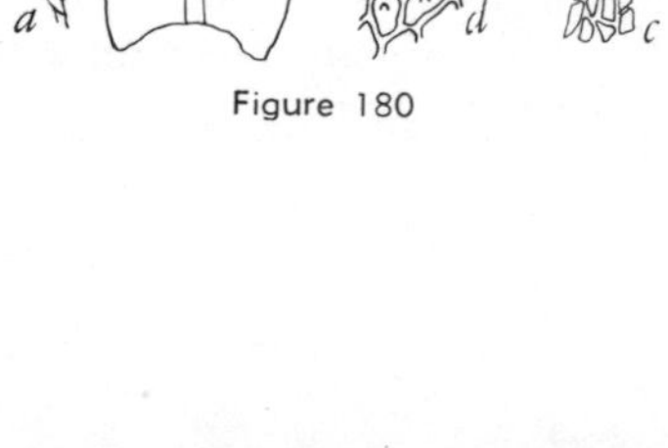

Figure 180

Fig. 180. *Pseudoleskea patens.* a, plant; b, leaf; c, apex of leaf; d, median cells; e, capsule. Mats on rocks, trees or ground, Newfoundland to British Columbia, California, Idaho and New Hampshire. f, median cells of *P. rigescens.* Leaves bent downward, without any papillae or lightly papillose on upper surface; capsules erect. Same range.

21b **Papillae from near ends of cells, on upper surface only. Cells usually longer. On trees. Stem leaves with acumen longer than body. Paraphyllia small, narrow. Capsules erect; cilia lacking. Fig. 180.................................*Pseudoleskea rigescens***

22a **Leaves longly and slenderly acuminate. Figs. 181-183.........23**

22b **Leaves blunt or acute or broadly acuminate; capsules erect. Figs. 184-188 ....24**

23a **(b, c) On trees; papillae single, large; leaves entire, apex colorless; capsule erect. Fig. 181........................Genus *Lindbergia***

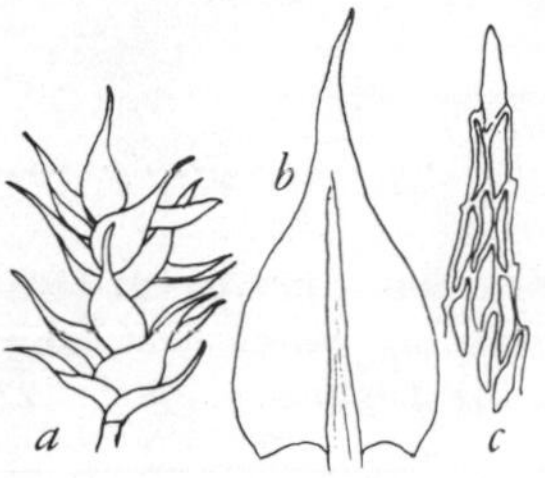

Figure 181

Fig. 181. *Lindbergia brachyptera* var. *austinii.* a, a wet twig; b, leaf; c, apex of leaf. Scattered shoots or little mats; capsule erect; inner peristome only a low membrane. Quebec to British Columbia, South Carolina and Arizona. Often associated with *Leskea.* Also found in the Caucasus Mountains of Europe. How come?

23b **On rocks and soil, California to Vancouver and Idaho. Leaves serrate; cells with 1 or more large papillae on each face; capsule curved and inclined; cilia of peristome well developed. Fig. 182. ....Genus *Claopodium***

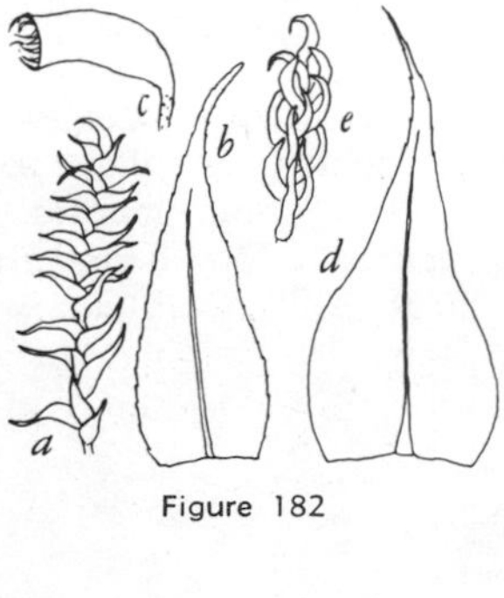

Figure 182

Fig. 182. *Claopodium whippleanum.* a, shoot; b, leaf; c, capsule; d, leaf of *C. crispifolium;* e, dry twig of same. With general appearance of *Thuidium,* which is very scarce on the West Coast. The midrib is colorless and conspicuous.

23c Leafy shoots cylindric wet or dry; leaf with slender colorless hair-like apex. Fig. 183 .... ***Anomodon rostratus***

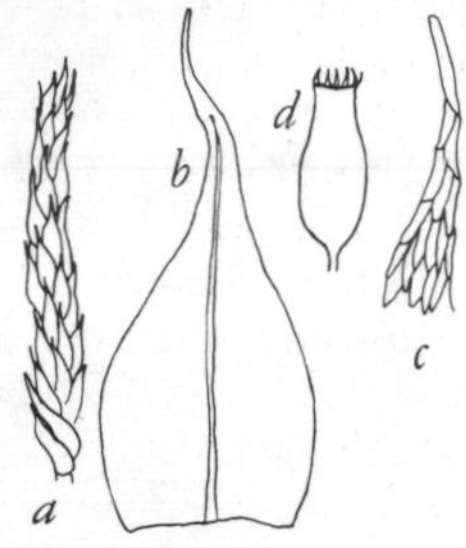

Figure 183

Fig. 183. *Anomodon rostratus.* a, shoot; b, leaf; c, apex of leaf; d, capsule. Common on rocks, earth or trees, eastern United States, Canada to the Gulf, Colorado and Arizona. Usually in dense mats 1 cm. deep, but often deeper, or at times in a very thin scraggly group. Perfect capsules are collected in October, but peristomes are still good in April.

24a Leaves clasping the stem at base **25**

24b Leaves not clasping, mostly ovate, acute or obtuse, not at all complanate, closely appressed when dry, spreading when wet; segments narrow, keeled. Figs. 187, 188. Genus *Leskea* **27**

25a Medium to large matted or tangled mosses. Segments linear. Figs. 183, 185, 186. Genus *Anomodon* **26**

25b Small thin patches on bark. Leaves much broken, tight against stem when dry. Fig. 184 .... ***Haplohymenium triste***

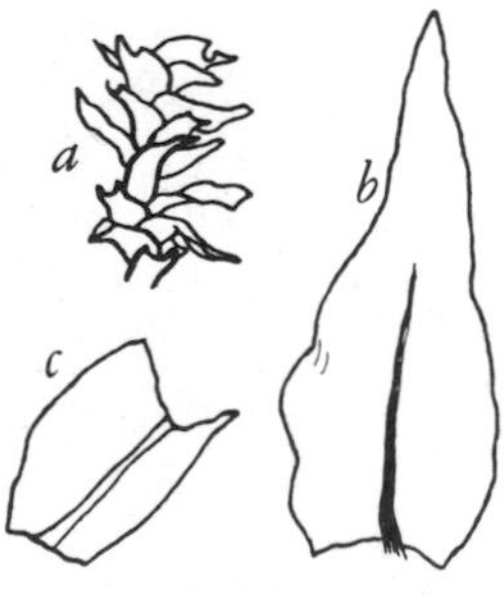

Figure 184

Fig. 184. *Haplohymenium triste (Anomodon tristis* of MFNA). a, shoot; b, a whole leaf; c, the usual broken leaf. Thin tangles on trees, dull green, loose. Most leaves are broken. Nova Scotia to South Carolina, Minnesota and Iowa. Italy. No capsules known from North America.

26a Leaves broad and concave at base, becoming tongue-shaped above, rounded at apex. Fig. 185..................... *Anomodon minor*

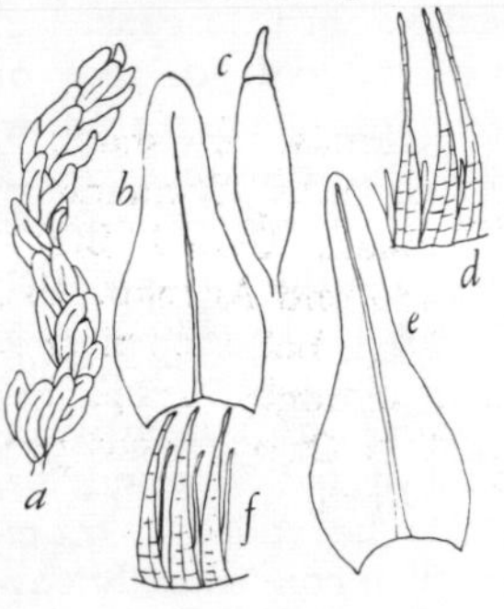

Figure 185

Fig. 185. *Anomodon minor*. a, a leafy shoot; b, detached leaf; c, capsule; d, peristome. Forming thin mats or scattered shoots on trees, or large (5-10 cm. long) wiry-stemmed clusters on rocks, New Brunswick to North Dakota, Texas and Florida. Inner peristome teeth short or lacking. *A. viticulosus* is similar, mostly on rocks, Canada to Virginia. The upper half of the leaf is narrower and more tapering than that of *A. minor*, Fig. 185 e, and the inner peristome, f, is better developed.

26b Apex of leaf distinctly apiculate. Fig. 186...*Anomodon attenuatus*

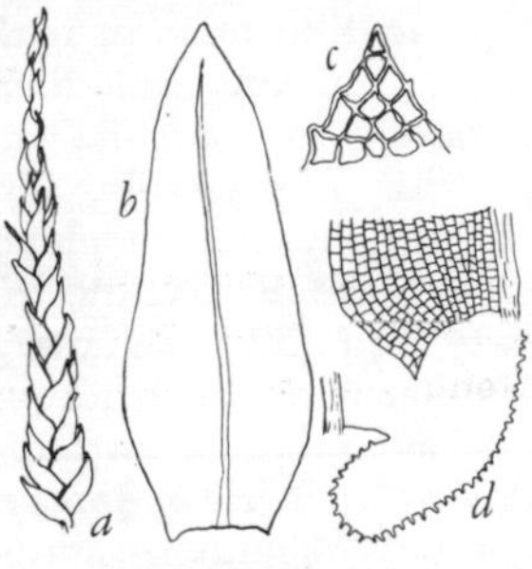

Figure 186

Fig. 186. *Anomodon attenuatus*. a, shoot with flagelliform end; b, leaf; c, apex and base of leaf; d, base of leaf of *A. rugelii*. *A attenuatus* is very abundant on rocks in the midwest, mostly smaller and on trees in the southeast. Capsules ripen in autumn, but peristomes are still good in April. *A. rugelli* is more restricted, northeast to Michigan, and Georgia, rare.

27a Median cells of leaves isodiametric, papillose; peristome teeth sharply bent inward at the base when dry..................28

27b Median cells longer than wide, oval-hexagonal, smooth or slightly papillose; teeth straight when dry. Fig. 187.......*Leskea nervosa*

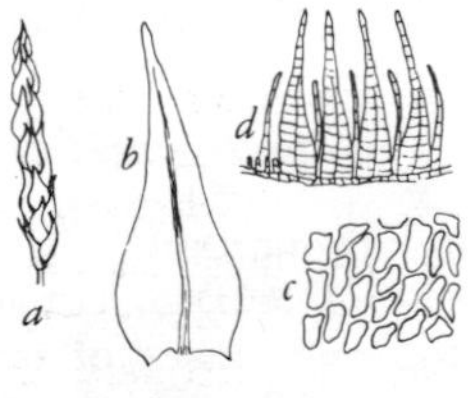

Figure 187

Fig. 187. *Leskea nervosa*. a, shoot; b, leaf; c, median cells of leaf; d, peristome. This species has the midrib reaching almost to the very tip; on trees, stones or rotten wood, Labrador to British Columbia, Pennsylvania and Colorado. Dioicous, *L. tectorum,* Yukon to New Mexico, Lake Superior and British Columbia, has a shorter midrib; margins of leaf entire; cells not over 3:1.

28a Leaves 0.6 mm. long or less; median cells .005-.007 mm. wide; midrib rough below; Florida to Texas................*Leskea australis*

28b Leaves 0.7 mm. long or longer; median cells .007-.01 mm. wide; midrib smooth. Fig. 188 .... ***Leskea gracilescens***

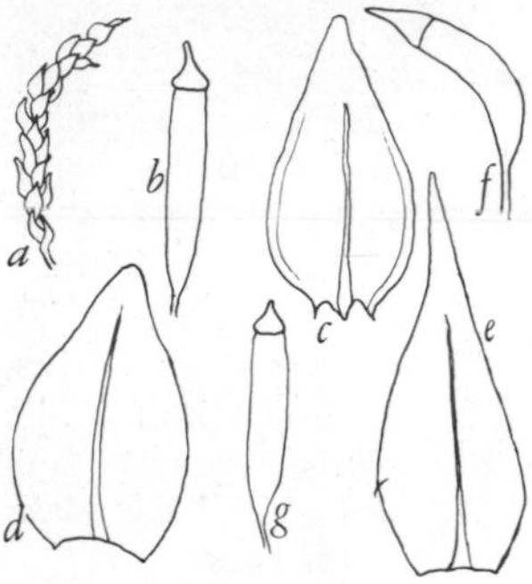

Figure 188

Fig. 188. *Leskea* gracilescens. a, shoot; b, capsule; c, leaf; d, leaf of *L. obscura;* e, leaf of *L. polycarpa;* g, capsule of same; f, capsule of *L. arenicola.* Small, dark green matted mosses on trees, rocks or earth, widely distributed east of the Rocky Mountains. The leaves figured here are "typical". Very many specimens are variously intermediate. If, as Best and Grout advise, intermediates are to be called *L. gracilescens,* that name will conveniently cover a multitude of forms!

29a Paraphyllia matted together on stem, and present on base of leaf. Fig. 189 .... **Genus *Helodium***

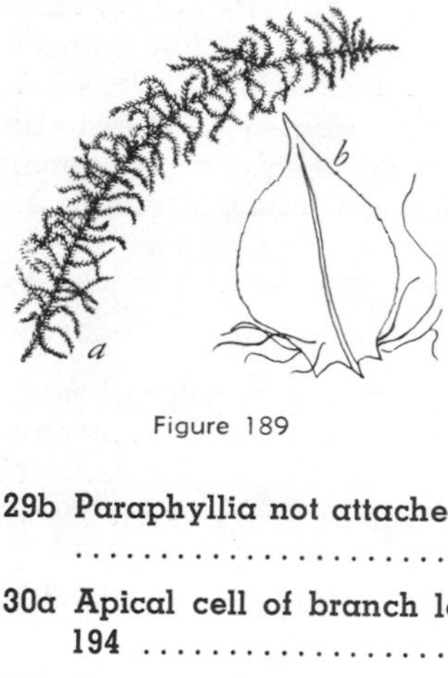

Figure 189

Fig. 189. *Helodium paludosum.* a, plant; b, leaf with paraphyllia. Irregularly branching; midrib reaching near to apex of leaf, papillae small. *H. blandowii* is very regularly pinnately branched with shorter midrib and larger papillae. The second inhabits swamps and wet meadows, from New Jersey, Illinois, Iowa and Washington northward; the first from northeast to Iowa and North Carolina.

29b Paraphyllia not attached to leaves. Figs. 190-194. Genus *Thuidium*. **30**

30a Apical cell of branch leaves crowned with 2-4 papillae. Figs. 191-194 .... **31**

30b Apical cell of branch leaves with one terminal papilla. Figs. 190, 194 .... ***Thuidium virginianum***

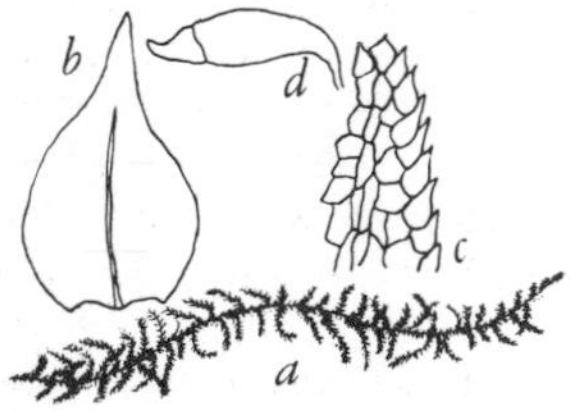

Figure 190

Fig. 190. *Thuidium virginianum.* a, plant; b, leaf; c, apical cells of leaf; d, capsule. In close mats on logs and bases of trees, or on soil, northeast to Minnesota and Mexico. *T. microphyllum* is similar, with wider range. The dry branches are smooth; the leaves taper evenly to the apex, "very abundant in Florida."

31a Paraphyllia numerous and long, branched. Figs. 192-194......32

31b Paraphyllia small, often few, 2-6 cells long; branch leaves curved when dry to make a chain-like effect. Fig. 191................ ....*Thuidium minutulum*

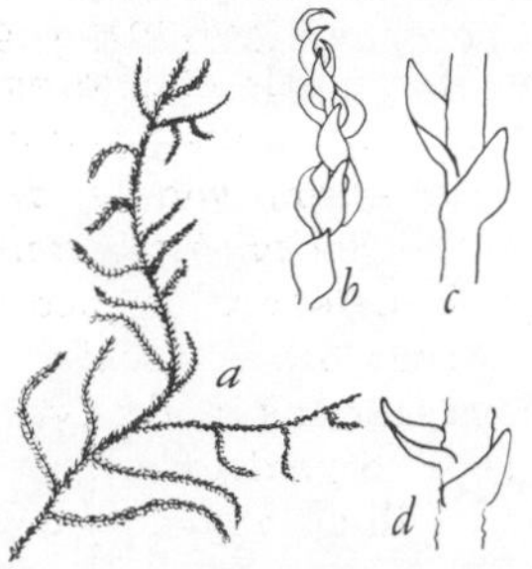

Figure 191

Fig. 191. *Thuidium minutulum.* a, plant; b, dry twig; c, twig. Thin dark green mats of very fine strands on bases of trees, New Brunswick to Minnesota, Mexico and Florida. *T. pygmaeum* is very similar, growing on limestone in damp, shady places, New Jersey to Iowa and Canada. The branches are papillose, Fig. 191d, whereas the branches of the previous one are smooth.

32a Stems closely once-pinnate, cylindrical when dry. Fig. 192...... ....*Thuidium abietinum*

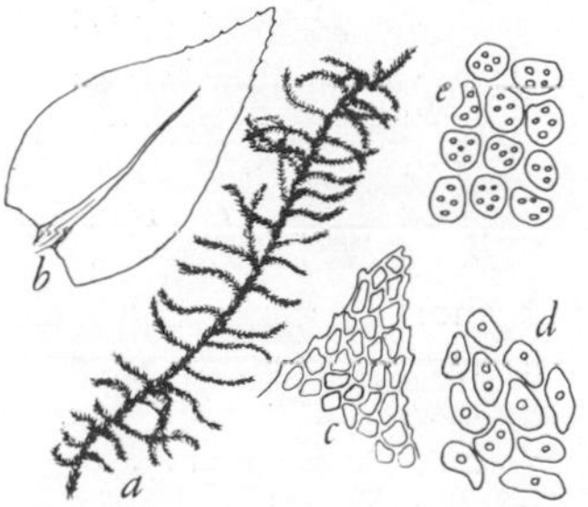

Figure 192

Fig. 192. *Thuidium abietinum.* a, plant; b, leaf; c, apical cells of leaf; d, median cells. A coarse, rigid plant, in mats on rocks or sterile soil, Greenland to Virginia, Iowa, Colorado, British Columbia and Alaska. *T. scitum* makes soft thin mats on bases of trees, Ontario to Wisconsin, Missouri and Georgia. Each cell has 3-6 small papillae on each surface, Fig. 192e.

32b Stems loosely pinnate, the branches again pinnate or bi-pinnate. Figs. 193, 194...33

33a Prongs (papillae) on paraphyllia near middle of cells. Perichaetial leaves with long cilia on the margin. Figs. 193, 194............. ....*Thuidium delicatulum*

Figure 193

Fig. 193. *Thuidium delicatulum.* a, plant; b, stem leaf; c, perichaetial leaf; d, capsule. In beautiful fern-like mats, often many feet across, in moist shaded places, Labrador to British Columbia and the Gulf. *T. philiberti* has the stem leaves ending in a colorless filament; in cool, wet places, New Jersey, Pennsylvania, Iowa, New Mexico. *T. alleni* is a loosely branched form with low papillae and without cilia on the perichaetial leaves; Connecticut to Florida.

33b Prongs near upper ends of cells. Perichaetial leaves without cilia. Fig. 194.................................*Thuidium recognitum*

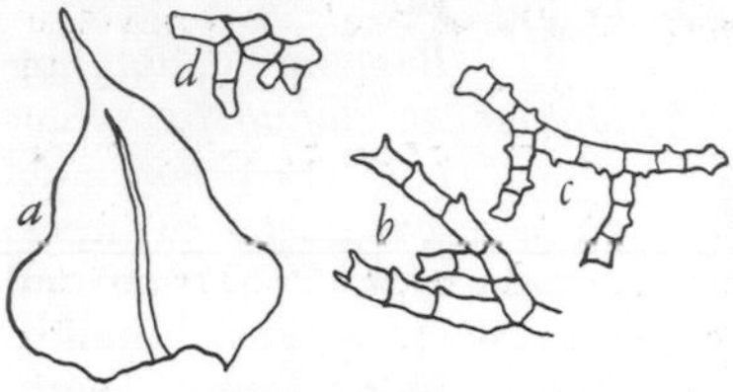

Figure 194

Fig. 194. *Thuidium recognitum.* a, stem leaf; b, paraphyllium; c, paraphyllium of *T. delicatulum;* d, paraphyllium of *T. virginianum.* Eastern United States and Canada; west to Iowa.

34a Paraphyllia numerous and conspicuous. Figs. 195-199.........35

34b Paraphyllia few or none, usually not seen.....................41

35a Plants with creeping rhizomes, erect scaly stems, and a cluster of spreading leafy branches. Fig. 195.............Genus *Climacium*

Figure 195

Fig. 195. *Climacium americanum.* a, plant; b, leaf; c, upper median cells of leaf; d, base of leaf of *C. dendroides;* e, cells of same; f, leaf cells of *C. kindbergii. C. dendroides* is in Europe and northern North America to Iowa; *C. kindbergii* is in wet places or water, east and southeast; *C. americanum* is common in woods, east of the Rocky Mountains.

35b Without rhizomes or dendroid habit...........................36

36a (b, c) Complanate-foliate; branches ending in slender flagella; paraphyllia lanceolate, serrulate; capsule longer than seta. Fig. 299. *Neckera menziesii*...See 142

36b Leaves strongly wrinkled (rugose), all bent toward one side of stem (secund); tips of branches hooked. Fig. 196.....Genus *Rhytidiopsis*

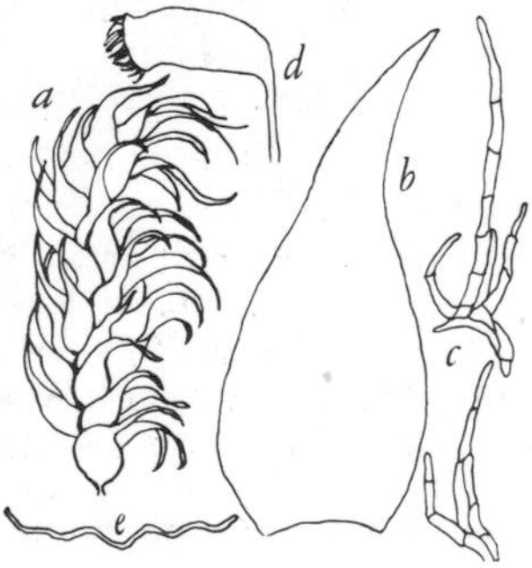

Figure 196

Fig. 196. *Rhytidiopsis robusta.* a, twig; b, leaf; c, paraphyllia; d, capsule; e, cross-section of leaf. A big dull-green moss of the northwest, east to Montana.

36c Leaves spreading in all directions, or bent to one side; not complanate or rugose....................................37

37a Midrib single and strong, to beyond middle of leaf. Paraphyllia lanceolate to linear....................................38

37b Midrib single or double, ending much below apex of leaf; paraphyllia branched. Figs. 198, 199....................................40

38a Midrib very strong to tip of leaf, or excurrent. Alar cells large and clear. Fig. 197. Genus *Cratoneuron*....................................39

38b Midrib never quite percurrent. Alar cells small, quadrate. Figs. 167, 180. Genus *Pseudoleskea*....................................See 7b, 20b

39a Leaves pleated lengthways, curved almost into a circle. Fig. 197. ....*Cratoneuron commutatum*

39b Leaves not plicate, not, or but little, curved. Fig. 197 ....*Cratoneuron filicinum*

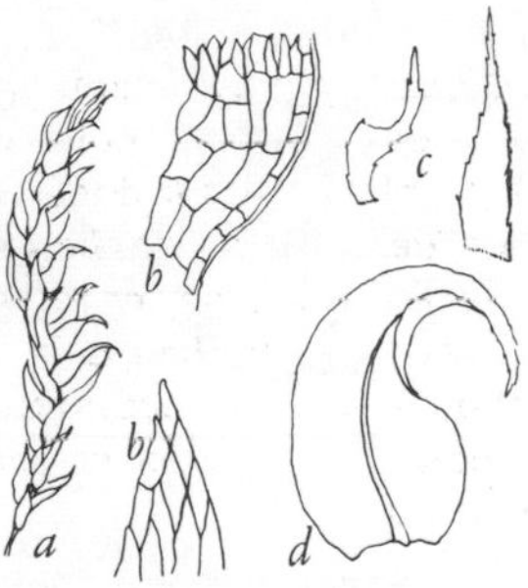

Figure 197

Fig. 197. *Cratoneuron filicinum*. a, twig; b, leaf base and apex; c, paraphyllia; d, leaf of *C. commutatum*. Mats in water or very wet places, pinnately branched, now dense, again very loose and irregular; leaves, midribs and paraphyllia very variable. Across the continent, especially northward.

40a Upper median leaf cells linear-flexuose; 5-10:1; stems red. Fig. 198. ....*Genus Hylocomium*

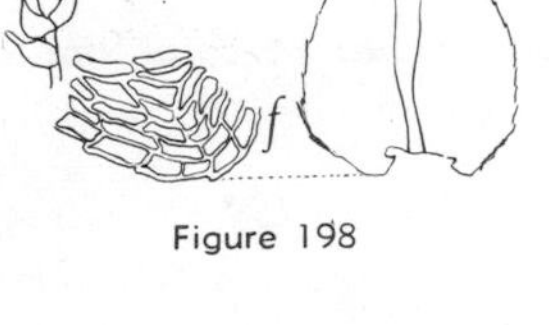

Figure 198

Fig. 198. *Hylocomium umbratum*. a, shoot; b, leaf; c, alar cells; d, cross-section of leaf; e, leaf of *H. brevirostre*; f, alar region of same. *H. pyrenaicum* has a single midrib reaching middle of leaf. Big loose patches, to 15 cm. tall, on stones, logs or humus; the first and third from northern Europe to Alaska and the mountains of North Carolina, the second from Nova Scotia to Missouri and Georgia. *Hylocomium splendens* will come here if you missed the papillae on upper back of leaves. See No. 12b, Fig. 172.

40b Upper median leaf cells oval-rhombic, 2-3:1, thick-walled, the alar quadrate or transversely elongated. Fig. 199 . . . . . Genus *Alsia*

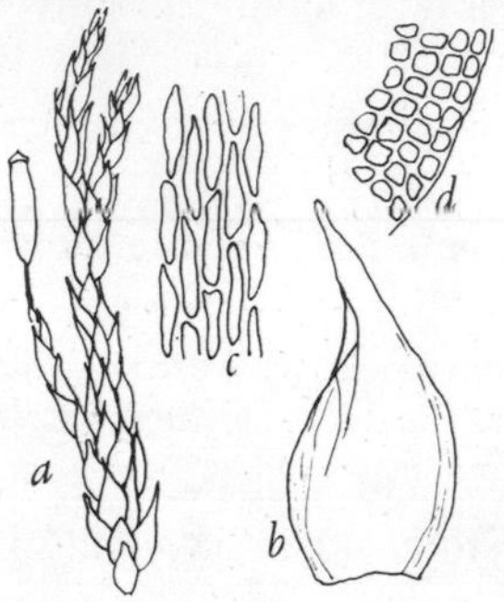

Figure 199

Fig. 199. *Alsia californica.* a, twig; b, leaf; c, median cells; d, alar cells. Midrib very variable; leaves entire; segments much shorter than teeth. Thick loose mats on trees, California to Washington near the coast.

41a (b, c) Midrib single and strong reaching to middle of leaf or beyond 42

41b Midrib strong, with one or two short accessory ribs on each side at base of leaf. (See Fig. 213.) . . . . *Antitrichia curtipendula*

41c Midrib lacking, or short and/or double 95

42a Aquatic, normally completely submerged. Leaves 2-7 mm. long; stems 10-30 cm. long 43

42b Terrestrial, on dry or wet substrates, not normally submerged* . . 50

43a (b, c) Leaves more or less falcate-secund; shoots hooked at tip. Figs. 200-203 44

43b Leaves complanate (lying in two opposite rows). *Leptodictyum riparium* forms. See Figs. 225, 226 . . . . See No. 70

43c Leaves appressed or erect or spreading, not falcate or complanate. 47

*Floating forms of *Climacium, Hygrophypnum, Brachythecium rivulare, Leptodictyum brevipes,* etc., trouble all of us. Leaf cells still come true.

44a Leaves 3-ranked, sharply folded along the midrib (keeled). Fig. 200 .... Genus *Dichelyma*

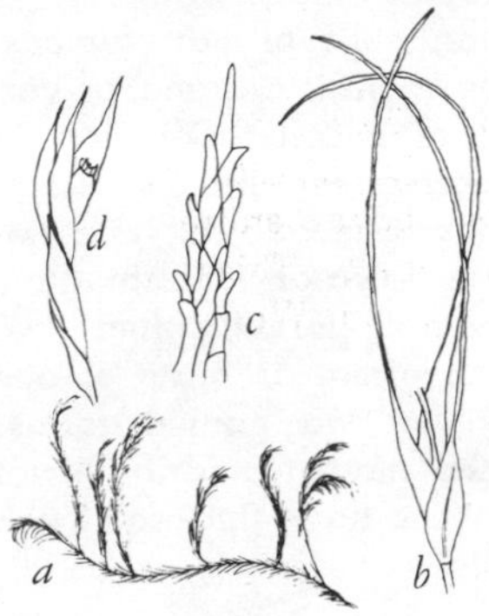

Figure 200

Fig. 200. *Dichelyma capillaceum.* a, shoot; b, leaves; c, apex of leaf; d, capsule and perichaetium. Normally wholly submerged in swamps, pools and slow streams, New Brunswick and Ontario to Tennessee and North Carolina. *D. uncinatum* occurs chiefly in British Columbia, Washington and Oregon. *D. falcatum,* Labrador to Maine, Minnesota and Oregon has the midrib little or not at all excurrent.

44b Leaves flat or tubulose, smooth or plicate. Figs. 201-203, 210. Genus *Drepanocladus* 45

45a Outer layer of cells of stem larger and thinner-walled than those within. Fig. 201 .... *Drepanocladus intermedius*

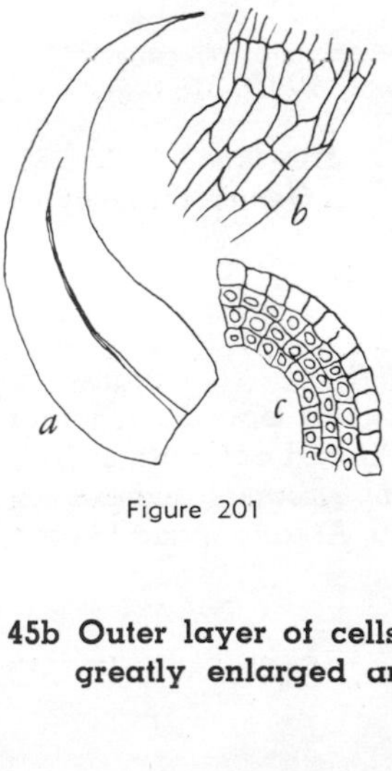

Figure 201

Fig. 201. *Drepanocladus intermedius.* a, leaf; b, alar cells; c, section of stem. In bogs across the continent, south to Michigan and Iowa. It is a slender plant, yellowish to green. *D. revolvens* is stouter, reddish, with leaves very longly and slenderly acuminate, Colorado to Alaska and Vancouver.

45b Outer layer of cells not different from underlying cells; alar cells greatly enlarged and conspicuous. Figs. 202-203 46

46a Leaves entire; capsules provided with an annulus. Fig. 202..*Drepanocladus aduncus*

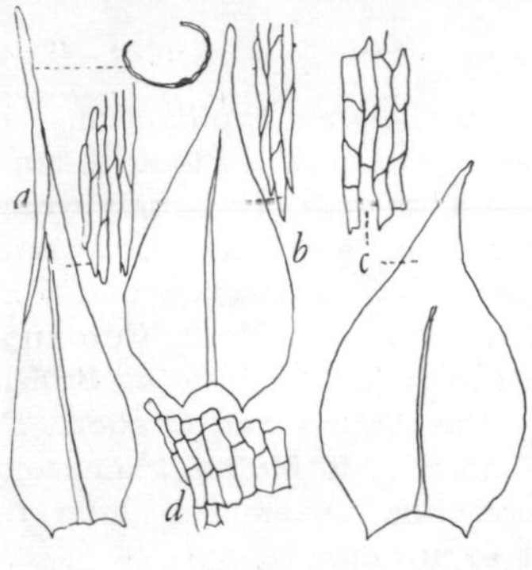

Figure 202

Fig. 202. *Drepanocladus aduncus.* a, leaf and median cells of var. *typicus;* b, same, of var. *kneiffii;* c, same, of var. *polycarpus;* d, alar cells Common in temporary or permanent shallow calcareous waters or wet meadows, New Jersey to Wisconsin, Iowa and Washington, with many named forms; often two branches of one plant, or parts of one branch, belong to two named forms! *D. sendtneri* has stouter midrib, fewer alar cells, but these have thickened yellow-brown walls.

46b Leaves serrulate at apex, often only very minutely so; without annulus. Fig. 203....................*Drepanocladus exannulatus*

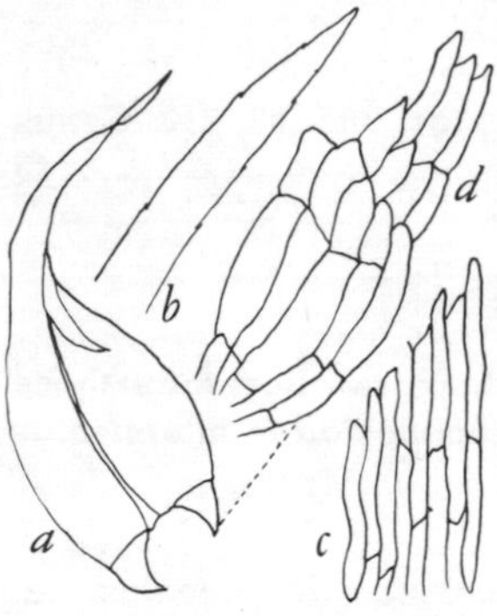

Figure 203

Fig. 203. *Drepanacladus exannulatus.* a, leaf; b, acumination; c, median cells; d, alar cells. New Jersey to Colorado and Washington, and northward, in non-calcareous waters, shores, and in swamps. Extremely variable, as is also *D. fluitans,* which has shorter and thinner midrib and less abruptly enlarged alar cells.

47a Leaves 3-ranked, sharply folded along the midrib (keeled), lanceolate. Fig. 204..............................Genus *Brachelyma*

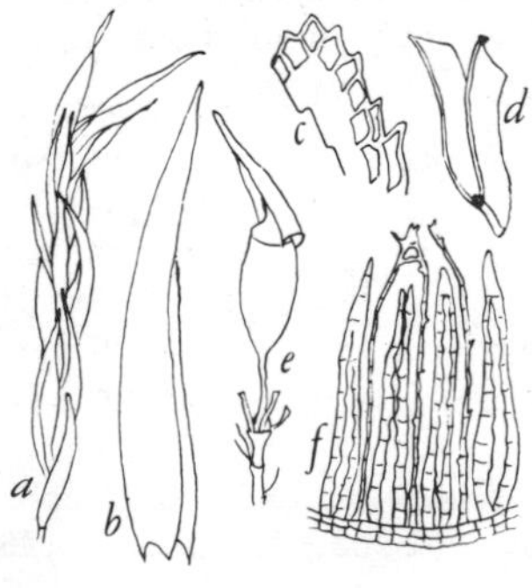

Figure 204

Fig. 204. *Brachelyma subulatum.* a, shoot; b, leaf; c, apex of leaf; d, section of leaf; e, seta, capsule and calyptra; f, peristome. Floating in streams and rivers, Georgia to Louisiana, Arkansas and Illinois.

47b Leaves flat or concave, not keeled 48

48a Leaves finely serrate all round, broadly ovate to orbicular. (See Fig. 232) .... *Eurhynchium rusciforme*

48b Leaves entire, flat or concave 49

49a Leaves thin, cordate-ovate; midrib slender, reaching to apex of leaf or nearly so. Fig. 205 .... *Calliergon cordifolium*

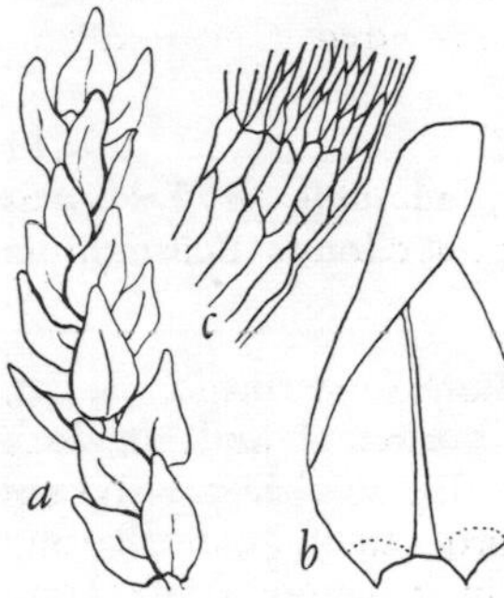

Figure 205

Fig. 205. *Calliergon cordifolium.* a, shoot; b, leaf; c, alar cells. In non-calcareous ponds or swampy places, New Jersey to Washington and northward. Eight similar species have similar range. They differ in length of midrib, thickness and color of alar cell walls, color and habit of plant.

49b Leaves thick, opaque, lanceolate to ovate; midrib stout, excurrent. Fig. 206 .... *Hygroamblystegium noterophilum*

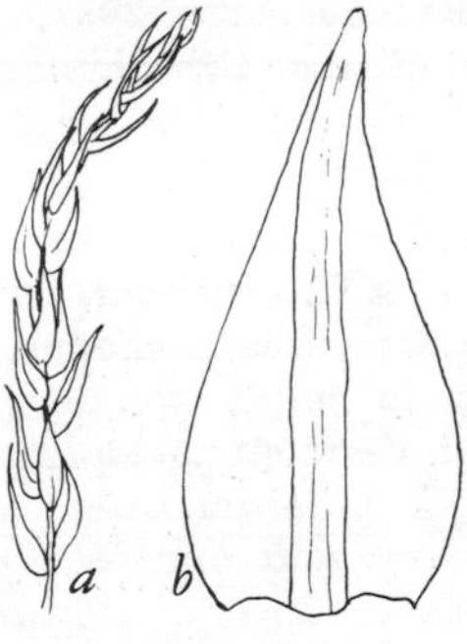

Figure 206

Fig. 206. *Hygroamblystegium noterophilum.* a, shoot; b, leaf. A big dark green moss in large calcareous springs, rarely more than 100 ft. from where the water emerges from the rocks. Leaves 2-3 mm. long; stems to 15 cm. long. Base and apex of leaf often 2 cells thick. New England to Pennsylvania and Montana. *H. irriguum* var. *spinifolium* is similar but smaller, and grows in many streams. *H. fluviatile* has the stout midrib spreading out and filling the apex of the leaf.

50a Plant with rhizomes, erect wiry stems and many leafy branches (dendroid). Fig. 207. (Compare *Mnium menziesii* and *Climacium.*) .... Genus *Porotrichum*

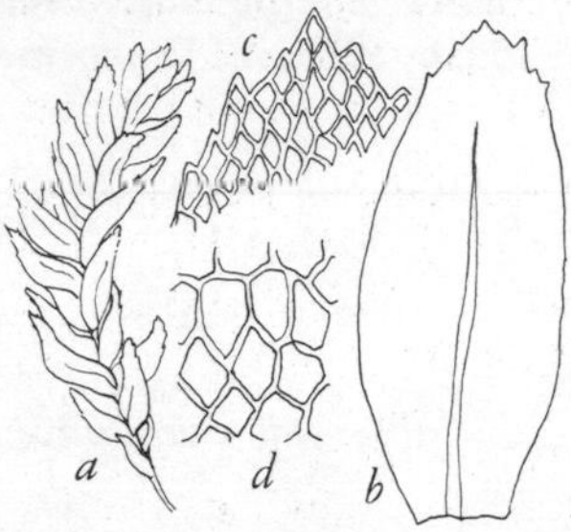

Figure 207

Fig. 207. *Porotrichum alleghaniense.* a, shoot; b, leaf; c, apex and serration of leaf; d, upper median cells. On damp rocks near streams, Southeastern Canada to Georgia, Arkansas and Missouri. Erect stems 2-3 cm. tall, leaves 1-2 mm. long.

50b Plants various but not dendroid 51

51a Leaves bordered with elongated, thick-walled cells in 2 layers; median cells rhomboid. Fig. 208 .... Genus *Sciaromium*

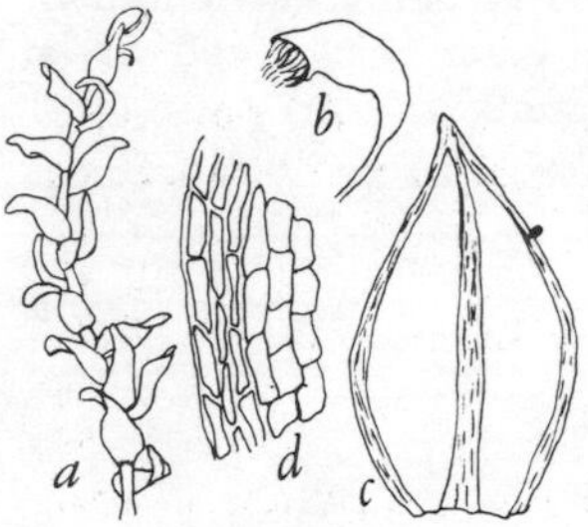

Figure 208

Fig. 208. *Sciaromium lescurii.* a, shoot; b, capsule; c, leaf; d, border of leaf. In dark green mats on stones in brooks, mostly not submerged. Midrib very stout. Ontario and western Pennsylvania to Cape Ann, Long Island, Georgia and Alabama. Several species are known from South America, and *S. fryei* from Cape Arago, Oregon.

51b Leaves not bordered 52

52a (b, c) Leaves nearly circular, appressed, deeply concave, with abrupt slender tips; shoots fat and cylindric (julaceous) Fig. 209.... .... Genus *Cirriphyllum*

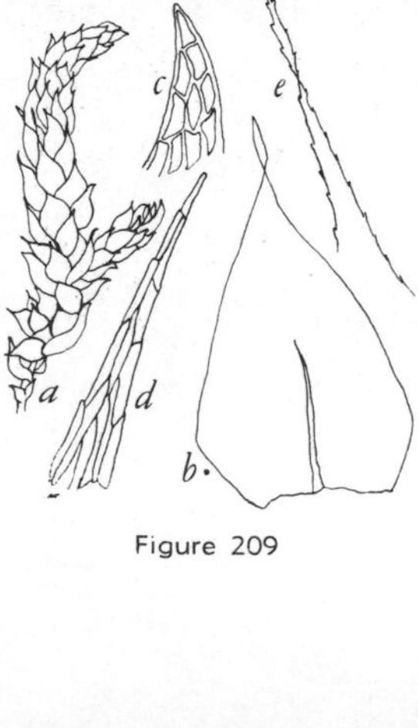

Figure 209

Fig. 209. *Cirriphyllum boscii.* a, shoot; b, leaf; c, apex of leaf; d, leaf apex of *C. piliferum;* e, leaf apex of *C. cirrosum.* Big shiny loosely julaceous mosses, sometimes in sods 20 ft. across, in shady woods or open fields. *C. boscii* Vermont to Florida, Louisiana and Iowa. *C. piliferum,* ocean to ocean, south to Pennsylvania and Washington. *C. cirrosum,* Colorado and Alaska; Europe.

52b Leaves narrowly lanceolate, long-tapering, falcate-secund to circinate 53
52c Leaves ovate to lanceolate, rarely falcate, never circinate......54
53a Leaves with many longitudinal folds, the slender tips bent around in a circle. Alar cells little or not at all enlarged. Fig. 210........ ....*Drepanocladus uncinatus*

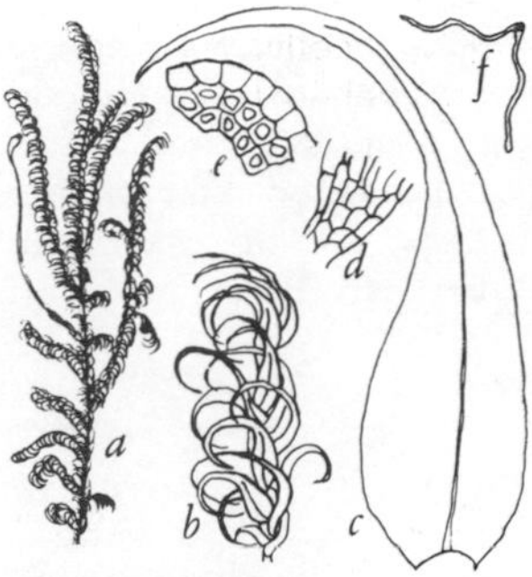

Figure 210

Fig. 210. *Drepanocladus uncinatus.* a, plant; b, twig; c, leaf; d, alar cells; e, section of stem, and f, section of leaf of *D. vernicosus.* Arctic ocean to Gulf, common in northern tier of States and northward, rare farther south. *D. vernicosus* is also strongly falcate-secund, with plicate leaves. It lives in swamps constantly wet, is more erect and has the outer layer of stem cells small and thick-walled.

53b Leaves smooth, tubulose above. Shoots hooked at tip. Alar cells distinctly enlarged. (See Fig. 202.)........*Drepanocladus aduncus*
54a Median cells of leaf short, 2-5:1.............................55
54b Median cells of leaf elongated, 5-20:1........................67
55a Cell walls very thick, the cavity elliptic to linear. Figs. 211-215. 56
55b Cell walls thinner, of equal thickness all round...............59
56a (b, c) Leaves entire near base, very shallowly denticulate above; plants of southeastern United States. Figs. 214, 215............58
56b Leaves ovate, abruptly short-acuminate, plane and sharply serrate from base to apex; alar cells numerous, very small, thick-walled, often colored. Fig. 211. Pacific slope only..........Genus *Bestia*

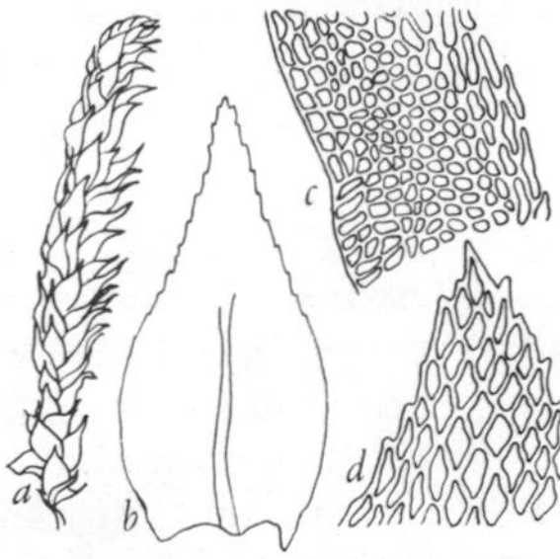

Figure 211

Fig. 211. *Bestia breweriana.* a, shoot; b, leaf; c, alar and median cells; d, apex and margin of leaf. Peristome perfect. Seta 10-15 mm. long. Branches curved, tapering at tips, julaceous. On trees and timbers, California to Vancouver. Three other species have been collected 3 or 4 times each, on the Pacific Coast, Oregon to Vancouver.

56c Leaves with tapering acumen, sharply serrate above..........57

57a Teeth of leaf margin broad, ascending. Southeastern. Fig. 212.. *Herpetineuron toccoae*

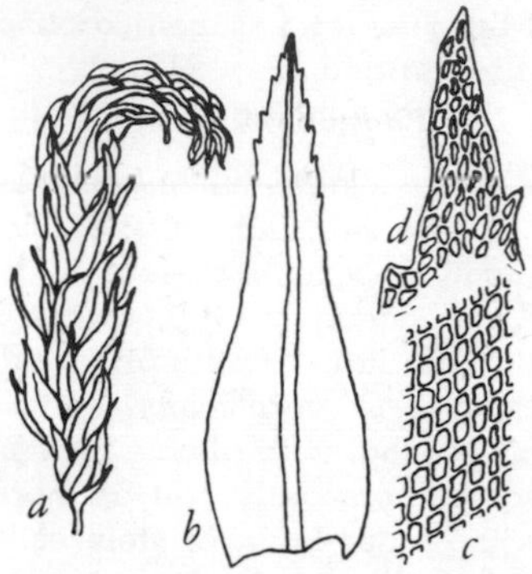

Figure 212

Fig. 212. *Herpetineuron toccoae*. a, plant; b, leaf; c, median cells; d, apex of leaf with teeth. Dark green mats on rocks, North Carolina to Florida and Louisiana. First described from Toccoa Falls, Georgia, but now known from Asia, East Indies, Africa and South America. Never fruiting in North America.

57b Leaves revolute below, sharply serrate above with long, slender, often reflexed teeth. Fig. 213. Pacific coast only..Genus *Antitrichia*

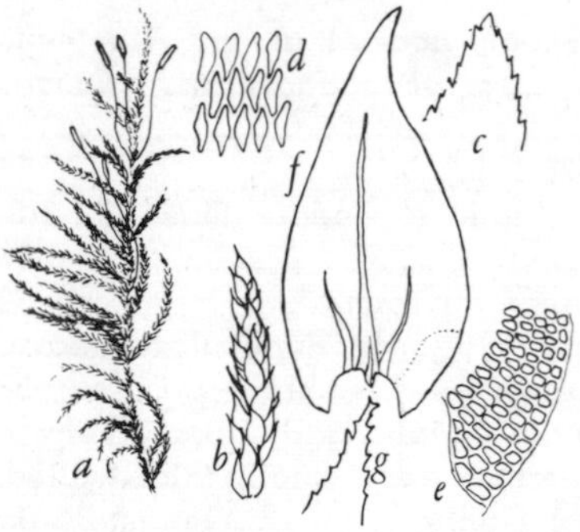

Figure 213

Fig. 213. *Antitrichia curtipendula*. a, shoot; b, twig; c, apex of leaf; d, median cells; e, alar cells; f, whole leaf with accessory ribs; g, apex of leaf of *A. californica*. On shaded trees and rocks, California to Alaska. *A. californica* lacks the accessory ribs, and has the capsule longer (3-5 mm.); California to Briitsh Columbia and Colorado.

58a Seta shorter than perichaetial leaves; leaves 1.5-2 mm. long. Fig. 214..Genus *Leptodon*

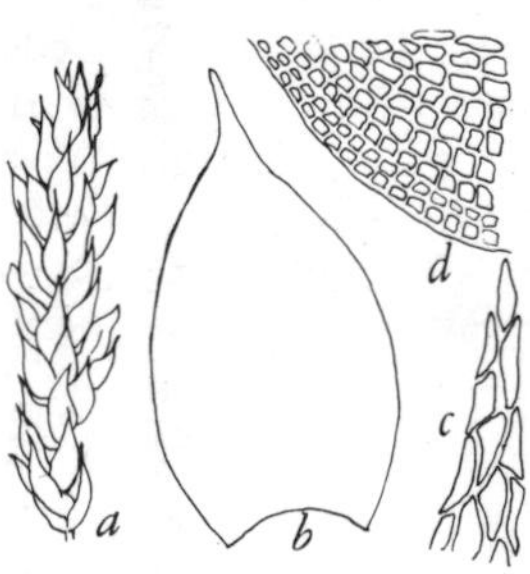

Figure 214

Fig. 214. *Leptodon trichomitrion*. a, shoot; b, leaf; c, apex of leaf; d, alar cells. Calyptra hairy; inner peristome rudimentary or lacking. On trees and rocks. New England to the Gulf. *L. ohioensis* is known only from central Ohio and southern Virginia and *L. nitidus* from one locality, now destroyed by clearing, near Belleville, Ontario.

58b Seta 3-4 mm. long, much longer than perichaetium. Leaves .5-.7 mm. long. Fig. 215........................Genus *Clasmatodon*

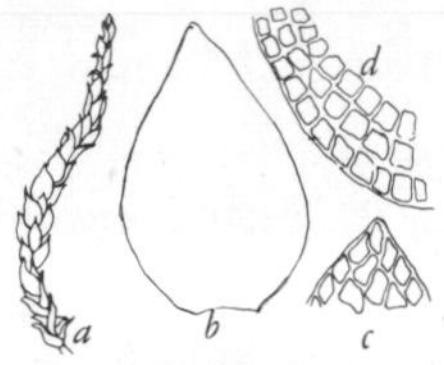

Figure 215

Fig. 215. *Clasmatodon parvulus.* a, shoot; b, leaf; c, apex of leaf; d, alar cells. Teeth of peristome are mere rudiments, rarely seen; segments irregular, fragile, smooth. On trees, shrubs or rocks, Virginia to Oklahoma and the Gulf, in thin, pale green mats.

59a Leaves distinctly serrate above the middle. Seta rough........60
59b Leaves entire, or slightly denticulate on lower half.............61
60a Small: leaves to .9 mm. long. Capsule horizontal. Figs. 245, 250. ....*Brachythecium reflexum, collinum*
60b Larger: leaves to 2 mm. long, plicate. Capsule nearly erect. Western.......................................*Camptothecium aeneum*
61a Leaves squarrose-recurved, especially when wet. Fig. 216....... ....*Campylium chrysophyllum*

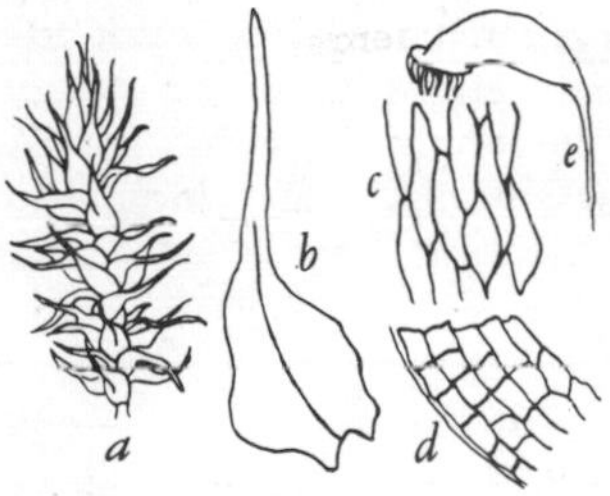

Figure 216

Fig. 216. *Campylium chrysophyllum.* a, shoot; b, leaf; c, median cells; d, alar region; e, capsule. In thin yellowish green mats on earth, soil or old wood, northeast North America to Georgia, Texas, Arizona and British Columbia. Leaves mostly crowded and overlapping, obscuring the stem; acumination long and slender, subtubular, often slightly denticulate at base. Very variable; extreme alar cells often markedly inflated. Dioicous. Leaves often falcate, North Carolina to Texas.

61b Leaves erect, spreading or appressed, not squarrose-recurved...62
62a Leaves nearly at right angles to stem. Fig. 217................ ....*Leptodictyum trichopodium*

Figure 217

Fig. 217. *Leptodictyum trichopodium.* a, shoot; b, leaf and stem; c, alar region; d, median cells; e, capsule; f, leaf of var. *kochii.* Thin mats, or mixed with other mosses. Easily recognized when the leaves are slenderly acuminate and stand at right angles to the stem. But some specimens are hardly distinguishable from *L. riparium,* others from *Amblystegium juratzkanum* or *A. varium.* The beginner had better ignore them! Var. *kochii* is fairly distinct, by reason of its shorter midrib.

62b Leaves erect or appressed (imbricate)........................63

63a Capsules erect. Slender mosses on trees. Leaves .8-1.5 mm. long.64

63b Capsules curved, strongly contracted under the mouth when dry.65

64a Midrib reaching tip of leaf. Cells small (.008-.012 mm.), dense. Fig. 187...*Leskea nervosa*

64b Midrib weak, ending near middle of leaf. Cells (.012 mm. wide), thin-walled, clear. Fig. 218..........*Anacamptodon splachnoides*

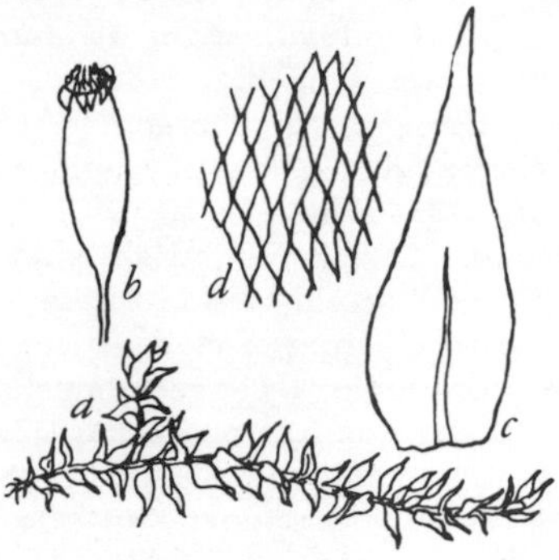

Figure 218

Fig. 218. *Anacamptodon splachnoides.* a, plant; b, open capsule with peristome; c, leaf; d, median cells. The Knot-hole Moss, because usually found on decaying wood in knot-holes of living trees—apple, sugar maple, etc. Maine to Illinois and Georgia, rare.

65a Midrib very strong, to apex of leaf or beyond. Fig. 219........... ....Genus *Hygroamblystegium*

Fig. 219. *Hygroamblystegium irriguum.* a, plant; b, leaf; c, basal cells; d, capsule; e, leaf of *H. orthocladon.* Very abundant in moist places. Northeast to Georgia, Arkansas and California. *H. orthocladon* is very similar, with the same range. *H. irriguum* varies greatly and is often hard to separate from *Amblystegium varium,* no. 66b. See also 49b.

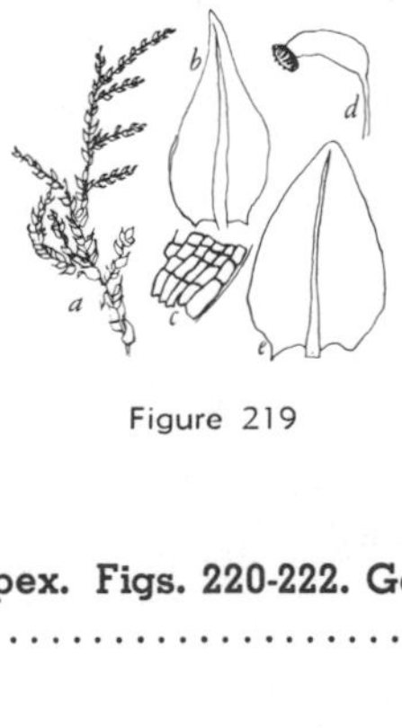

Figure 219

65b Midrib strong or weak, stopping short of apex. Figs. 220-222. Genus *Amblystegium* 66

66a (b, c) Midrib weak, ending near middle of leaf; margin entire; marginal cells at base quadrate or transversely elongated. Fig. 220. .... *Amblystegium serpens*

Figure 220

Fig. 220. *Amblystegium serpens.* a, shoot with capsule; b, leaf; c, dry twig; d, median cells. In thin mats on earth or trees or old wood; leaves lanceolate, to 1.2 mm. long. *A. juratzkanum* has the leaves widely spreading when dry, without transversely elongated basal-marginal cells, and is slightly larger.

66b Midrib strong, reaching apex of leaf or nearly so; leaves entire; median cells 4 or 5 times as long as wide. Fig. 221............ .... *Amblystegium varium*

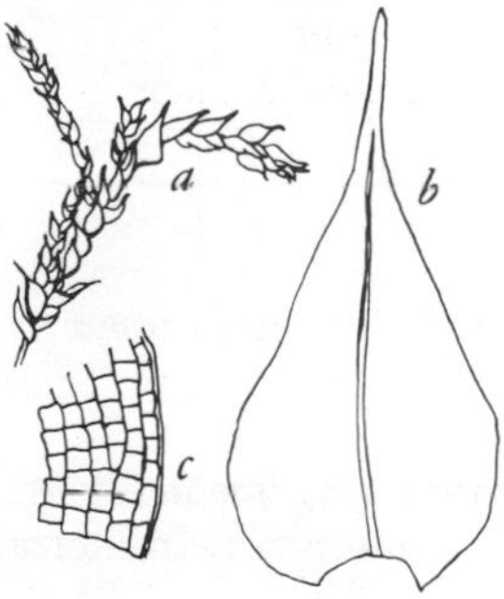

Figure 221

Fig. 221. *Amblystegium varium.* a, plant; b, leaf; c, alar cells. When the apex is as acuminate as figured, and the alar cells are in several parallel rows, recognition is easy. Many specimens closely resemble *Hygroamblystegium irriguum,* no. 65a, or *H. orthocladon.* On trees, wood, stones, earth, everywhere.

66c Midrib thin; cells 6 to 10 times as long as wide; margins serrulate. Fig. 222............................. *Amblystegium compactum*

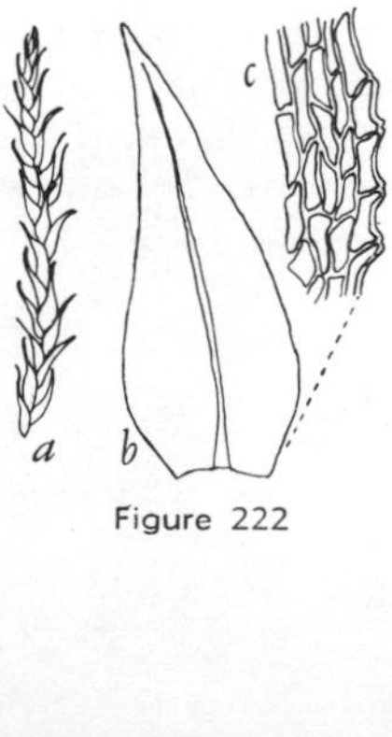

Figure 222

Fig. 222. *Amblystegium compactum.* a, shoot; b, leaf; c, cells of leaf. New York to Washington, in dense mats, to 2.5 cm. deep; slender; frequently with delicate broad filaments attached to back of midrib. *A. americanum,* Wisconsin to British Columbia, has more numerous paraphyllia; it is too much like *A. compactum.*

67a Shoots complanate-foliate..................................68

67b Leaves equally placed all around the stem....................71

68a Leaves acuminate or acute....................................69

68b Leaves rounded-obtuse, oblong-scimitar-shaped, minutely serrulate above. Cilia lacking. Fig. 223....................Genus *Homalia*

Figure 223

Fig. 223. *Homalia jamesii*. a, shoot; b, leaf; c, capsule with operculum. Little flat shiny sheets on shaded rock-faces, Newfoundland to British Columbia, Pennsylvania and Washington; upper Michigan. Stems to 1.5 cm. long, leaves to 1.5 mm. Leaf cells linear fusiform, the apical and marginal broadly rhomboidal. Other species in Europe and Asia.

69a Leaves entire, the base often obliquely attached to stem......70

69b Leaves sharply serrate, the apex twisted; seta smooth. Fig. 224. ....*Eurhynchium serrulatum*

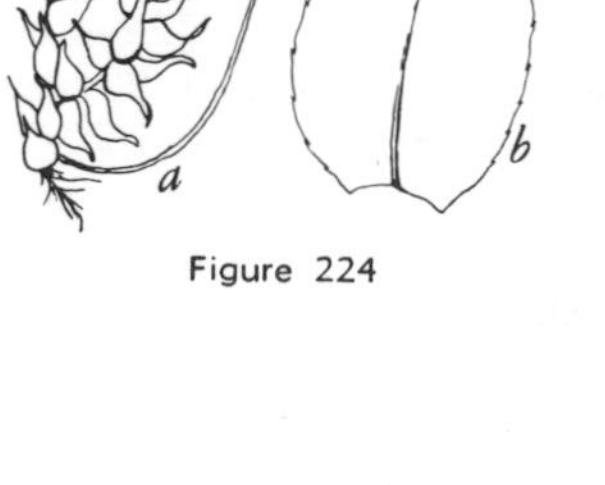

Figure 224

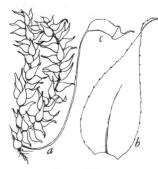

Fig. 224. *Eurhynchium serrulatum*. a, shoot; b, leaf; c, capsule and operculum. Irregularly branched, in thin mats on soil or bark. Eastern United States. Common in shady places. Fr. autumn.

70a Leaves slenderly acuminate. In damp places, often submerged. Fig. 225.................................*Leptodictyum riparium*

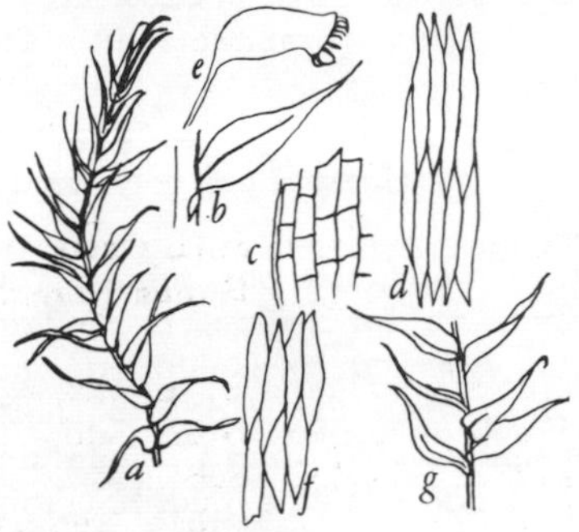

Figure 225

Fig. 225. *Leptodictyum riparium.* a, shoot; b, leaf with portion of stem; c, alar cells; d, median cells; e, capsule; f, median cells of f. *laxirete;* g, shoot of f. *fluitans.* Extremely variable in outline and habitat. Usually on moist soil or rotten wood; f. *fluitans* dangles a foot long in cold spring water; f. *longifolium* in quiet pools. In the extreme southeast *L. sipho* takes the place of *L. riparium.*

70b Leaves acute; cells 5-6:1. On soil in shade. Fig. 226.. *Leptodictyum brevipes*

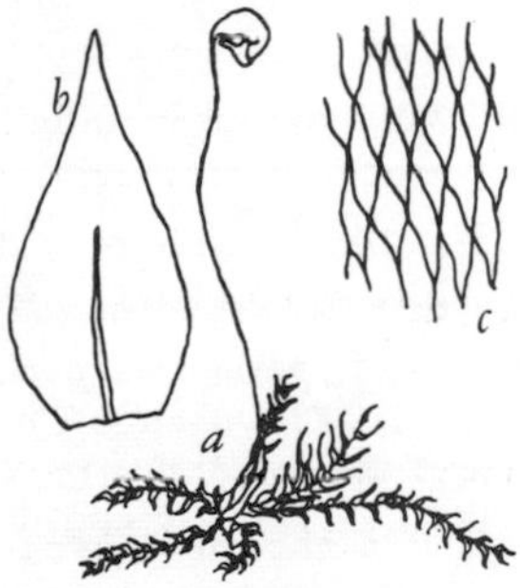

Figure 226

Fig. 226. *Leptodictyum brevipes.* a, plant; b, leaf; c, median cells. Common in lawns and low woods, Minnesota to Iowa and Indiana. Rarely submerged. Large submerged mosses that might trace to here are *L. riparium obtusum, laxirete* and *L. vacillans.*

71a Alar cells thin-walled, clear, inflated..........................72

71b Alar cells less or not at all enlarged. Leaves acute or acuminate, straight or nearly so, not recurved..........................75

72a Leaves entire, rounded at apex. Fig. 205....*Calliergon cordifolium*

72b Leaves distinctly pointed at apex..........................73

73a Inflated alar cells broadly decurrent. Fig. 248.. *Brachythecium rivulare,* 93b

73b Inflated alar cells clustered, not decurrent....................74

74a (b, c) Leaves slenderly acute, all bent to one side of stem (falcate-secund) at least at the hooked tips of stems. Figs. 201-203, 210..................................Genus *Drepanocladus,* 44b

74b Leaves widely spreading, very long-acuminate, perfectly entire. In very wet places. Fig. 227............*Campylium polygamum*

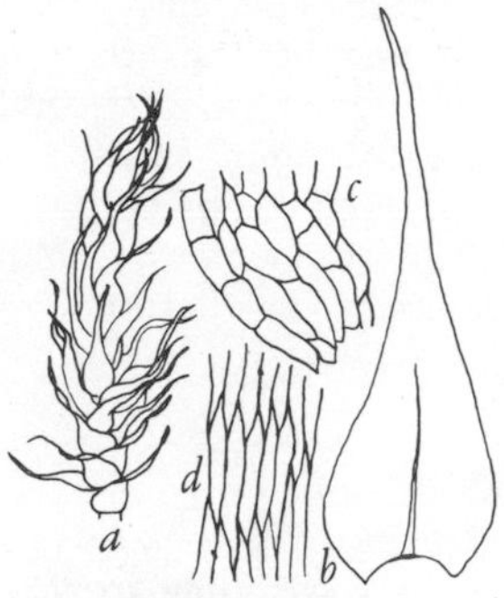

Figure 227

Fig. 227. *Campylium polygamum.* a, shoot; b, leaf; c, alar region; d, median cells. Arctic America to California and Virginia. This, when the midrib is short, is hardly distinguishable from *C. stellatum,* 110b, when it has a single midrib. From *Leptodictyum riparium,* 70a, it differs by having the apical region of the leaf concave, and the base transversely attached to the stem.

74c Leaves broad, blunt or with short tips. Figs. 270-274. Genus *Hygrohypnum* 113a

75a Leaves evenly tapering to a slender point, with several longitudinal folds (plicate). Figs. 228-230...............................76

75b Leaves ovate to lanceolate, with curved outlines, with only two folds or none at all. Figs. 231-250.........................78

76a Capsules oblong-cylindric, more or less curved; peristome perfect; large matted mosses, often yellowish. Figs. 229-230. Genus *Camptothecium* 77

76b Capsules erect and symmetric; inner peristome imperfect, even the segments often reducd. Fig. 228............Genus *Homalothecium*

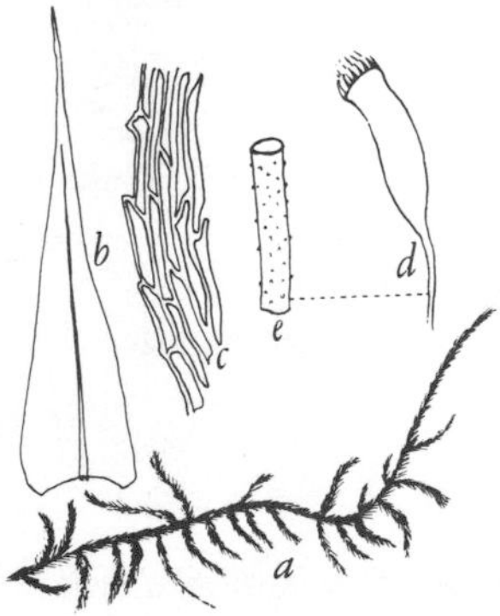

Figure 228

Fig. 228. *Homalothecium nuttallii.* a, shoot; b, leaf; c, cells of leaf; d, capsule; e, seta. Seta rough, at least above; leaves dentate at base. More slender than *Camptothecium,* with slender, curved, tapering golden yellow branches. California to British Columbia and Montana. *H. nevadense* is more slender, with leaves not dentate at base; same range.

77a Stems mostly erect, densely felted with brown radicles; in bogs and swamps. Fig. 229.......................... *Camptothecium nitens*

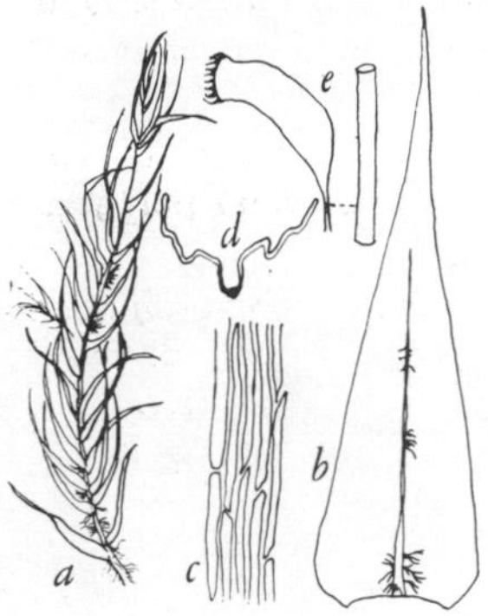

Figure 229

Fig. 229. *Camptothecium nitens.* a, shoot; b, leaf; c, median cells; d, section of leaf; e, capsule and seta. Seta smooth. Across North America in northern tier of states and northward; also in Europe. It forms dense sods, with stems 6 to 15 cm. tall.

77b Stems creeping and matted together, with few if any radicles. Fig. 230.................................. *Camptothecium lutescens*

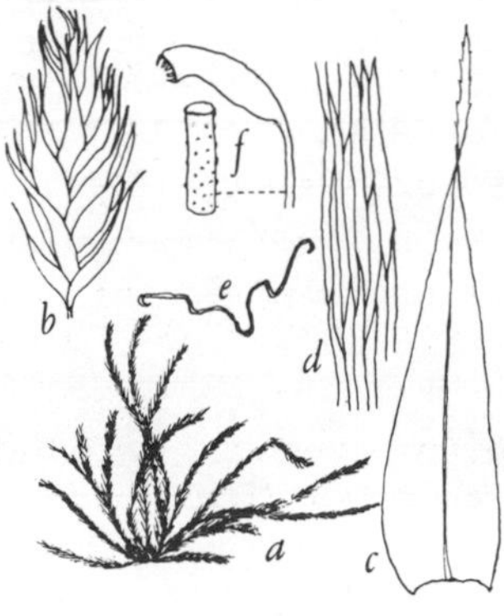

Figure 230

Fig. 230 *Camptothecium lutescens.* a, shoot; b, twig; c, leaf; d, cells of leaf; e, section of leaf; f, capsule and seta. Seta rough. Branching abundantly and irregularly, forming big glossy patches on trees, stumps and logs, northern U. S. and Canada west of the Rocky Mountains; also in Europe. *C. pinnatifidum* has regular, pinnate branching. On soil and rocks, California to British Columbia.

78a Beak of operculum as long as urn; plants glossy (except *E. rusciforme*); alar cells little or not at all differentiated. Figs. 231-234. Genus *Eurhynchium*..79

78b Beak conic or long-conic; alar cells quadrate; plants not glossy..83

79a Apical cells of leaf short-rhomboidal to circular. Figs. 232-234...80

79b Apical cells not differentiated. Seta smooth. Robust, pinnately branched. Stem leaves clasping the stem. Fig. 231 .... *Eurhynchium oreganum*

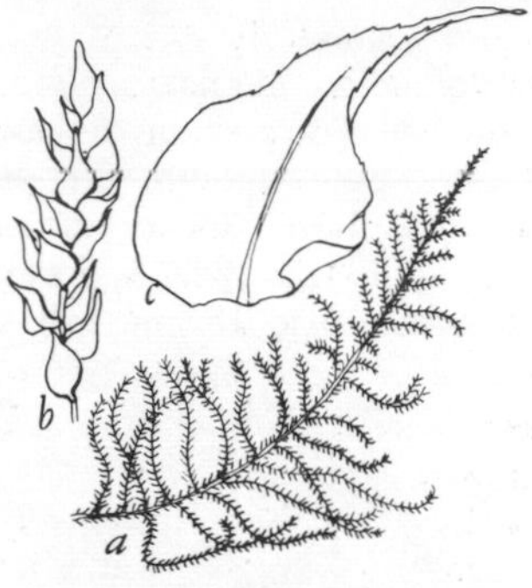

Figure 231

Fig. 231. *Eurhynchium oreganum.* a, shoot; b, twig; c, stem leaf; stems to 25 cm. long, in large cushions. Small specimens merge into *E. stokesii,* and this is often considered a variety of *E. praelongum* of Europe. There is an unbroken series from a slender, diffusely branched plant to the big golden-yellow or green *E. oreganum.*

80a Broad-leafed aquatic in wiry tufts on stones in streams; seta smooth. Fig. 232 .... *Eurhynchium rusciforme*

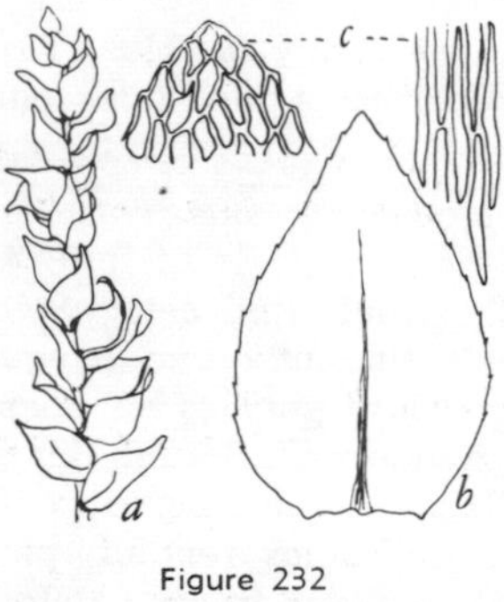

Figure 232

Fig. 232. *Eurhynchium rusciforme.* a, shoot; b, leaf; c, cells of middle and apex of leaf. Leaves erect-spreading when dry, serrulate nearly to the base, somewhat decurrent; alar cells thick-walled. A blackish moss, entangling much sand. Eastern United States, and in Europe.

80b On soil and bases of trees in woods 81

81a Leaves broadest 1/3 above base; seta rough. Fig. 233 .... *Eurhynchium hians*

Figure 233

Fig. 233. *Eurhynchium hians.* a, shoot; b, leaf; c, cells from middle, and d, from apex of leaf; e, capsule; f, stem leaf of *E. strigosum.* In delicate loose mats on soil, often among other mosses, Canada to the Gulf, west to Minnesota, Iowa and Missouri. *E. strigosum* has a smooth seta. The slender typical form is northern: Labrador to New York, Colorado, Washington and Alaska. Var. *robustum* has the same range as *E. hians,* but is more common northward.

81b Leaves broadest at base. Seta smooth......................82

82a Branches cylindrical, julaceous. Stem leaves slenderly acuminate, branch leaves rounded at apex. Fig. 234..*Eurhynchium diversifolium*

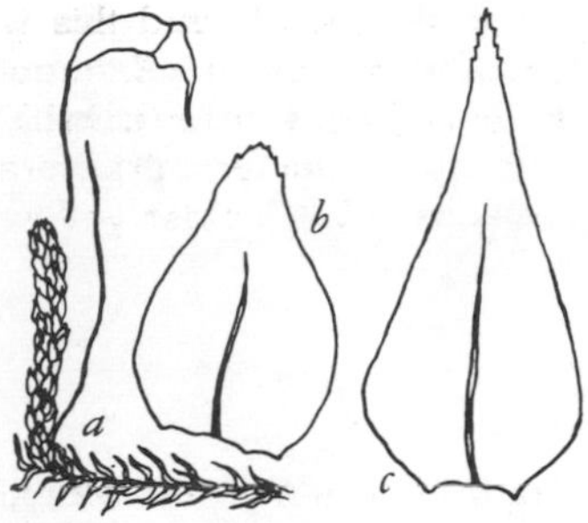

Figure 234

Fig. 234. *Eurhynchium diversifolium.* a, branch; b, leaf from branch; c, stem leaf. In dense dull green mats on stones or earth, South Dakota to Washington and New Mexico. *E. strigosuum* var. *praecox* is similar, New York to Iowa and Texas. *E. fallax,* Colorado to British Columbia and Alaska, differs in that the shoots are loosely foliate, not truly julaceous, the capsule is longer: 2.5 mm.

82b Branches not julaceous, the leaves spreading, acute. Branching often pinnate and complanate. Fig. 233...*Eurhynchium strigosum**

83a (b, c) With a large area of small, thick-walled, rounded alar cells; cilia well-developed. Fig. 235.............Genus *Pseudisothecium*

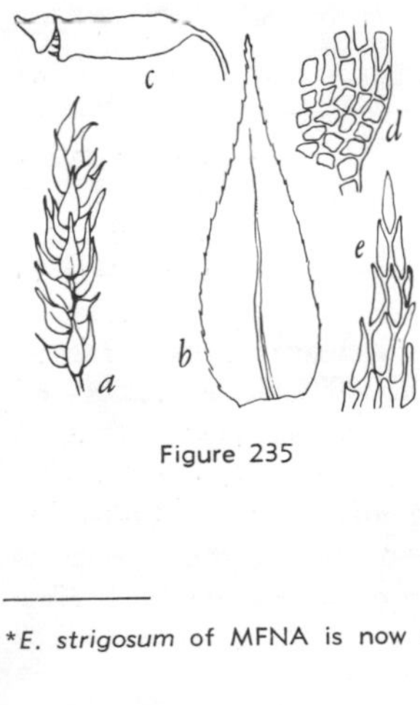

Figure 235

Fig. 235. *Pseudisothecium stoloniferum.* a, shoot; b, leaf; c, capsule; d, alar region of *P. myosuroides;* e, leaf apex of same. Almost dendroid, with stems to 5 cm. long; leaves to 2 mm. The small dense alar cells and inclined to nodding capsules are characteristic; California and Colorado to Alaska. In the East, *P. myosuroides* is found, rarely, from Newfoundland to North Carolina, in high mountains. Common in western Europe.

**E. strigosum* of MFNA is now called *E. pulchellum* (Hedw.) Jenn.

83b With a large area of thin-walled, quadrate cells at base of leaf, from margin to midrib; cilia lacking; capsules erect. Fig. 236. ....Genus *Chamberlainia*

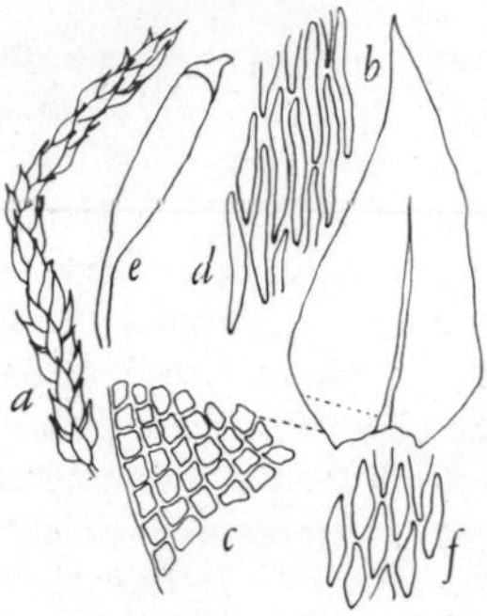

Figure 236

Fig. 236. *Chamberlainia acuminata.* a, shoot; b, leaf; c, basal cells; d, median cells; e, capsule; f, median cells of *C. cyrtophylla.* In dense mats on bark, rarely on rocks or soil, eastern United States to Minnesota and the Gulf. *C. cyrtophylla* is a poorly delimited species. *C. acuminata* varies from filiform to robust and julaceous.

83c With fewer alar cells, not reaching midrib, usually thin-walled, sometimes inflated; cilia well-developed.......................84

84a Small glossy mats on trees. Leaves about 1 mm. long. Inner peristome adherent to outer. Eastern. Fig. 237..Genus *Homalotheciella*

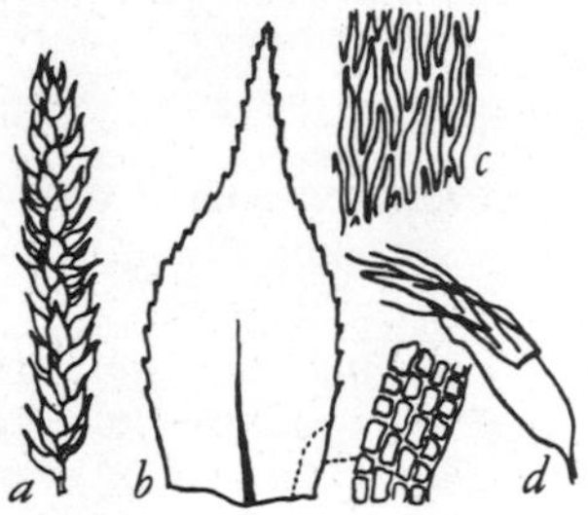

Figure 237

Fig. 237. *Homalotheciella subcapillata.* a, shoot; b, leaf; c, cells of leaf; d, capsule with calyptra. Seta rough; spores in autumn. United States east of the Mississippi River; Missouri. Not common.

84b Larger. Peristome separate...............................85

85a Branches julaceous (cylindrical, densely and closely leafed); leaves smooth, concave; seta rough; western. Figs. 238, 239. Genus *Scleropodium* 86

85b Branches with leaves erect or appressed; if sub-julaceous the leaves have longitudinal folds (plicate); falcate-secund in one group of species; very abundant east of the Sierras and Cascades. Figs. 240-250. Genus *Brachythecium*..............................87

86a Leaves broadly ovate to suborbicular; median cells 8-10:1, alar distinctly inflated; in water or wet places. Fig. 238................ ....*Scleropodium obtusifolium*

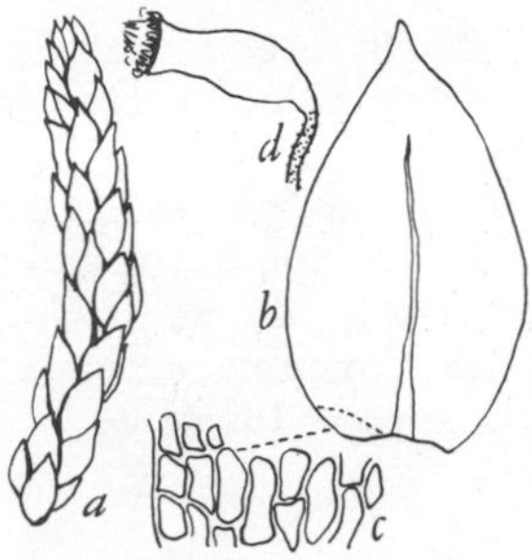

Figure 238

Fig. 238. *Scleropodium obtusifolium.* a, shoot; b, leaf; c, alar region; d, capsule. A stout, matted moss, attached to stones in streams, California to British Columbia, Montana and Nevada. *S. illecebrum* has leaves abruptly short-acuminate, and very few quadrate alar cells; but it merges into *S. obtusifolium,* and has a similar range, on drier ground.

86b Leaves ovate to lanceolate; stem leaves slenderly acuminate; alar cells numerous; only slightly julaceous. Fig. 239................ ....*Scleropodium cespitans*

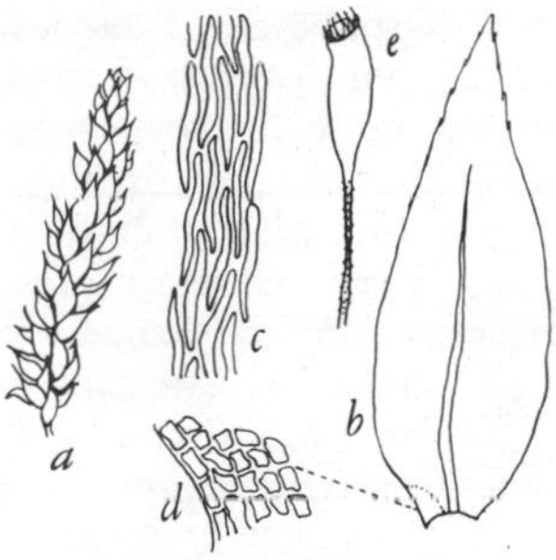

Figure 239

Fig. 239. *Scleropodium cespitans (S. caespitosum* of MFNA). a, shoot; b, leaf; c, median cells; d, alar cells; e, capsule. In loose mats on stumps, logs and rocks, California to Alaska. *S. colpophyllum* Grout has but few alar cells; it is hardly distinguishable from *S. cespitans.* Two other species occur in North America.

87a Leaves plicate..88

87b Leaves not plicate....................................91

88a (b, c) Alar cells small, numerous, quadrate, sharply differentiated, not notably dense or thick-walled..........................89

88b Alar cells mostly open, similar to lower cells of leaf. Seta smooth, at least near base..90

88c Alar cells much larger than those above, often with a row of large clear cells across base of leaf, probably belonging to the stem. Seta rough. Fig. 240............. *Brachythecium lamprochryseum*

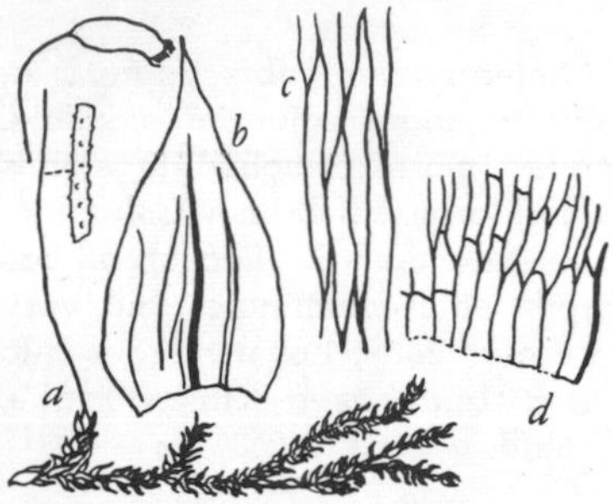

Figure 240

Fig. 240. *Brachythecium lamprochryseum*. a, shoot; b, leaf; c, median cells; d, basal cells. Large, light green moss of damp places, easily mistaken for *B. rivulare*, but the alar cells are not really inflated. California to British Columbia, Colorado and Idaho. Common. Dioicous.

89a Large, in dense mats. Leaves straight; seta smooth. Dioicous. Fig. 241................................. *Brachythecium oxycladon*

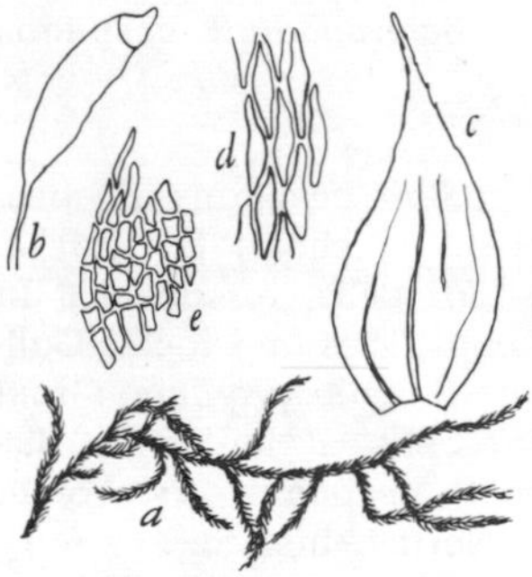

Figure 241

Fig. 241. *Brachythecium oxycladon*. a, shoot; b, capsule; c, leaf; d, median cells of var. *dentatum;* e, alar region. Dioicous, and distinguished by the plicate leaves, long slightly curved capsules and alar cells. Very variable in size and arrangement of leaves, serration and acumination, sometimes falcate. Very common and abundant in northeast United States, to Minnesota, Kansas and North Carolina, in woods, pastures, lawns. Merges into *B. salebrosum* in vegetative characters.

89b Medium size, loosely spreading. Leaves falcate-secund. Monoicous; seta rough. Fig. 242..................... *Brachythecium leibergii*

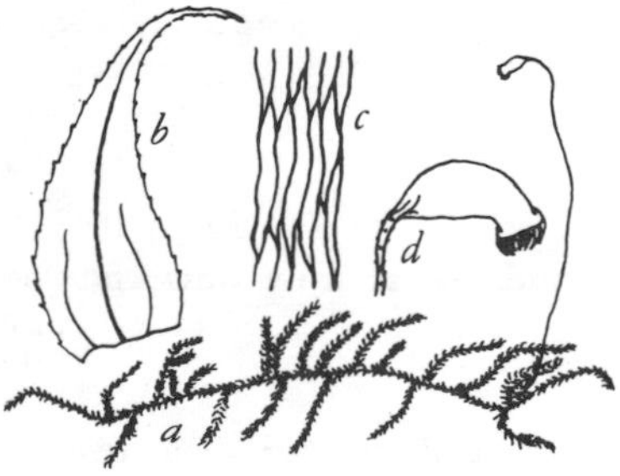

Figure 242

Fig. 242. *Brachythecium leibergii*. a, shoot; b, leaf; c, median cells; d, capsule. On soil or duff, Colorado to Montana and Washington, frequent.

90a Leaves distinctly serrate. Fig. 243. Monoicous.................... ....*Brachythecium salebrosum*

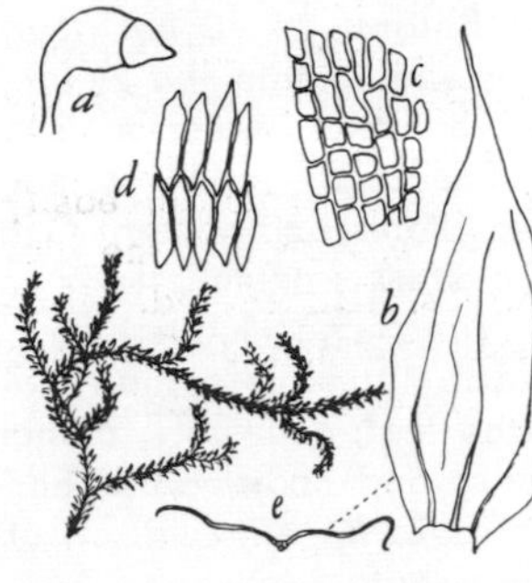

Figure 243

Fig. 243. *Brachythecium salebrosum*. a, capsule; b, leaf; c, alar cells; d, median cells; e, section of leaf. Monoicous, and characterized by the short horizontal capsules and alar cells. More mesic than the preceding, the leaves more spreading. Very wide-spread over the same area as the preceding. At Grinnell, Iowa, it is abundant in shaded parts of the college campus, whereas on roadsides and in woods and pastures *B. oxycladon* is everywhere. Europe. A form with seta rough above is *B. campestre.*

90b Leaves entire or very finely denticulate, with a long, fine acumination. Dioicous. Large plants. Fig. 244.....*Brachythecium albicans*

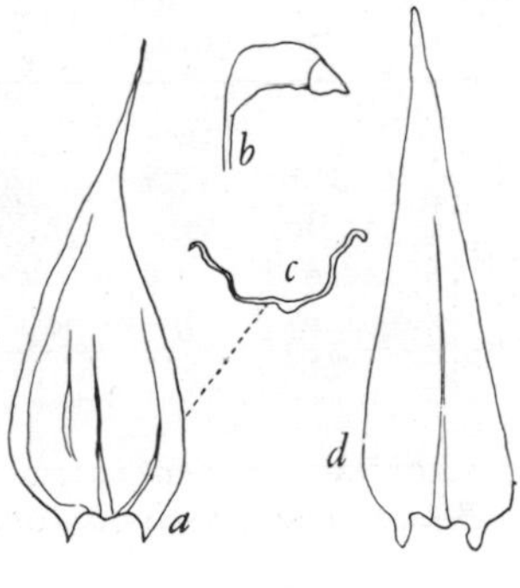

Figure 244

Fig. 244. *Brachythecium albicans*. a, leaf; b, capsule; c, section of leaf; d, leaf of *B. acutum*. A big moss, in light green mats on rocks or soil, Colorado northward and westward; dioicous; leaf apex very slender. *B. flexicaule*, Newfoundland, New Jersey, Iowa, British Columbia, is monoicous, with leaves very much like those of *Leptodictyum riparium*. I consider it a wet habitat form of *B. salebrosum*. *B. acutum* is monoicous, with leaves wedge-shaped, i.e., the sides are straight, from the broad base to apex.

91a Leaves straight, not secund.................................92

91b Leaves more or less secund...............................94

92a (b, c) Leaves ovate-deltoid. Seta rough. Large plants.........93

92b Stem leaves triangular-ovate, decurrent; median cells 3-5:1. Small species. Fig. 245........................*Brachythecium reflexum*

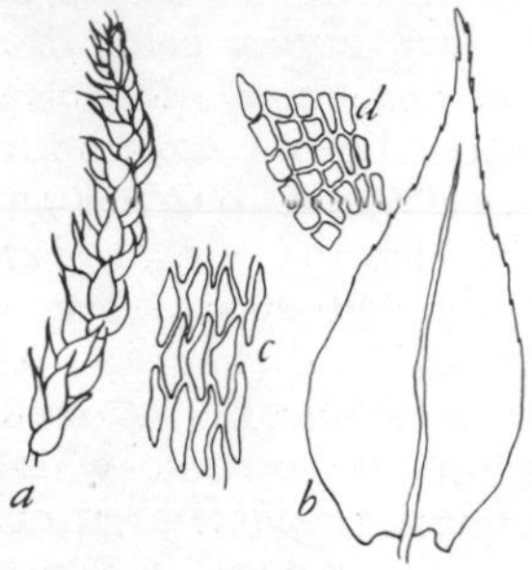

Figure 245

Fig. 245. *Brachythecium reflexum.* a, plant; b, leaf; c, median cells; d, alar region. Stems filiform, to 10 cm. long; midrib stout, extending into the slender acumen; cells short; monoicous; seta very rough. On logs, roots or soil, northern United States and eastern Canada, Alaska. *B. starkei* extends to Pennsylvania and Vancouver; leaves to 1.7 mm. long, midrib little more than half the length of the leaf, cells 13:1, monoicous; rough seta and short, dark, horizontal capsule as in *B. reflexum;* shoots somewhat complanate.

92c Leaves ovate-lanceolate, concave. Monoicous. Fig. 246.......... ....*Brachythecium flagellare*

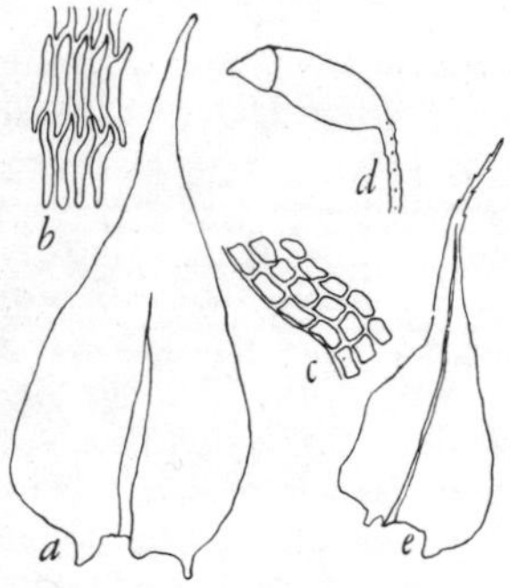

Figure 246

Fig. 246. *Brachythecium flagellare (B. plumosum* of MFNA). a, leaf; b, median cells; c, alar region; d, capsule; e, leaf of *B. populeum. B. flagellare* has smooth spoonshaped-concave leaves, seta rough above, nearly black; capsule horizontal to sub-erect; operculum long-conic. On moist rocks in brooks, northeast United States and Canada to Iowa and British Columbia. *B. populeum* has a similar leaf, slightly shorter cells (5-8:1), more numerous alar cells, the midrib extending to tip of leaf; autoicous; seta rough above.

93a Alar cells large but not inflated; in mesic habitats. Fig. 247...... ....*Brachythecium rutabulum*

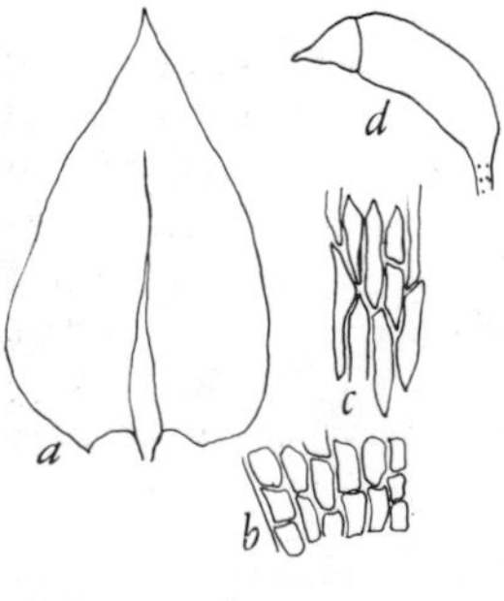

Figure 247

Fig. 247. *Brachythecium rutabulum.* a, leaf; b, alar region; c, median cells; d, capsule. A big moss in bright green mats on soil or rocks, trees or old logs, in damp woods, northeast United States and Canada, to Pennsylvania, Missouri and Montana. Monoicous; seta rough. Leaves to 2 mm. long. Variable, sometimes resembling *B. salebrosum.*

93b Alar cells numerous, inflated, colorless, decurrent; hydric. Fig. 248. .... *Brachythecium rivulare*

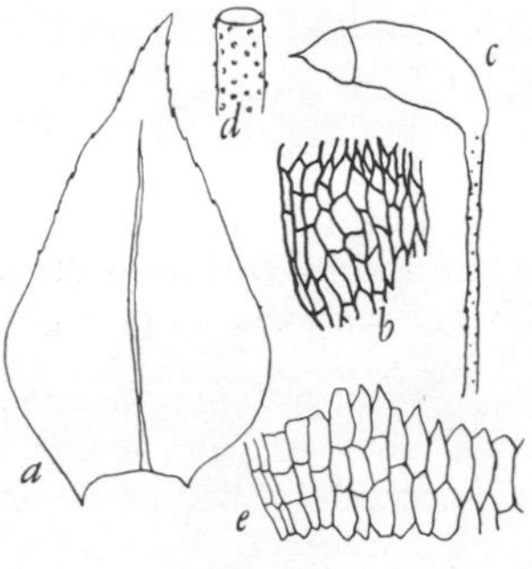

Figure 248

Fig. 248. *Brachythecium rivulare.* a, leaf; b, alar region; c, capsule; d, seta; e, alar region of *B. nelsoni.* A big, light green moss, in or near springs or brooks, ocean to ocean, south to Virginia and Missouri. Leaves ovate-lanceolate, to 1.5 mm. long, concave, acute or broadly acuminate, serrate; median cells 10-15:1; dioicous; seta very rough. Variable, often approaching *B. rutabulum. B. nelsoni* is a form with long-acuminate leaves and more numerous inflated alar cells. Colorado and Wyoming.

94a Seta very rough; cells 12:1; capsule short, curved. Fig. 249....... .... *Brachythecium velutinum*

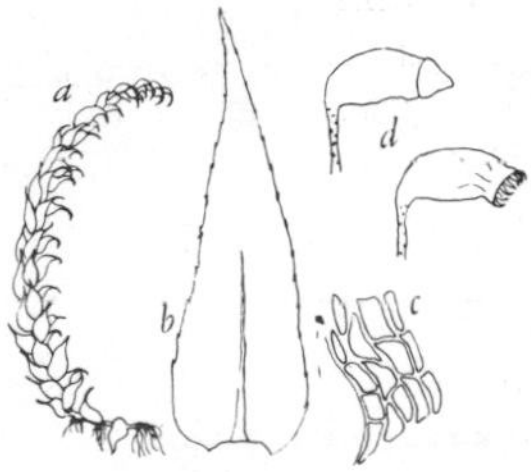

Figure 249

Fig. 249. *Brachythecium velutinum.* a, shoot; b, leaf; c, alar region; d, capsule, with operculum, and open. In slender velvety dark green mats on earth, stones or trees; leaves serrate, more or less falcate. Monoicous. Northern United States and Canada, to New Jersey and California. Europe.

94b Seta smooth or slightly roughened; cells 3-6:1; capsule more or less curved. Fig. 250........................ *Brachythecium collinum*

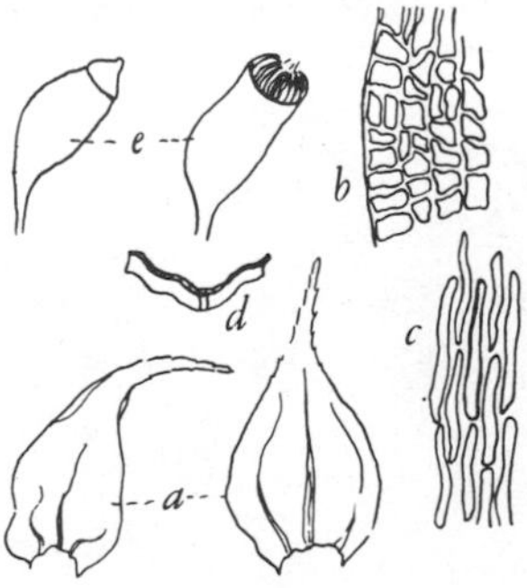

Figure 250

Fig. 250. *Brachythecium collinum.* a, leaf; b, alar region; c, median cells; d, section of leaf; e, capsule with and without operculum. In thin interwoven mats on earth and rocks in mountains: New Mexico to Peace River; Mt. Shasta; Greenland; Europe. Leaves ovate, to 0.9 mm. long; midrib extending to middle; monoicous. Var. *idahense* is falcate, larger.

95a Aquatic, long and dangling, often in dense tufts; alar cells inflated. Figs. 251-253. Genus *Fontinalis*....................................96

95b Terrestrial; xeric, mesic or hydric, not constantly submerged....98

96a. Leaves folded and sharply keeled along the midrib, at least, above. Fig. 251....................................*Fontinalis antipyretica*

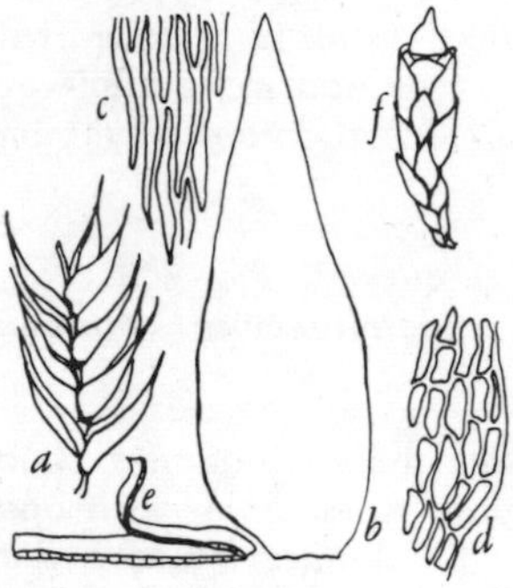

Figure 251

Fig. 251. *Fontinalis antipyretica*. a, shoot; b, leaf; c, median cells; d, alar cells; e, section of leaf; f, capsule with operculum. Var. *gigantea* has leaves to 8 mm. long and 6 mm. wide. Capsules rarely seen; inner peristome a cone-shaped network. Formerly reputed as a febrifuge, because it grows in cold water, not because it really reduces a fever! North America, Europe, Asia and Africa. *F. neomexicana* Rocky Mountains to Pacific Coast, has leaves relatively broader and more acute.

96b Leaves rounded on the back, not keeled. Figs. 252, 253.......97

97a Stem leaves more or less concave and channeled, rather firm in texture. Fig. 252............................*Fontinalis dalecarlica*

Figure 252

Fig. 252. *Fontinalis dalecarlica*. a, shoot; b, leaf; c, apex of leaf; d, section of leaf; e, perichaetium and capsule. Leaves 2-4 mm. long; shoots slender. Greenland and Labrador to Wisconsin, Indiana and Tennessee. Europe. *F. novae-angliae*, northeast to Oklahoma and Georgia, has broader leaves, 3-7.5 mm. long; shoots more robust.

97b Stem leaves flat or slightly concave, soft and limp. Fig. 253..... .... *Fontinalis duriaei*

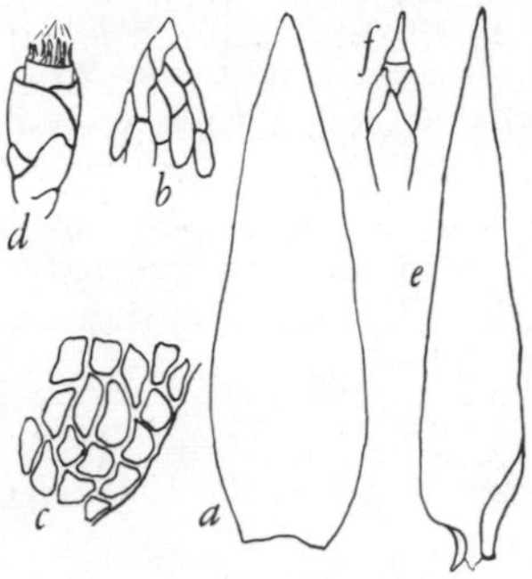

Figure 253

Fig. 253. *Fontinalis duriaei.* a, leaf; b, apex of leaf; c, alar cells; d, perichaetium and capsule; United States and Canada. *F. lescurii* e, leaf; f, perichaetium and capsule. Nova Scotia to Alabama and the Rocky Mountains. Leaves rather distant. A difficult group. Twenty-four species of *Fontinalis* are recognized in North America by Dr. Winona Welch in MFNA.

98a Median leaf cells 2-5:1, that is, relatively short. Figs. 254-260...99

98b Median leaf cells 5-20:1, that is, long to very long. Figs. 261-301..106

99a Cell walls very thick, the lumen elliptic to linear; alar cells very numerous. Figs. 254, 255...100

99b Cell walls thinner, equally thick all around.................102

100a Secondary stems little branched; calyptra smooth. Figs. 254, 255. Genus *Leucodon* 101

100b Secondary stems freely and often pinnately branched. Calyptra hairy. Fig. 214. Genus *Leptodon*......................See 58a

101a Seta shorter than perichaetial leaves; leaves gradually acuminate. Fig. 254 .... ***Leucodon brachypus***

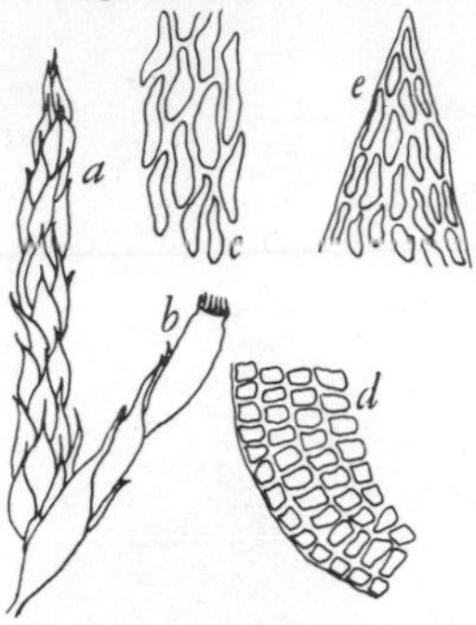

Figure 254

Fig. 254. *Leucodon brachypus.* a, shoot; b, sporophyte and perichaetium; c, median cells of leaf; d, basal cells of leaf; e, apex of leaf. Branches julaceous, hard and smooth when dry, making large, harsh, curly tufts and sheets, 2 to 4 cm. deep, on trees or rocks, northeast to Ontario, Georgia and Kansas. Leaves plicate.

101b Seta longer than perichaetium; leaves slenderly acuminate, very strongly plicate, wet or dry. Fig. 255 .... ***Leucodon sciuroides***

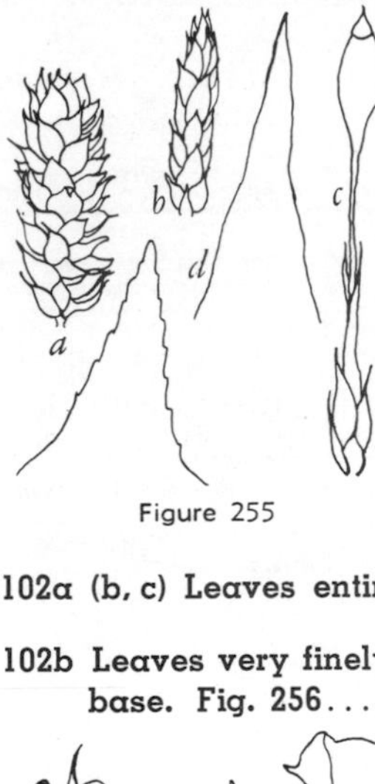

Figure 255

Fig. 255. *Leucodon sciuroides.* a, wet shoot; b, dry shoot; c, sporophyte and perichaetium; d, apex of leaf; e, apex of leaf of *L. julaceus.* These two species are very much alike. Beside the difference in acumination and plication, *L. julaceus* leaves are mamillose-roughened on the back at the apex. The first occurs from northeast to Pennsylvania and Iowa, the second to Minnesota, Texas and Florida.

102a (b, c) Leaves entire **103**

102b Leaves very finely denticulate, squarrose-recurved from a concave base. Fig. 256 .... ***Campylium hispidulum***

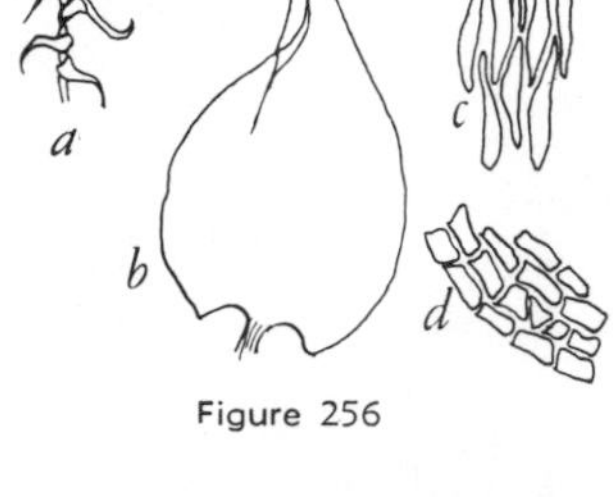

Figure 256

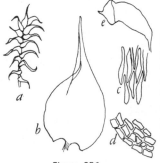

Fig. 256. *Campylium hispidulum.* a, shoot; b, leaf; c, median cells; d, alar region; e, capsule. In thin yelowish mats on old wood, bark or earth in woodlands, northeastern North America to North Carolina, Texas, Idaho and British Columbia. Leaves to 0.75 mm. long, widely spreading, abruptly contracted to the acumination, finely serrulate all round. Monoicous.

102c Leaves coarsely toothed with whole projecting cells. Fig. 257... ....Genus *Fabronia**

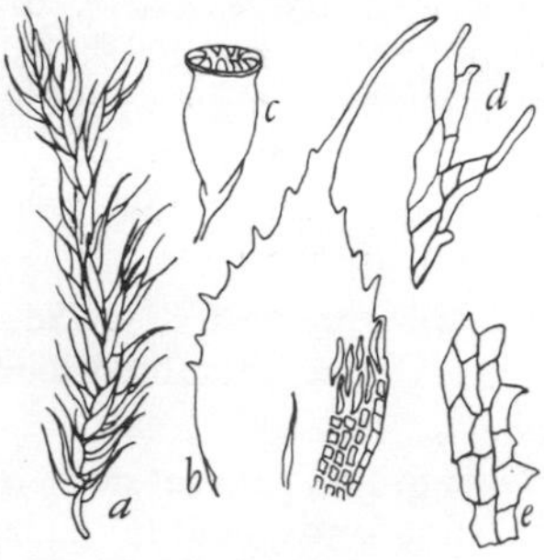

Figure 257

Fig. 257. *Fabronia ciliaris.* a, shoot; b, leaf; c, capsule; d, margin of leaf; e, margin of leaf of *F. pusilla.* Very small pale green mats on bark or rocks; peristome teeth easily broken off. *F. ciliaris* ranges from New Jersey to Minnesota, Arizona and Georgia. *F. pusilla* from New Mexico to Colorado, California and British Columbia; *F. ravenelii,* with leaves nearly entire, is found from Pennsylvania to Tennessee and Georgia.

103a Cells very large and clear, .05-.06 mm.; alar cells not different. Fig. 258..................................Genus *Hookeria*

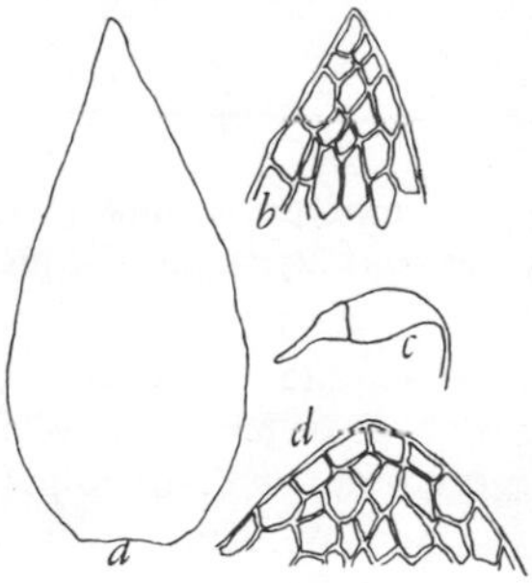

Figure 258

Fig. 258. *Hookeria acutifolia.* a, leaf; b, cells of apex of leaf; c, capsule of *H. lucens;* d, apex of leaf of same. Pale watery mosses, the former on dripping ledges, Connecticut to Ohio and Georgia (also India, Ceylon, Java, West Indies and South America!), the latter California to Vancouver, and in Europe. The cells are easily seen with an ordinary hand lens.

---

*A whole series of intergrading forms as to shape of leaf, size of marginal teeth, size and shape of cells, size of spores. Some combinations are named, others fortunately, are not. "Their name is legion."

Peristome teeth single, the teeth broad and obtuse

Leaves ovate-lanceolate

Teeth of leaf longer than the body of the cell. Spores .012-.017 mm. .... *Fabronia pusilla*

Teeth intermediate in length. Spores .015-.018 mm. ..... *Fabronia ciliaris*

Teeth mere serrulations. Spores .017 mm........................*F. ravenelii*

Leaves lanceolate. Teeth ¼-½ as long as the cell body. Spores .011 mm........ .... *Fabronia wrightii*

Peristome imperfect or lacking; probably due to drought at a critical time .... *Fabronia imperfecta, F. gymnostoma*

Otherwise like *F. ciliaris*

103b Cells .007-.008 mm. wide; quadrate alar cells small, numerous. 104

104a Leaves minute, to .6 mm. long. Fig. 260. Genus *Amblystegiella*. 105

104b Leaves larger, .8-1.2 mm. long, concave. Cilia perfect. Fig. 259. ....Genus *Homomallium*

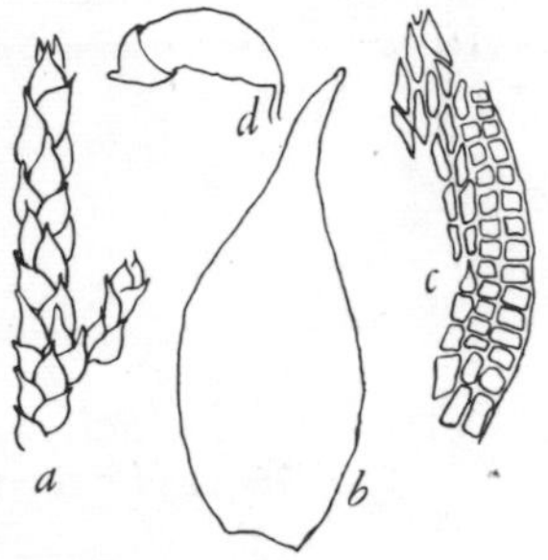

Figure 259

Fig. 259. *Homomallium adnatum.* a, shoot; b, leaf; c, alar and median cells; d, capsule and operculum. Thin dark green mats adhering closely to rocks or stones, to be scraped off with a knife. Ontario to Colorado, Texas and West Virginia; common in midwest. Superficially resembling *Leskea* and *Sematophyllum*, but easily distinguished when capsules are present.

105a On base of trees. Leaves about .5 mm. Cilia of peristome rudimentary. Fig. 260........................*Amblystegiella subtilis*

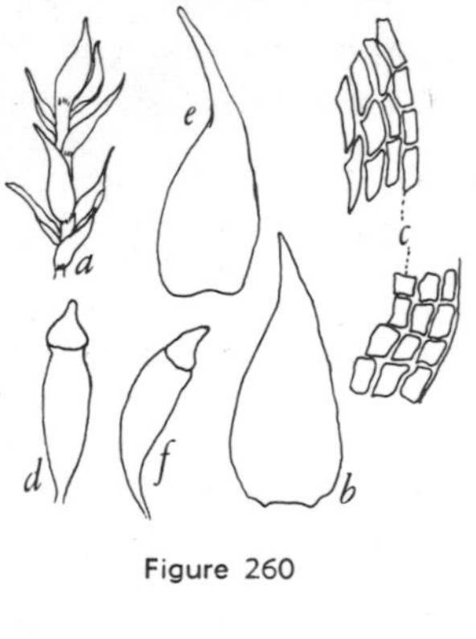

Figure 260

Fig. 260. *Amblystegiella subtilis.* a, shoot; b, leaf; c, alar and median cells; d, capsule and operculum; e, leaf of *A. confervoides;* f, capsule of same. Very small matted mosses, the former on bark, Ontario to Minnesota, Illinois and Pennsylvania; the latter on limestone rocks, northeast to Iowa and Colorado. Two species, still smaller, are reported. *A. subtilis* lacks cilia in the peristome; *A. confervoides* has cilia.

105b On rocks. Leaves .1-.3 mm. Cilia perfect. Fig. 260............. ....*Amblystegiella confervoides*

106a (b, c, d) With one inflated cell at extreme basal angle, and many quadrate cells; tips of shoots often crowded with buds (gemmae). Fig. 261 .... Genus *Platygyrium*

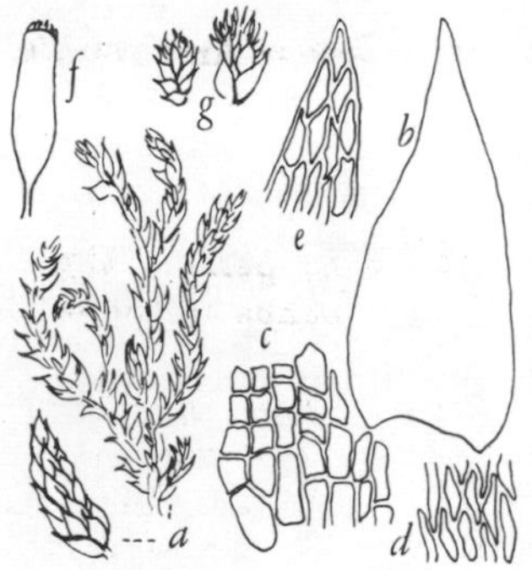

Figure 261

Fig. 261. *Platygyrium repens.* a, shoot; b, leaf; c, alar region; d, median cells; e, apex of leaf; f, capsule; g, gemmae. In dark green mats on bark. Common east of the Rocky Mountains. Characterized by the straight leaves, the erect cylindric capsule, and segments very narrow; no cilia. With a hand lens the clustered gemmae are distinctive.

106b With several (2 or more) inflated alar cells. Figs. 262-284 107

106c With small quadrate alar cells. Figs. 285-291 128

106d With little or no differentiation of alar cells. Figs. 292-301 134

107a (b, c) Alar cells in a transverse row of 3 or 4 adjacent to stem. Operculum with beak as long as urn. Figs. 262, 263. Genus *Sematophyllum* 108

107b Alar cells in a cluster, 3 or 4 transversely and 3 or 4 up margin of leaf. Figs. 264-265 109

107c Alar cells more numerous, less swollen, thicker walled, often colored. Figs. 266-285 110

108a Slender plants on trees or old wood; capsules erect. Fig. 262 .... *Sematophyllum adnatum*

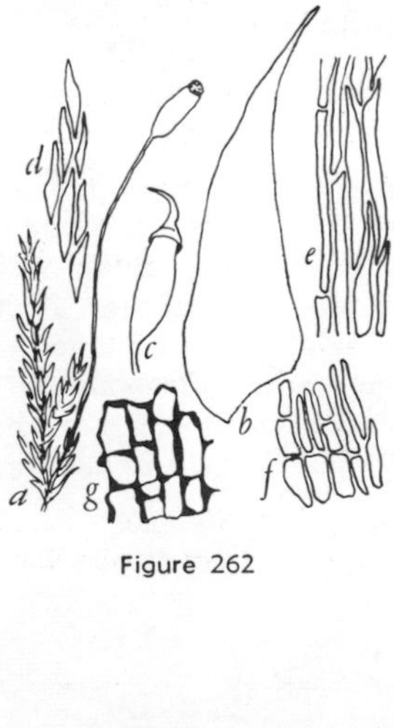

Figure 262

Fig. 262. *Sematophyllum adnatum.* a, shoot; b, leaf; c, capsule with operculum; d, apex of leaf; e, median cells; f, alar cells; g, cells of capsule wall. In patches on bark of living trees, Rhode Island to Iowa, Florida and Texas. Ends of shoots may be curved away from the substratum somewhat as in *Pylaisia*. A similar plant with shorter, broader cells, in Florida, is *S. caespitosum*. The operculum, the thick-walled outer cells of the urn, the alar cells, and the broadly reflexed margins of the leaves, and their yellowish color, characterize *Sematophyllum*.

108b In mats on rocks; capsules inclined and curved, contracted below the mouth when dry. Fig. 263...... *Sematophyllum carolinianum*

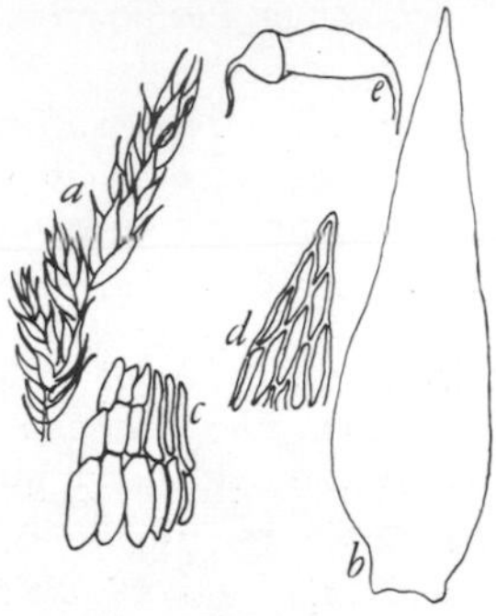

Figure 263

Fig. 263. *Sematophyllum carolinianum.* a, shoot; b, leaf; c, alar cells; d, apex of leaf; e, capsule with operculum. In yellowish green mats closely attached to moist rocks, Canada to Georgia and Iowa. Like the preceding species, except as to capsule. *S. marylandicum* is much larger, with leaves 1.5-2.5 mm. long; otherwise much like the preceding; on damp stones in mountains, New Hampshire to Georgia.

109a Alar cells scarcely decurrent; leaves complanate and falcate-secund, sharply serrate on the slender acumination; capsules inclined, smooth. Fig. 264...................... Genus *Brotherella*

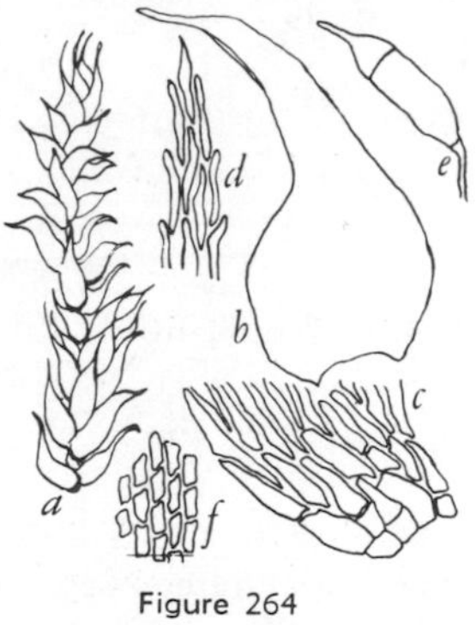

Figure 264

Fig. 264. *Brotherella recurvans.* a, shoot; b, leaf; c, alar cells; d, apex of leaf; e, capsule with operculum; f, outer cells of capsule. Glossy, pale green mats on rotten wood, soil or bases of trees. Newfoundland to Manitoba and Georgia. The thin-walled outer cells of the urn distinguish this from *Sematophyllum.* A similar plant of the northwest coast is *B. roellii.* Two very similar species occur in the east.

109b Alar cells decurrent; leaves squarrose, finely serrulate above; capsules longitudinally furrowed when dry. Fig. 265...................................... *Plagiothecium striatellum*

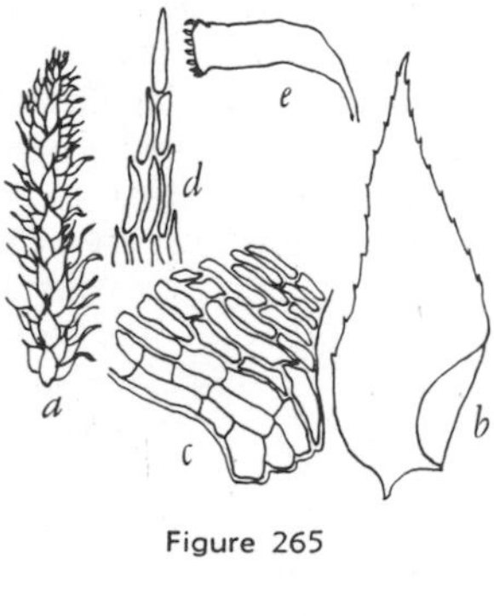

Figure 265

Fig. 265. *Plagiothecium striatellum.* a, shoot; b, leaf; c, alar cells; d, apex of leaf; e, capsule. On stones, rotten wood or peaty soil in damp shady places, Arctic America to North Carolina. Common on Long Island, New York. Resembling a small *Campylium,* but easily distinguished by the alar cells and the furrowed capsules.

110a (b, c) Leaves erect, straight, broad, blunt, sometimes more or less falcate. Figs. 267-274 111

110b Leaves squarrose-recurved, long tapering, entire. Fig. 266 .... *Campylium stellatum*

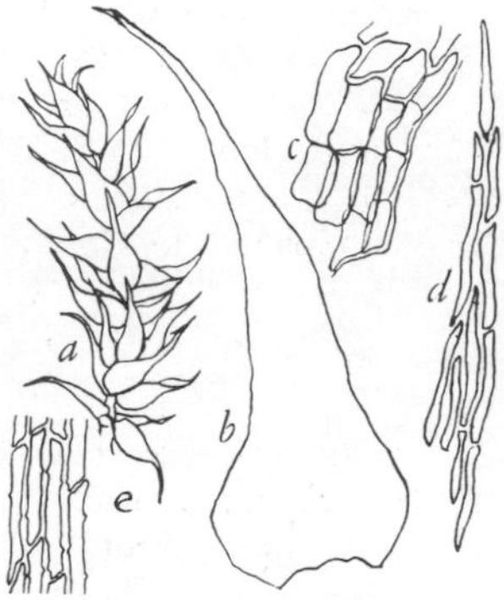

Figure 266

Fig. 266. *Campylium stellatum*. a, shoot; b, leaf; c, alar region; d, apex of leaf; e, cells from lower part of leaf. Mostly erect, in dense patches in bogs or fens, Pennsylvania, Ohio, Iowa, and Washington to Canada and Alaska. Stems to 10 cm. long, leaves to 3 mm. with apex semi-tubular; cell walls thick and porose, especially at base. Approaches *C. polygamum*, Fig. 227.

110c Leaves complanate. Figs. 275-285 118

111a (b, c) Leaves deeply concave, spoon-shaped, obtuse and rounded at apex. Figs. 268-269. Genus *Calliergonella* 112

111b Leaves deeply concave, curved so that the shoots are hooked at the tips, rugose (wrinkled) when dry. Fig. 267. . Genus *Scorpidium*

Figure 267

Fig. 267. *Scorpidium scorpioides*. a, shoot; b, leaf; c, alar region; d, median cells; e, capsule. Big erect moss, to 30 cm. long, in tufts or masses, in bogs or still shallow water, ocean to ocean in northern United States and Canada, to New Jersey, Michigan, Montana. Leaves 2-4 mm. long, very concave, making the shoots very stout. Rarely fruiting. In fact it is a rare find.

111c Leaves ovate to orbicular, acute or abruptly short-acuminate, spreading, more or less falcate-secund. A very variable group. Figs. 270-274. Genus *Hygrohypnum*........................113

112a Tips of stems ending in a firm acute bud; alar cells much inflated, thin-walled, clear. Fig. 268.............*Calliergonella cuspidata*

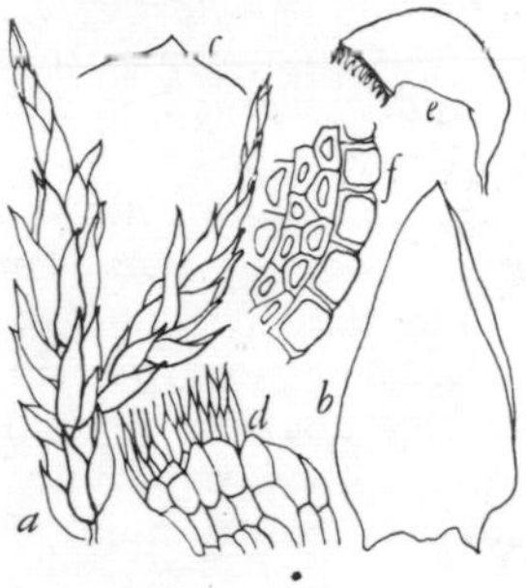
Figure 268

Fig. 268. *Calliergonella cuspidata.* a, shoot; b, leaf; c, apex of leaf; d, alar region; e, capsule; f, section of stem. A stout moss of wet meadows, swamps and fens, ocean to ocean in northern United States and Canada, to New Jersey and Iowa. Tolerant of lime, if not actually preferring calcareous waters. Characterized by the cuspidate terminal buds; dioicous. Europe.

112b Tips loose; stems red; alar cells somewhat enlarged, usually colored and opaque. Fig. 269.............*Calliergonella schreberi*

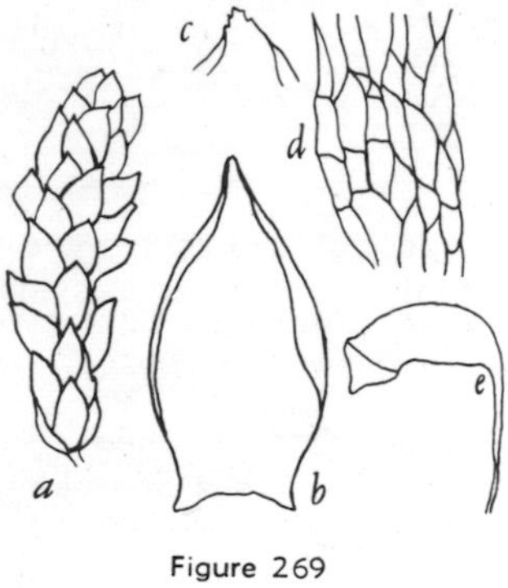
Figure 269

Fig. 269. *Calliergonella schreberi.* a, shoot; b, leaf; c, apex of leaf; d, alar region; e, capsule. Usually pinnately branched, forming great cushions, often over wide areas, 10-15 cm. deep, in many kinds of soil and exposure, ocean to ocean in northern United States and Canada, to Virginia, Iowa and Colorado. The red stems, smooth concave leaves with turned-back points, and alar cells easily characterize this abundant moss. Europe.

113a Outer cells of stem thin-walled, clear and colorless. Fig. 270. ....*Hygrohypnum ochraceum*

Figure 270

Fig. 270. *Hygrohypnum ochraceum.* a, shoot; b, leaf; c, alar and adjacent cells; d, apex of leaf. Medium size to large, to 9 cm. long; very variable. On stones in cool mountain brooks, New Jersey, West Virginia, Colorado, British Columbia and northward. Europe.

113b Outer cells of stem small and thick-walled..................114

**114a Leaves very large, 3 x 2 mm., rigid, harsh. Fig. 271...........
..................................*Hygrohypnum bestii***

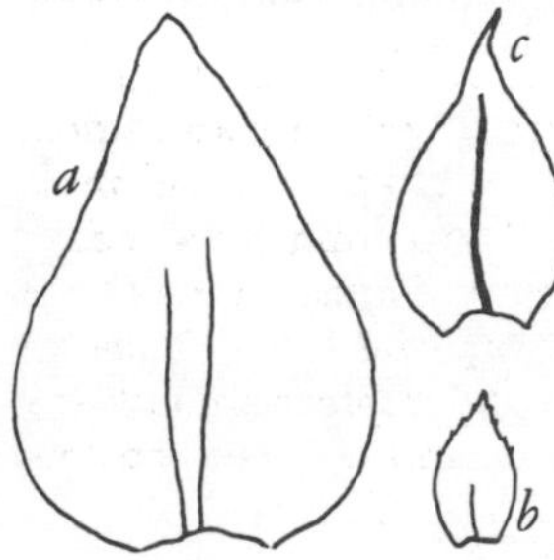

Figure 271

Fig. 271. *Hygrohypnum bestii.* a, leaf; b, leaf of *H. montanum;* c, leaf of *H. palustre.* a, on stones in spray of alpine streams, Montana to Washington and British Columbia. b, similar places, Newfoundland to Ontario and Vermont. c, Canada to New Jersey, Pennsylvania, Colorado and Washington. Europe.

114b Smaller 115

115a (b, c) Leaves small (.7x.3 mm.), lanceolate, serrulate to base. Fig. 271..........................*Hygrohypnum montanum*

115b Larger. Leaves entire, or finely serrulate at apex...........116

115c Leaves distinctly serrulate above the middle. Alar cells large, clear, with brown walls. Fig. 272.......*Hygrohypnum novae-caesareae*

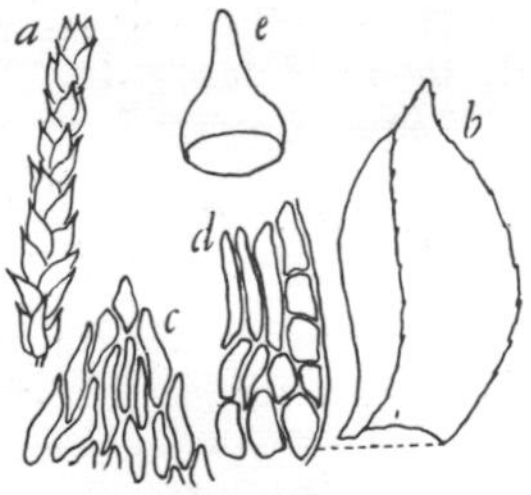

Figure 272

Fig. 272. *Hygrohypnum novae-caesareae.* a, shoot; b, leaf; c, apex of leaf; d, basal cells; e, operculum. Cilia lacking. Thin mats on stones in cold mountain streams, Vermont to Georgia and western Pennsylvania. Europe. Our large specimens are *var. badense* Herzog. Braithwaite considered it a *Sematophyllum,* and it is so treated (*Raphidostegium)* in Grout's Mosses with Hand lens and Microscope.

116a Leaves entire, sub-tubulose near apex. Alar cells not inflated. Figs. 271, 273.........................*Hygrohypnum palustre*

116b Leaves flat, not tubulose 117

117a Alar cells abruptly enlarged, clear, the inner ones with brown walls. Fig. 273 .... *Hygrohypnum eugyrium*

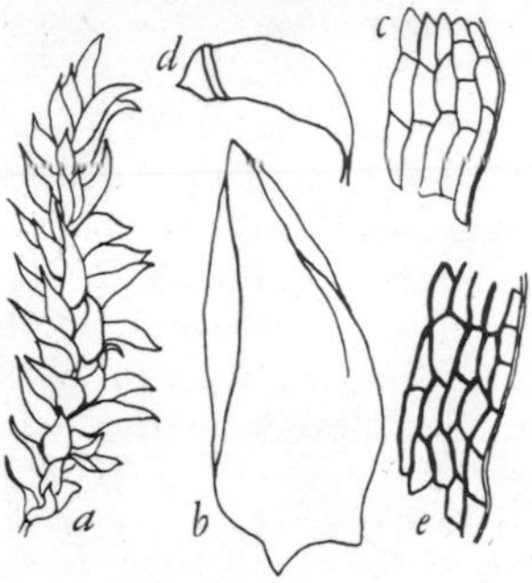

Figure 273

Fig. 273. *Hygrohypnum eugyrium.* a. shoot; b, leaf; c, alar cells; d, capsule; e, alar cells of *H. palustre*. *H. eugyrium* is found in cool mountain streams, North Carolina to Colorado, Washington and northward; *H. palustre* New Jersey to Colorado, Washington and northward. *H. palustre* is extremely variable. Both occur also in Europe.

117b Alar cells colored but not inflated. Leaves broadly ovate to suborbicular. Fig. 274 .... *Hygrohypnum dilatatum*

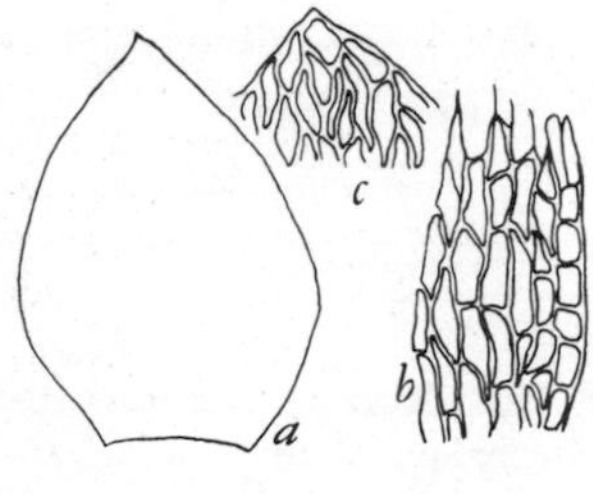

Figure 274

Fig. 274. *Hygrohypnum dilatatum.* a, leaf; b, alar and adjacent cells; c, apex of leaf. This (Virginia to New Mexico, Washington and northward) and *H. molle* of the northwest are much alike, and grade into one another. *H. molle*, as the name implies, is soft and flaccid; *H. dilatatum is* "stiff and harsh to the touch when dry."

118a Leaves shiny, not falcate-secund; alar cells in a cluster, enlarged and clear. Fig. 275 .... Genus *Heterophyllium*

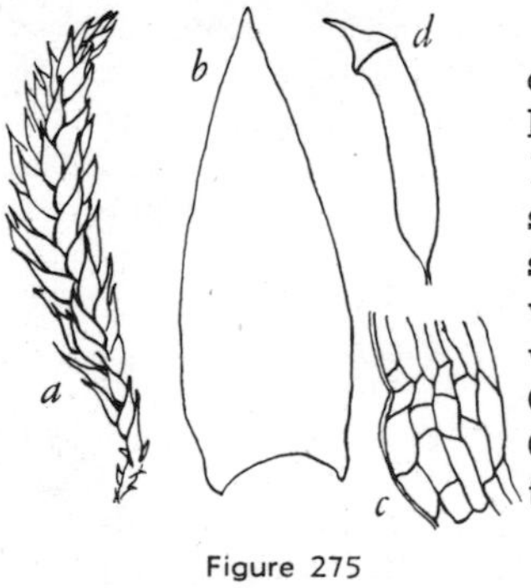

Figure 275

Fig. 275. *Heterophyllium haldanianum.* a, shoot; b, leaf; c, alar cells; d, capsule. Leaves entire, margins plane, median cells 16:1, not decurrent. The very smooth flat sprays in wide mats, and nearly erect capsules are characteristic. Common on old wood, stones and peaty soil in mesic woods, Nova Scotia to Montana and the Gulf, Europe. *H. nemorosum,* Virginia to Georgia, has serrate leaves, especially on the slender acumen.

118b Leaves falcate-secund. Figs. 276-285. Genus *Hypnum*........119

119a Outer cells of stem large, thin-walled and colorless. Figs. 276, 277. 120

119b Outer cells small and thick-walled. Figs. 278-285............121

120a Alar cells conspicuously inflated, colorless; leaves broadly acuminate, acute or obtuse. Fig. 276..............*Hypnum patientiae*

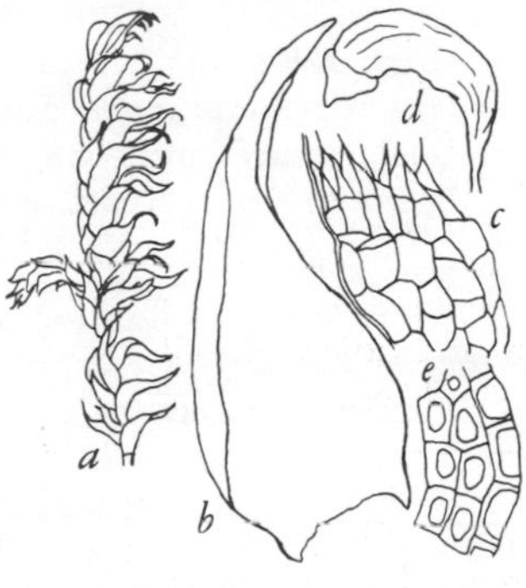

Figure 276

Fig. 276. *Hypnum patientiae*. a, shoot; b, leaf; c, alar cells; d, capsule; e, section of stem. Florida, Colorado, and Washington to the Arctic Ocean, common in moist places; shiny, with leaves broad-pointed, and decurrent; stems red. *H. pratense*, complanate but not falcate-secund, has less marked alar cells, bordered by smaller quadrate cells; merges into *H. patientiae*, with similar range, south to New Jersey, Colorado and Vancouver.

120b With 3 or 4 sub-quadrate alar cells; leaves long-filiform-acuminate. Fig. 277............................*Hypnum subimponens*

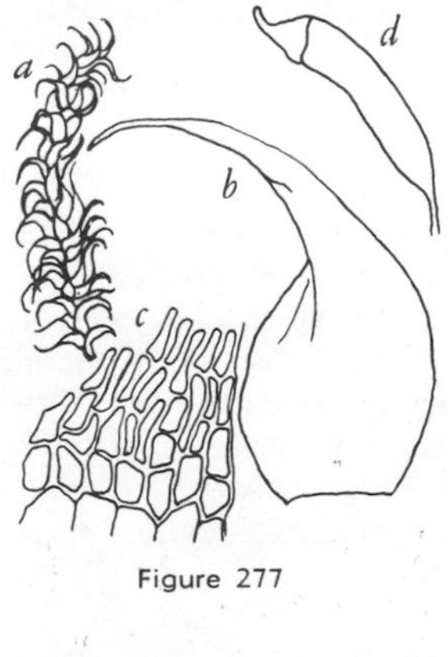

Figure 277

Fig. 277. *Hypnum subimponens*. a, shoot; b, leaf; c, alar cells with thin-walled cortical cells of stem; d, capsule. Stems green or brown; branching regularly complanate-pinnate; median cells 7-10:1. In wide thick mats in moist woods, California to Alaska. *H. callichroum*, with similar stem, has leaves long acuminate and coiled, entire; alar cells hyaline-inflated, numerous; Nova Scotia to British Columbia and northward. Europe.

121a Margins of leaves strongly revolute nearly to apex, entire. Fig. 278..*Hypnum revolutum*

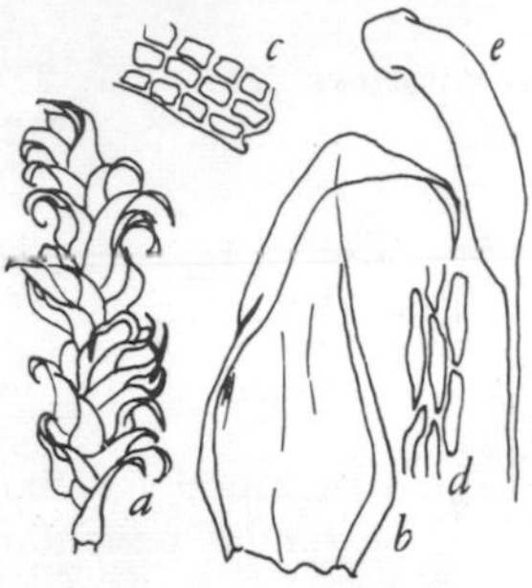

Figure 278

Fig. 278. *Hypnum revolutum.* a, shoot; b, leaf; c, alar cells; d, median cells; e, capsule. On bare rocks, New Mexico to California, Black Hills and the Arctic; abundant in the Colorado Rockies. Very variable in size—filiform to robust—irregularly branched to regularly pinnate—tufted or matted—but always with leaves revolute, at least near base, numerous quadrate alar cells, and short leaf cells, 3-7:1.

121b Margins plane or more or less reflexed. Figs. 279-285........122

122a Branching evenly pinnate, the branches crowded-complanate, and of equal length; leaves plicate, the tips bent toward the base of the main stem. Fig. 279...............*Hypnum crista-castrensis*

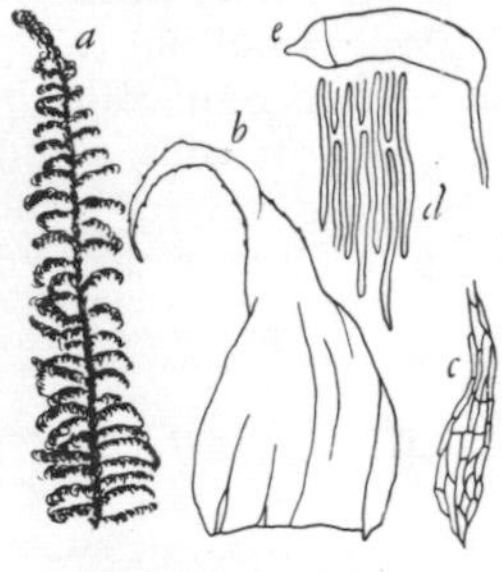

Figure 279

Fig. 279. *Hypnum crista-castrensis.* a, shoot; b, leaf; c, alar cells; d, median cells; e, capsule. The most beautiful of feathery or frondose mosses, said to be on the Coat of Arms of the House of Lancaster. In dense mats, the crowded fronds more or less erect. On rocks, old logs or peaty soil, North Carolina, Iowa, Washington and northward.

122b Branching less precise to irregular; leaves bent toward the substratum 123

123a Stem leaves cordate-auriculate at base, slenderly long-acuminate, serrate from base to apex; branch leaves much smaller, more serrate; mostly pinnate and frondose, yellowish. Fig. 280......... ....*Hypnum molluscum*

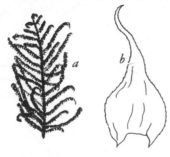

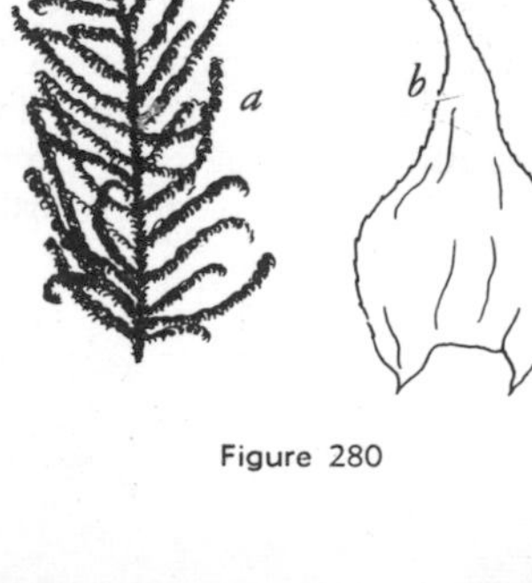

Figure 280

Fig. 280. *Hypnum molluscum.* a, shoot branching; b, leaf. A pretty, golden-green moss in moist shaded woods of Europe and America, south to Georgia and Oklahoma, west to the Rocky Mountains. Leaves more or less papillose on the back above. Related to *Hylocomium* by the dimorphic, serrate, papillose leaves.

123b Not exactly as above....................................124

124a Leaves cordately contracted to the stem. Figs. 281-282.......125

124b Leaves not cordate at base, tapering to the insertion. Figs. 283-285 126

125a Leaves entire, or serrulate near apex; decurrent cells at basal angles inflated, colorless; E. Canada to Georgia and Colorado. Fig. 281................................*Hypnum curvifolium*

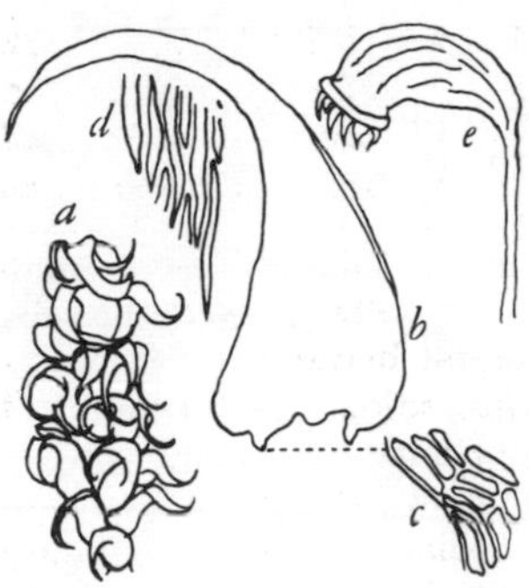

Figure 281

Fig. 281. *Hypnum curvifolium*. a, shoot; b, leaf; c, alar region; d, median cells; e, capsule. A handsome golden-green moss, in wide firm mats; leaves very evenly falcate secund. Often used by florists as "sheet moss", for whom it is collected in the southeast. On rocks, old logs or peaty soil, Georgia, Missouri and Colorado to Arctic America. The base of the leaf, and the furrowed curved capsules are characteristic.

125b Leaves serrulate; acumination very long and slender, circinately coiled; California to Alaska and Idaho. Fig. 282...*Hypnum circinale*

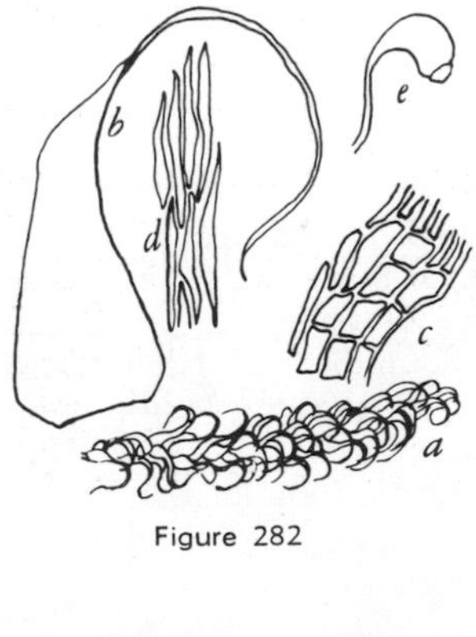

Figure 282

Fig. 282. *Hypnum circinale*. a, shoot; b, leaf; c, alar region; d, median cells; e, capsule. In broad mats; branching regularly pinnate. The slender, coiled leaves and small capsules are very characteristic. Common from California to Alaska and Idaho, on trees, stones and old wood.

126a Leaves entire; alar cells very numerous, opaque. Fig. 283...... ....*Hypnum cupressiforme*

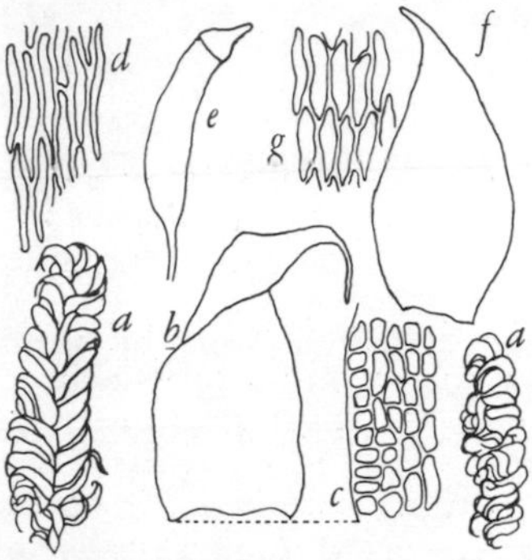

Figure 283

Fig. 283. *Hypnum cupressiforme*. a, shoot from top (left) and from side (right); b, leaf; c, alar cells; d, median cells; e, capsule; f , leaf, and g, median cells of *H. vaucheri*. Rare, but everywhere in North America. Extremely variable, especially in western Europe, where it is very abundant. Var. *filiforme* hangs in sheets of green threads on bark or rocks. Our most robust form is *H. vaucheri*, Arizona to British Columbia, Nebraska, Minnesota, Newfoundland and Grant Land! It has much shorter leaf-cells, and more numerous alar cells, 12-15 on the margin of the leaf (6-10 in *H. cupressiforme*).

126b Leaves serrulate to the base. Figs. 284, 285................127

127a Leaves 2 mm. long; alar cells thick-walled, orange-brown when old. Fig. 284...............................*Hypnum imponens*

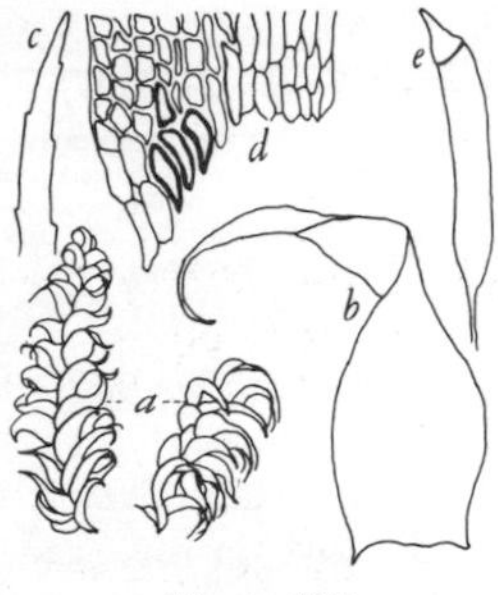

Figure 284

Fig. 284. *Hypnum imponens*. a, shoot from top (left) and from side (right); b, leaf; c, apex of leaf; d, alar cells; e, capsule. Dioicous. Mostly very evenly pinnate, in broad sheets on soil, rocks or old wood, rich green, the leaves strongly falcate-secund. The alar cells and nearly erect capsules are characteristic. Quebec to British Columbia, California and Georgia. *H. fertile* has slightly different alar cells, curved capsule, and is monoicous. Newfoundland to British Columbia, Tennessee and North Carolina.

127b Leaves 1 mm. long; quadrate alar cells very numerous, none inflated. Fig. 285...............................*Hypnum reptile*

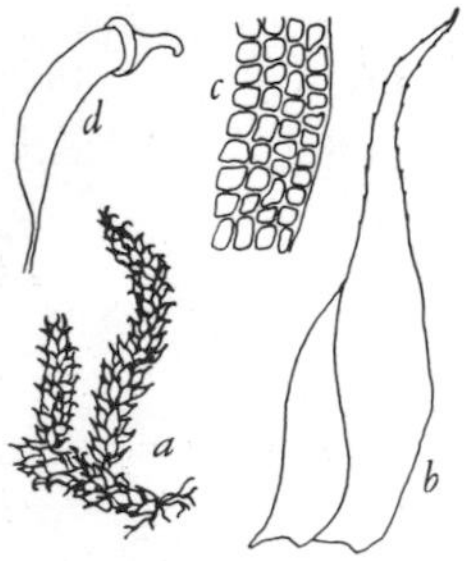

Figure 285

Fig. 285. *Hypnum reptile*. a, shoot; b, leaf; c, alar cells; d, capsule. Monoicous. A neat little moss, in dense mats on bark, stones or old wood; mesic. Nova Scotia to Alaska, Arizona and the mountains of North Carolina. *H. pallescens* is similar: leaves more slender, farther apart (loose); northern United States and adjacent Canada.

128a (b, c) Leaves spreading....................................129

128b Leaves complanate to falcate-secund........................130

128c Leaves appressed, broad and entire. Shoots julaceous to slightly flattened. Peristome teeth with few, long, smooth joints. Cilia lacking. Fig. 286.......................... *Entodon seductrix*

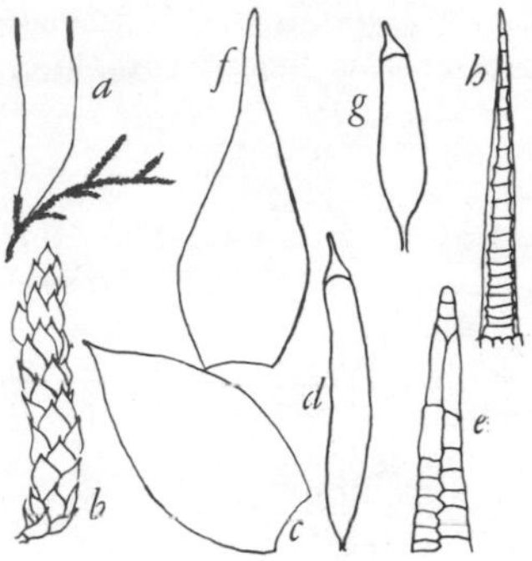

Fig. 286. *Entodon seductrix.* a, plant; b, shoot; c, leaf; d, capsule; e, peristome tooth. f, leaf; g, capsule; h, peristome tooth of *E. brevisetus.* In dense mats on bark, earth or rocks, common from Ontario to Minnesota, Texas and Florida; rather variable. The peristome teeth are the most reliable marks of the species. *E. brevisetus* has leaves narrowly acuminate, and segments completely adherent to the closely-jointed teeth; New Brunswick to Virginia and Missouri; rare.

Figure 286

129a Leaves slenderly acute, finely denticulate; stem leaves much larger than branch leaves. Compare Figs. 168 and 289........ ....*Rhytidiadelphus triquetrus and R. squarrosus*

129b Leaves nearly orbicular, rounded and obtuse and denticulate at apex. Cilia present in peristome. Fig. 274.................... ....*Hygrohypnum dilatatum*

130a (b, c) Branches bent upward by reason of upwardly pointing leaves. Cilia lacking. Figs. 287, 288. Genus *Pylaisia*........131

130b Leaves curved downward or backward..........................132

130c Leaves not curved; shoots very flat (complanate-foliate). Cilia lacking. Figs. 290, 291. Genus *Entodon*.........................133

131a Inner peristome attached to outer; quadrate alar cells numerous (15-20 along margin of leaf). Fig. 287.........*Pylaisia selwynii*

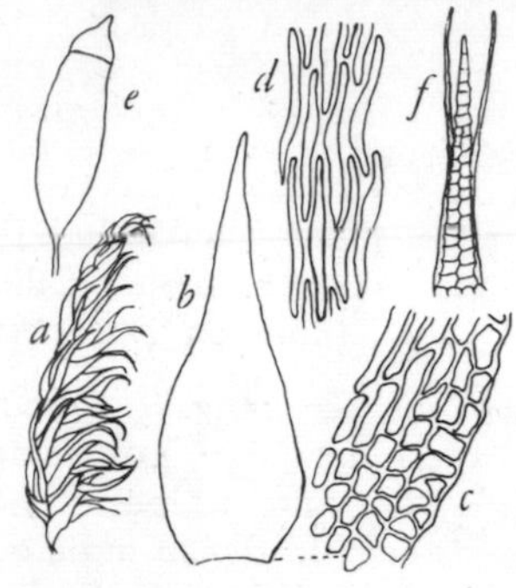

Figure 287

Fig. 287. *Pylaisia selwynii.* a, shoot; b, leaf; c, alar region; d, median cells; e, capsule; f, teeth and segments of peristome. In dense mats on trees, common east of the Rocky Mountains. About the size of *Platygyrium,* much larger than *Leskea.* Capsules widest at the middle; teeth united with segments in lower half only; spores .018-.024 mm. *P. intricata,* New Brunswick to South Carolina, Indiana and Minnesota, has teeth and segments united completely; spores .024-.03 mm.

131b Inner peristome free from outer; quadrate alar cells 3 to 9 along margin of leaf. Fig. 288......................*Pylaisia polyantha*

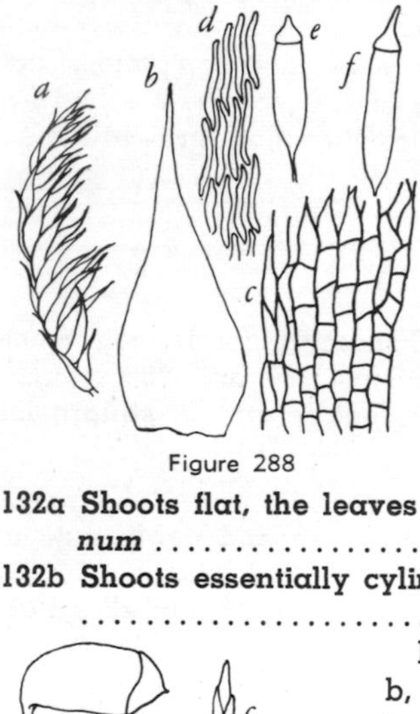

Figure 288

Fig. 288. *Pylaisia polyantha.* a, shoot; b, leaf; c, alar region; d, median cells; e, capsule and operculum; f, capsule and operculum of *P. subdenticulata.* In dense mats on trees; alar cells 3-9 on margin of leaf; spores .014 mm.; across the continent in Canada and extreme northern United States. *P. subdenticulata* has 10-15 marginal quadrate cells, spores .01-.012 mm., and occurs from New York to Minnesota, New Mexico and North Carolina.

132a Shoots flat, the leaves both complanate and falcate. Genus *Hypnum* ....See 118b

132b Shoots essentially cylindric, but the large leaves falcate. Fig. 289. ....*Rhytidiadelphus loreus*

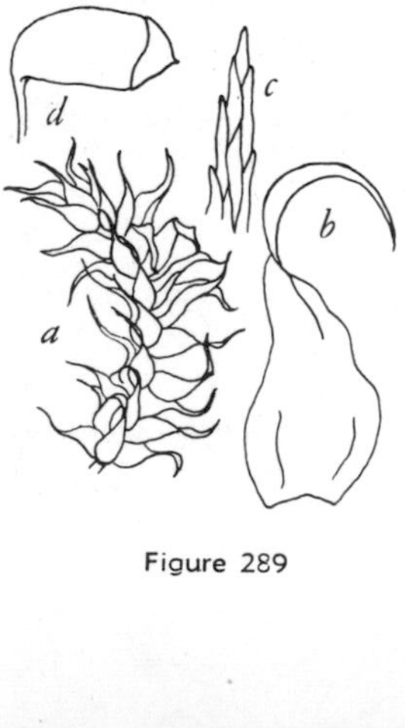

Figure 289

Fig. 289. *Rhytidiadelphus loreus.* a, shoot; b, leaf; c, apex of leaf; d, capsule. Big long irregularly branching plants, 10-20 cm. long, in large loose masses on soil, rocks and old wood, in moist spruce-fir forests, common from Oregon to Alaska; in the East, south to Ontario, Nova Scotia and Newfoundland. *R. squarrosus* is very similar, equally squarrose, not secund, and scarcely plicate, with numerous broad, colored alar cells; ocean to ocean in Canada, south to the mountains of Tennessee.

133a Shoots 2-3 mm. wide; leaves 1.5 mm. long; teeth sculptured with wavy lines. Fig. 290......................***Entodon cladorrhizans***

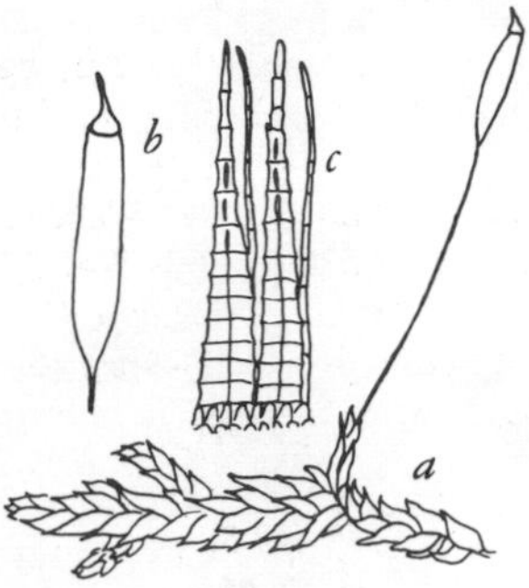

Figure 290

Fig. 290. *Entodon cladorrhizans.* a, shoot; b, capsule with operculum; c, teeth of peristome. In large mats on bark, old logs or rocks, Minnesota to Texas and eastward. *E. drummondii* has a conspicuous yellow seta, that of the preceding species being red; on trees and logs, Tennessee and North Carolina to the Gulf.

133b Shoots 1 mm. wide or less; leaves 1 mm. long; teeth densely papillose. Fig. 291..............................***Entodon compressus***

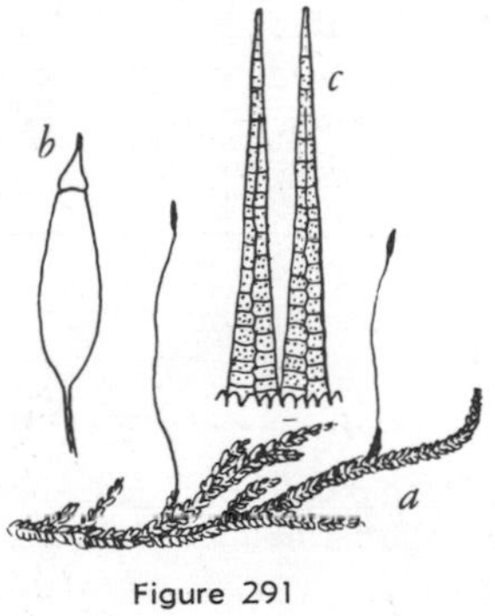

Figure 291

Fig. 291. *Entodon compressus.* a, shoot; b, capsule; c, teeth of peristome. The dry shoots have the leaves sloping down from the stem like shingles from the comb of a roof. The peristome is the certain recognition character; on bark, old logs or earth, Rhode Island to South Dakota, Kansas and Ohio, "not common."

134a (b, c) Shoots complanate-foliate; leaves not falcate...........**135**

134b Leaves falcate-secund, the branches hooked at tip. Fig. 289. *Rhytidiadelphus loreus*..............................See No. 132b

134c Leaves erect-open. Try *Hygrohypnum novae-caesareae* Fig. 272, or *Plagiothecium roeseanum* Fig. 292.

135a Leaves ovate to ovate-lanceolate; cells thin-walled, spindle-shaped. Figs. 292-298. Genus *Plagiothecium*.........................136

135b Leaves ovate to oblong; cells thick-walled, linear-flexuose. Figs. 299-301. Genus *Neckera*..........142

136a Leaves decurrent on stem; plants relatively large. Figs. 292-295. 137

136b Leaves not decurrent; plants medium sized to small. Figs. 296-298. 140

137a Leaves not truly complanate, but not quite equally spreading. Fig. 292..........*Plagiothecium roeseanum*

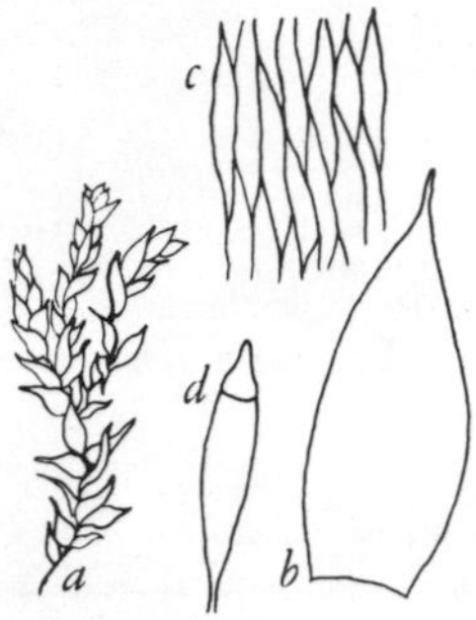

Figure 292

Fig. 292. *Plagiothecium roeseanum.* a, shoot; b, leaf; c, median cells; d, capsule. Leaves and cells of *Plagiothecium*. In cushion-like mats on soil in shade. Midrib sometimes well developed. Canada to Georgia and Colorado. Only rarely fruiting.

137b Decidedly complanate. Figs. 293-295..........138

138a Shoots 3-4 mm. wide, whitish; leaves transversely rugose (wrinkled). Fig. 293..........*Plagiothecium undulatum*

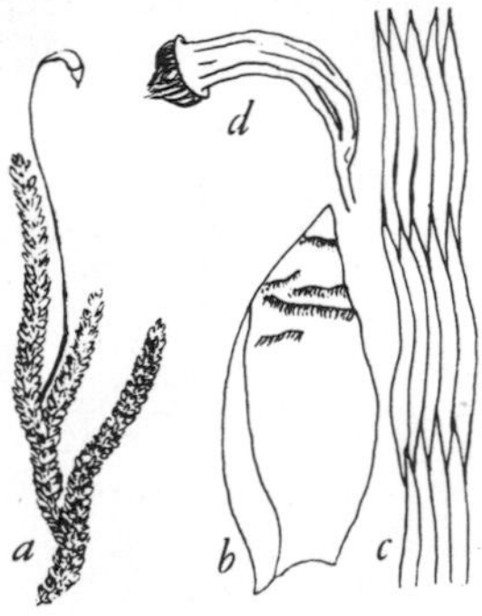

Figure 293

Fig. 293. *Plagiothecium undulatum.* a. shoot; b, leaf; c, median cells; d, capsule. Much the largest of the genus; on moist soil or rocks, often mixed with other mosses; British Columbia to California. Europe.

138b Narrower; green or yellowish; not rugose....................139

139a Leaves acute to slenderly acuminate. Fig. 294................ ....*Plagiothecium denticulatum*

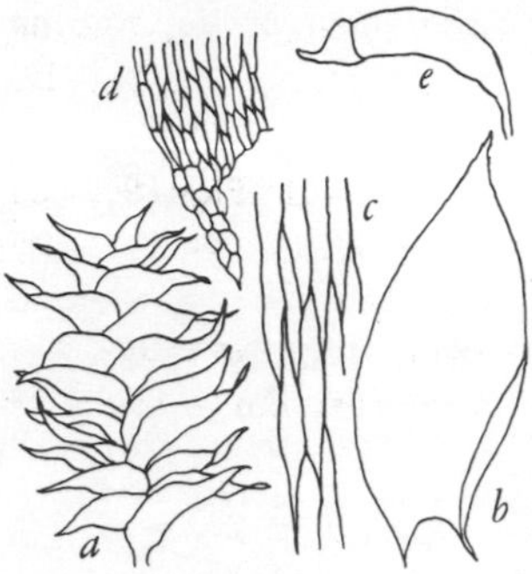

Figure 294

Fig. 294. *Plagiothecium denticulatum.* a, shoot; b, leaf; c, median cells; d, alar region; e, capsule. Monoicous. In glossy-green mats on earth, stones or rotten wood in moist woodlands, Canada to Georgia and Colorado. On the northwest coast is Var. *aptychus. P. sylvaticum* extends north to Alaska and south to Alabama. It is more yellowish, and the leaves when dry do not overlap; dioicous. *P. ruthei* is a large lowland, northeastern form with leaves folded and clasping the stem at base.

139b Leaves tapering to a hair point. Northwestern. Fig. 295........ ....*Plagiothecium piliferum*

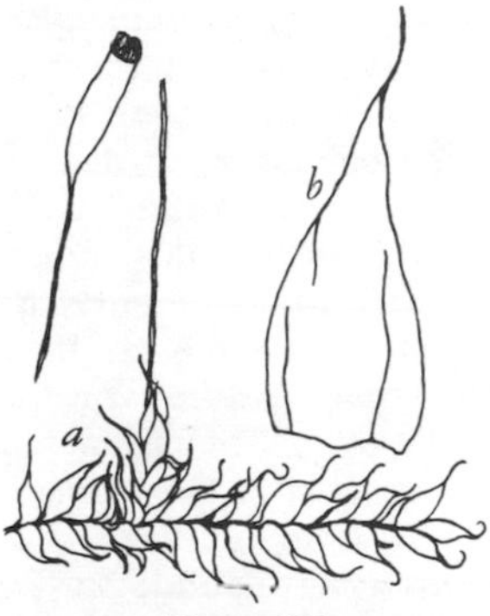

Figure 295

Fig. 295. *Plagiothecium piliferum.* a, shoot; b, leaf. Leaves 1-2 mm. long, concave; margin entire, narrowly reflexed. Cilia lacking. Monoicous. British Columbia to Oregon and Wyoming. Europe.

140a Leaves obtuse at apex, yellowish, glossy, with short double midrib; serrate above. Fig. 296............*Plagiothecium geophilum*

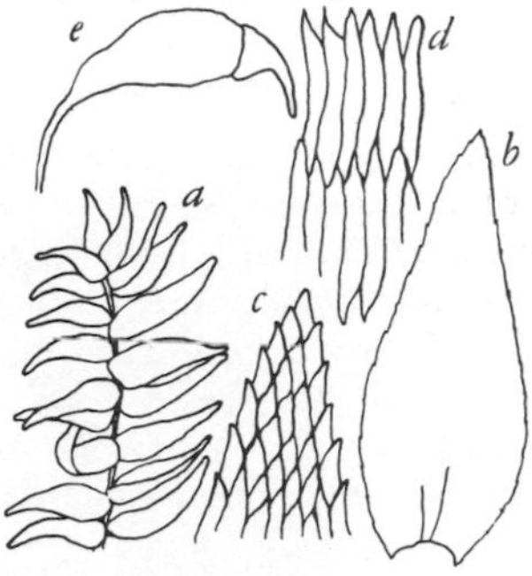

Figure 296

Fig. 296. *Plagiothecium geophilum.* a, shoot; b, leaf; c, apex of leaf; d, median cells; e, capsule. A very glossy yellowish moss, in thin mats on soil. Characterized by the luster and the blunt leaves, which are so far apart as hardly to touch one another. New York to Georgia, New Mexico and Wisconsin.

140b Leaves more or less longly acuminate. Figs. 297, 298........141

141a Leaves distinctly serrulate from base to apex, crowded on the stem and overlapping; with leaflike paraphyllia. Fig. 297...... ....*Plagiothecium deplanatum*

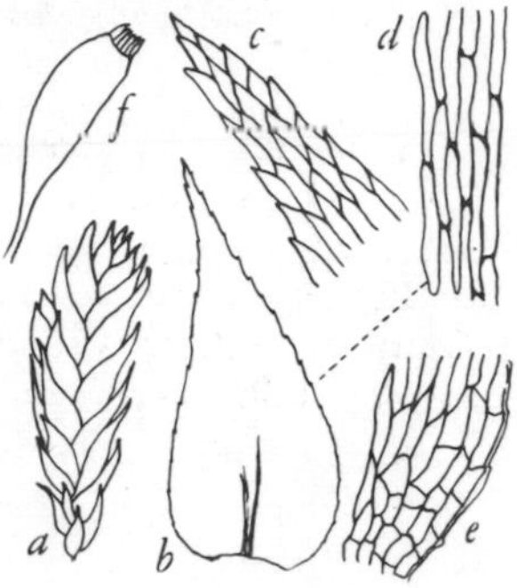

Figure 297

Fig. 297. *Plagiothecium deplanatum.* a, shoot; b, leaf; c, apex of leaf; d, median cells; e, alar region; f, capsule. Light green, very flat and close-leafed, the leaves overlapping, usually with long-acuminate, serrate apex. Dioicous; without annulus. Sporophytes rare. On earth, stones and bark, Nova Scotia to Minnesota, Arizona and North Carolina.

141b Leaves serrulate near apex only. Fig. 298..*Plagiothecium micans*

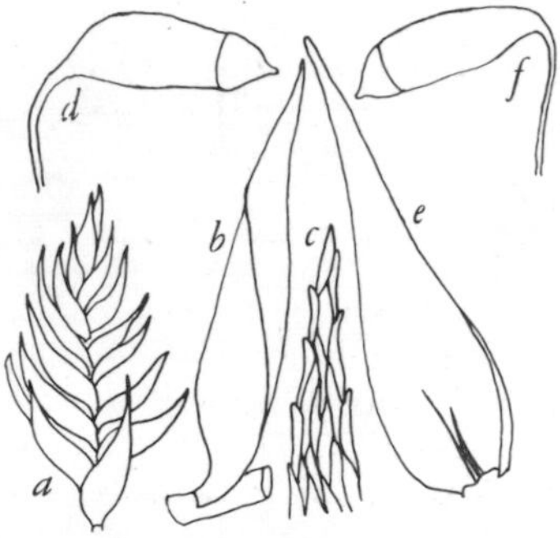

Figure 298

Fig. 298. *Plagiothecium micans.* a, shoot; b, leaf; c, apex of leaf; d, capsule with operculum; e, leaf and f, capsule of *P. elegans.* The first is monoicous, without annulus, and occurs on soil, old wood or bark, New York to Missouri and the Gulf. The second is dioicous, and has a narrow annulus. Both often bear branch-like gemmae in the axils of the leaves. *P. elegans* occurs from northern United States and adjacent Canada to North Carolina and California.

142a Midrib reaching middle of leaf or beyond; branches tapering to a point; with abundant lanceolate paraphyllia. Fig. 299......... ....*Neckera menziesii*

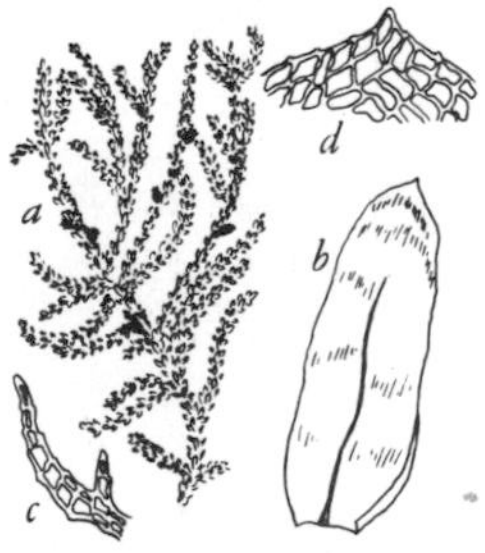

Figure 299

Fig. 299. *Neckera menziesii.* a, shoot with capsules; b, leaf; c, paraphyllium; d, apex of leaf. A big glossy moss, 10-20 cm. long, in loose masses on trees and rocks, California to Montana and Alaska. Peristome segments well-developed. *N. undulata* of Florida has truncate leaves (cut straight across at apex).

142b Without midrib or paraphyllia; leaves wrinkled (undulate)....143

143a Leaves entire or slightly denticulate above; eastern United States. Fig. 300..................................*Neckera pennata*

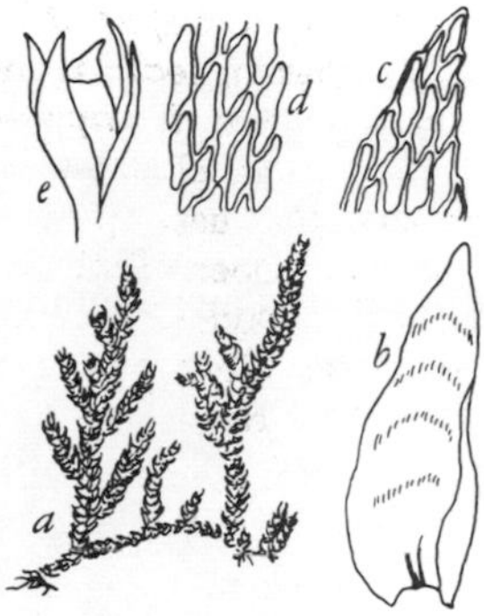

Figure 300

Fig. 300. *Neckera pennata*. a, shoot; b, leaf; c, apex of leaf; d, median cells; e, capsule. Shoots or mats hanging on bark of trees, very flat. Perianth segments short and imperfect. Ontario to North Carolina and west to about the 100th meridian.

143b Leaves with numerous slender sharp teeth above; western. Fig. 301...*Neckera douglasii*

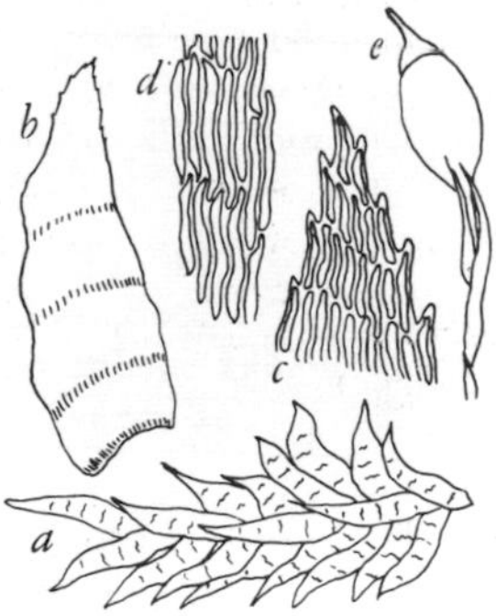

Figure 301

Fig. 301. *Neckera douglasii*. a, shoot; b, leaf; c, apex of leaf; d, median cells; e, capsule. Characterized by the big sharp teeth of the leaf. Segments slender, about as long as the teeth. On rocks and trees, California to Alaska, Colorado and Idaho.

PICTURED-KEY

TO LIVERWORTS OF NORTH AMERICA

1a Plants growing flat, scale-like or ribbon-like, usually fork-branched, without distinction of stem and leaf, green or purplish. Figs. 302-322. Class 2. HEPATICAE (in part) 2

1b Plants with stem and leaves; erect, ascending, prostrate, or hanging from trees 3

2a Plant opaque by reason of air-spaces inside of it, often showing air-pores and polygonal markings. Rhizoids with pegs on the inside of the walls. Figs. 305-316 8

2b Plant translucent, watery-looking, without inner air-spaces. Rhizoids without pegs. Figs. 302-304; 317-322. Class HEPATICAE (in part) . . . 4

3a Leaves in 2 rows near upper side of stem, without midrib, and with cells isodiametric. Leaves very often notched at apex, or lobed, sometimes with a smaller lobe folded against a larger one. Sporophyte short-lived. Figs. 323-372. Order JUNGERMANNIALES 31

3b Leaves equally spaced all around the stem, usually with midrib; margins entire or toothed, never notched at apex or lobed; cells elongate to isodiametric. Sporophyte persisting for weeks or months. Figs. 24-301. Class 1. MUSCI .... See page 23

4a (b, c) Small rosettes or scales, with surface covered with pear-shaped sacs (involucres) each containing a capsule. No elaters. Fig. 302. Order SPHAEROCARPALES, Family SPHAEROCARPACEAE, Genus *Sphaerocarpus.*

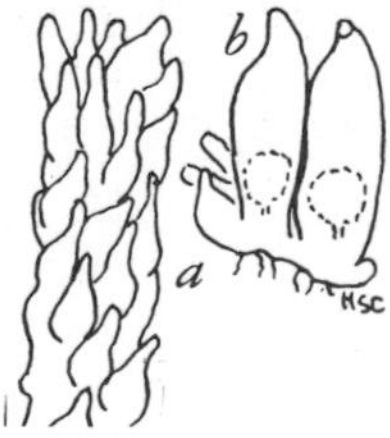

Figure 302

Fig. 302. *Sphaerocarpus texanus*. a, male plant; b, female plant. The plants of this family and order are quite small and are found on damp ground. The species name of this one was given because the type specimen came from Texas. Four other species occur in the southern United States.

4b Larger (1 cm. or longer at maturity). Spores in a long rod-like capsule which splits in two above as it grows up from the base, emitting spores and irregular elaters. No midrib and no gemmae, but sometimes the plant is rough. One large chloroplast in each cell. Figs. 303-304. Class 3 ANTHOCEROTAE, Order ANTHOCEROTALES, Family ANTHOCEROTACEAE................................5

4c Spores in an oval or globular capsule on a slender watery stalk. Capsule splitting into four lobes, emitting spores and spiral-banded elaters. Midrib or mid-furrow usually distinct. Chloroplasts numerous in each cell. Order METZGERIALES. Figs. 317-322..........22

5a Capsule erect, 1-3 cm. long, becoming black after splitting. Fig. 304. Genus *Anthoceros*..6

5b Capsules horizontal, short, slightly projecting from the margins of the thallus. Fig. 303............................Genus *Notothylas*

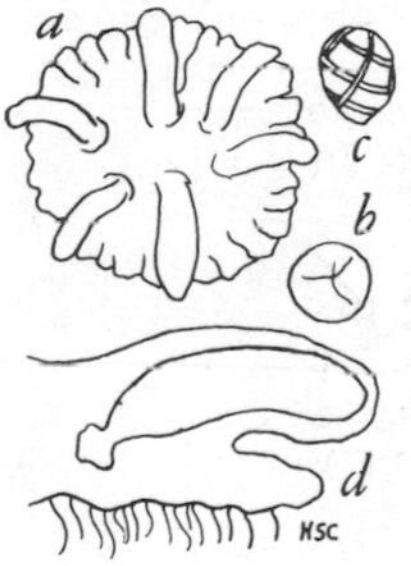

Figure 303

Fig. 303. *Notothylas orbicularis.* a, plant; b, spore; c, elater; d, section of sporophyte in perianth. The rosettes, to 1 cm. in diameter, grow on damp, firm soil, clay or silt, in shade, N. E. to N. C., Wisconsin, Nebraska, and Texas. Though rarely collected the species is probably everywhere.

6a Spores yellow. Thallus without cavities. Fig. 304............... ....*Anthoceros laevis*

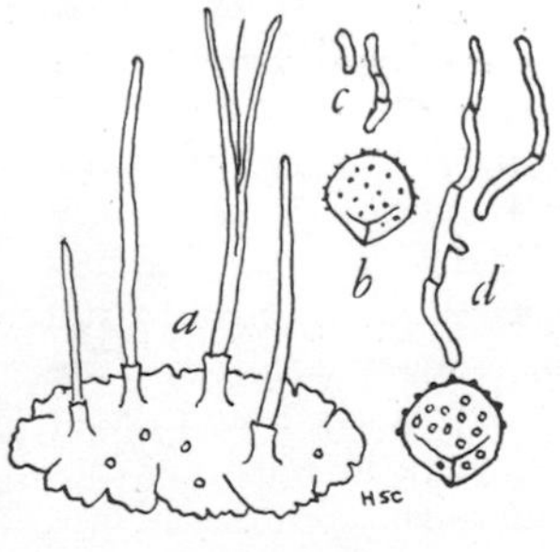

Figure 304

Fig. 304. *Anthoceros laevis.* a, plant; b, spore; c, elaters; d, spore and elaters of *A. punctatus.* Both are worldwide in distribution. Capsules of *A. punctatus (A. fusiformis)* are up to 4 cm. tall and resemble a tuft of burned grass; seen in Washington State.

6b Spores dark brown to black. Thallus with interior cavities.......7

7a Spores with granules or papillae on surface. Thallus smooth. Fig. 304 ....*Anthoceros punctatus*

7b Spores spinose and reticulate. Thallus crested and pleated around the margin. Northeastern United States; Europe...............
....*Anthoceros crispulus*

8a (b, c) Air pores visible without a lens, each in a polygonal area. Capsules borne on the under side of an umbrella-shaped receptacle, with spirally banded elaters among the spores. Wall cells of capsules with ring-shaped thickenings. Figs. 305-308. Family MARCHANTIACEAE 9

8b Air pores not visible without a strong lens. Plants on moist or dry rocks or banks, rarely, if ever, in neat rosettes. Capsules as in 8a, with or without ring-like thickenings. Figs. 309-312. ....
....12

8c Air pores, if any, not visible with a hand lens. Plants submerged or floating, or in circular rosettes on very wet ground. Capsules imbedded in the plant, with no elaters among the rough spores. Figs. 313-316. Family RICCIACEAE..........................15

9a With open cups or half-cups of disc-shaped gemmae on the thallus; archegonia (and sporophytes) on the under side of long-fingered umbrellas with 4 to 9 fingers. Figs. 305, 306...................10

9b Without gemmae, and without marginal scales on under side of thallus. Figs. 307, 308..11

10a Gemma cups round, fringed; female umbrellas 9-lobed; thallus with thin scales along the margins beneath; air pores elliptic. Fig. 305 ....Genus *Marchantia*

Figure 305

Fig. 305. *Marchantia polymorpha.* a, female plant; b, male plant; c, scales on under side of thallus; d, elater; e, surface of thallus; f, pore; g, section of pore. All over North America and Europe, on freshly disturbed clayey or silty soil, especially on burned places. Spores yellow. The umbrella-like female receptacles grow to full size even if not one egg is fertilized. The golden yellow sporophytes are found under the umbrellas in late June in Iowa. *M. paleacea* and *M. domingensis,* both southern, lack the marginal scales. The inner opening of the pores of *M. paleacea* is cross-shaped.

10b Gemmae in half-cups; female umbrella 4-lobed; thallus without marginal scales beneath; found only in greenhouses and sterile, except in southern California. Fig. 306...........Genus *Lunularia*

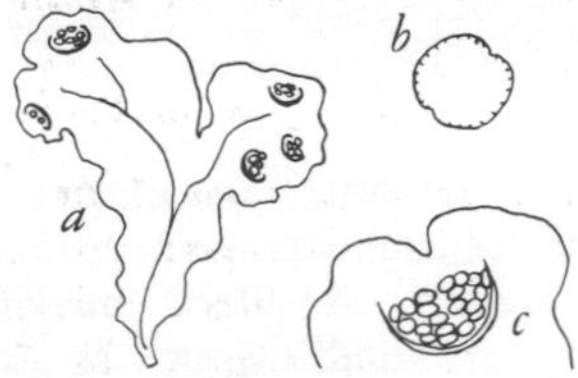

Figure 306

Fig. 306. *Lunularia cruciata.* a, plant; b, gemma; c, gemma cup. Introduced from Europe; common in greenhouses from Iowa to the Atlantic coast.

11a Air pore on a low mound of colorless cells; antheridia in a warty spot on the thallus; sporophytes beneath a cone-shaped umbrella. Fig. 307..................................Genus *Conocephalum*

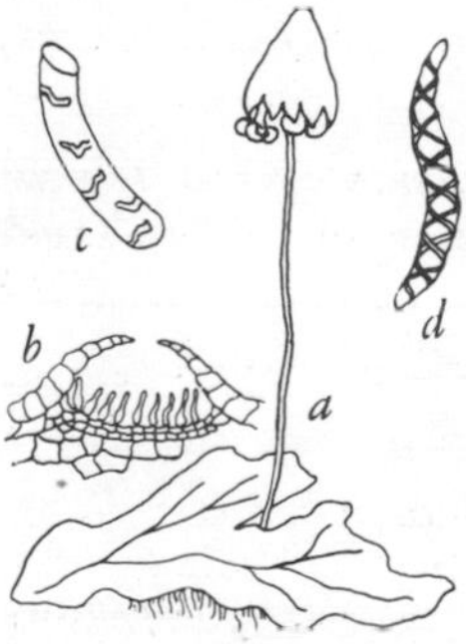

Figure 307

Fig. 307. *Conocephalum conicum.* a, plant; b, section of pore; c, rhizoid with pegs; d, elater. The largest of our thalloid liverworts, very common on moist earth or rocks, often covering many square feet. The conical umbrella is only raised up on its stalk in spring when the spores are ripe. It is watery and short-lived, maturing in late April or May in Iowa. North America and Europe. Emits an aromatic odor when bruised.

11b Air pores circular, surrounded by a low cylinder of cells; antheridia and sporophytes on upraised scalloped umbrellas. Fig. 308...... ....Genus *Preissia*

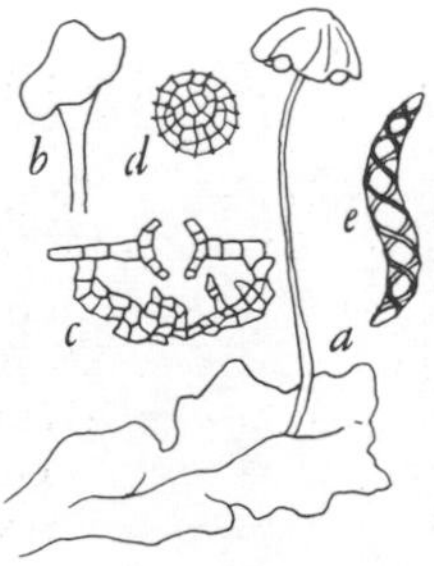

Figure 308

Fig. 308. *Preissia quadrata.* a, plant with capsules; b, antheridial receptacle; c, section of pore; d, spore; e, elater. Northern United States, New Jersey, Kentucky, Iowa, Colorado, Oregon, to Alaska and Greenland; Europe, Asia. Thalli 3-4 cm. long, 1 cm. wide or less, often purplish, often in extensive sods on moist earth or rocks. Spores umber-brown, ripe in May in Iowa, in July in Colorado at 8000 ft. elevation.

12a Cell walls radiating from pores strongly thickened, giving the pore a star-like appearance. Fig. 309 .... *Clevea hyalina*

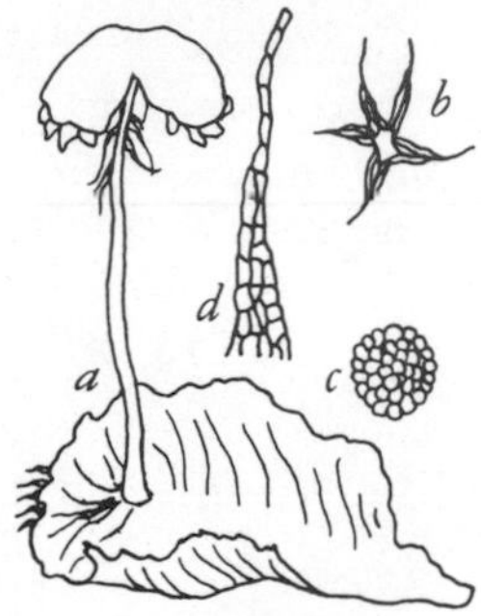

Figure 309

Fig. 309. *Cleva hyalina.* a, plant with archegonial umbrella; b, pore; c, spore; d, scale. The abundant broad white scales around the margin of the thallus and clustered at the growing points are unique and characteristic. Antheridia are in the surface of a separate plant. On earth among limestone rocks, Greenland to British Columbia, California, Colorado, Iowa and Vermont.

12b Radiating walls not thickened 13

13a Cells of the epidermis with thin walls with or without prominent trigones; .025-.03x.04—.05 mm. Figs. 311-312 14

13b Cells of epidermis with the walls thickened all round, and at the corners, .014x.017 mm.; cells around the pores in 2-3 concentric rows; stalk of umbrella with broad (4-8 cells wide) white scales around base and summit. Fig. 310 .... Genus *Mannia*

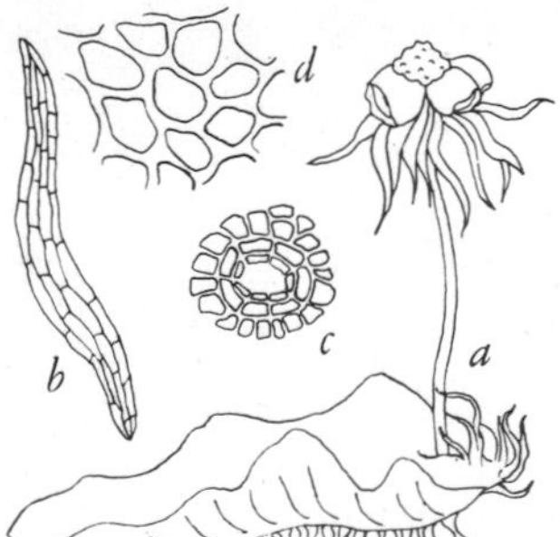

Figure 310

Fig. 310. *Mannia fragrans.* a, plant; b, scale; c, pore; d, cells of epidermis. Thalli 2-4 mm. wide, curling up at the edges when dry, completely covering the upper surface, exposing the deep-purple under side. On dry stony soil and rocks, Greenland to Alabama, Texas, Nebraska and Minnesota. Sporophytes in May in Iowa. A very similar species in Arizona and California is *M. californica.*

14a Cells around the pores in 4 or 5 concentric rows, the walls thickened; capsule embraced in a 2-lipped involucre; stalk of umbrella with hair-like scales (2-4 cells wide) at summit. Fig. 311..Genus *Reboulia*

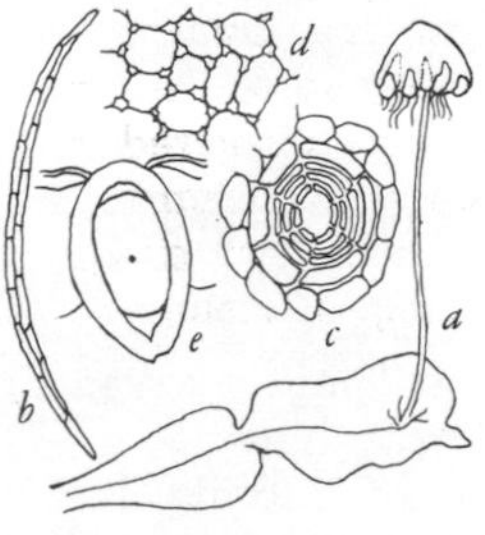

Figure 311

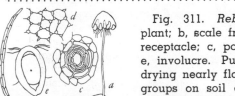

Fig. 311. *Reboulia hemisphaerica*. a, plant; b, scale from upper end of stalk of receptacle; c, pore; d, cells of epidermis; e, involucre. Purplish on the margin but drying nearly flat; 6-7 mm. wide; in small groups on soil or rocks. Sporophytes in mid-May in Iowa. Maine to Washington and South America; Europe; Asia, East Indies, Australia. The only species.

14b Cells around the pores irregular, thin-walled; stalk of umbrella naked at both ends; capsule surrounded by several scales, remnants of a tubular pseudo-perianth. Fig. 312......Genus *Asterella*

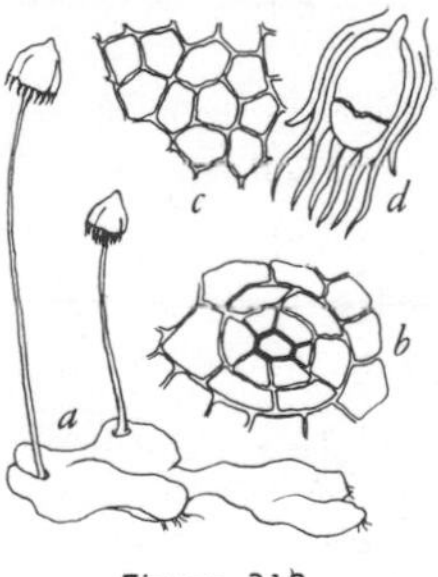

Figure 312

Fig. 312. *Asterella tenella*. a, plant; b, pore; c, cells of epidermis; d, sporophyte and pseudoperianth. Slender, 1.5-3 mm. wide, with a rounded ventral keel. Spores .08-.09 mm. with netted surface. On moist soil, Maine to Georgia, Texas, Missouri and Illinois. *A. ludwigii* is similar, California to Alaska, New York, Greenland, Iceland, Europe. Six other species occur in North America.

15a Lobes of the thallus 5-10 mm. wide, with air spaces in 3 or 4 irregular layers; in rosettes 2-3 cm. across on muddy shores, or floating in triangular pieces bearing many thin scales beneath. Fig. 313..Genus *Ricciocarpus*

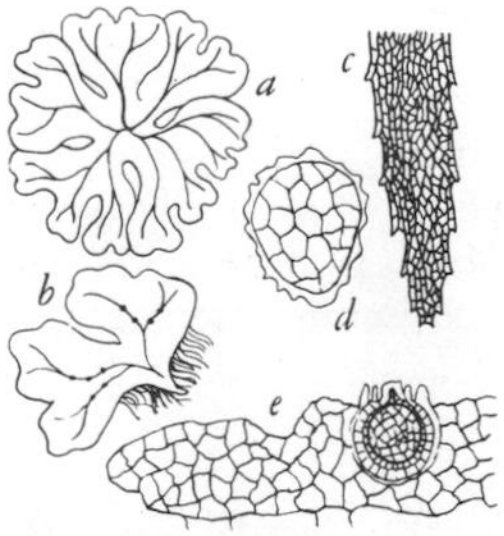

Figure 313

Fig. 313. *Ricciocarpus natans*. a, land form; b, floating form; c, ventral scale; d, spore; e, section of thallus and sporophyte. The floating form bears capsules in April in north central states; the land form is very fertile in Louisiana in November. Common: Maine to Florida, Texas and Minnesota. Europe, Asia, Australia, South America, West Indies.

15b Lobes 3 mm. to 1 mm. wide, with air chambers in 1 or 2 layers, or with mere chinks between the chains of upper cells. Figs. 314-316. Genus *Riccia* 16

16a In rosettes on earth, in gardens, fields or on river banks. Lobes 1 to 3 mm. wide. Figs. 315, 316 17

16b Floating branching ribbons, 1 mm. wide, often in tangled masses. Fig. 314 .... *R. fluitans*

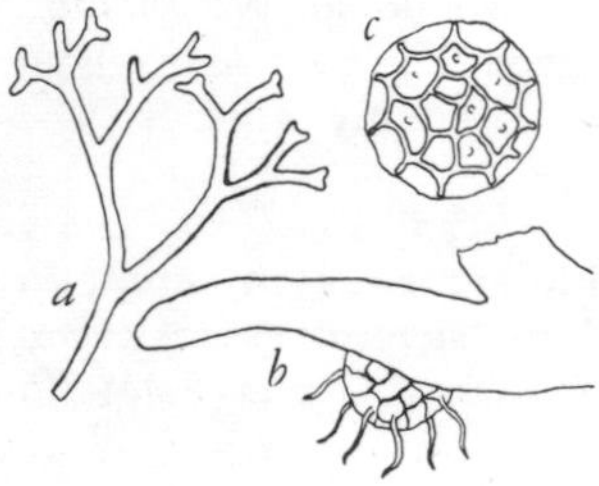

Figure 314

Fig. 314. *Riccia fluitans*. a, plant; b, plant with capsule bulging out beneath; c, spore. In shallow water, Quebec to Montana, British Columbia, California, Mexico, Florida, West Indies, South America., Europe, Asia, Africa, East Indies, Samoa, New Zealand. At sea level on Long Island, New York, and 7500 ft. in Yellowstone Park. Fruits are rare; of 27 specimens in my herbarium only one has capsules; it was collected in late October near Washington, D. C. A composite species about to be split into 3.

17a Spores permanently in tetrads. Thallus chambered. Fig. 316 .... *Riccia curtisii*

17b Spores separate at maturity 18

18a Thallus thin, the margin 1 cell thick and 1-5 cells wide. Thallus chambered. Spores .04-.06 mm., spiny, not winged, North Carolina, New Mexico, South America .... *Riccia membranacea*

18b Thicker; margin not membranous 19

19a Photosynthetic layer composed of vertical filaments 20

19b Photosynthetic layer composed of irregular chambers separated by walls 1 cell thick 21

20a Margin of thallus smooth or papillose, not ciliate. Spores with wide, irregular, sinuous ridges. Fig. 315 .... *Riccia dictyospora*

20b Margin with clear, stiff, short bristles (cilia). Spores coarsely and irregularly reticulate, winged. Fig. 315........*Riccia beyrichiana*

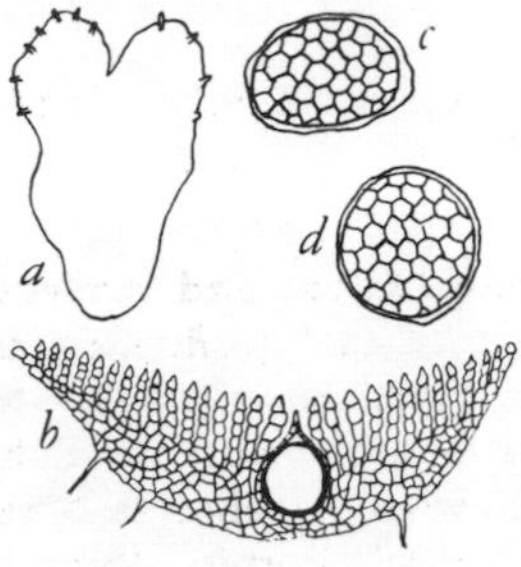

Figure 315

Fig. 315. *Riccia beyrichiana*. a, thallus with cilia; b, section of thallus; c, spore. About 2 mm. wide. United States, Europe, Africa. d, spore of *R. dictyospora;* Connecticut to Georgia and Texas. 14 species are recognized in North America with thallus like Fig. b. The species of Riccio are difficult to identify with certainty. Ripe spores are almost necessary, mature in autumn, but sometimes found in decaying thalli in spring.

21a Lobes of thallus short, broad (1-2 mm.), touching or overlapping. Spores winged, "granulate-crenulate." Fig. 316......*Riccia frostii*

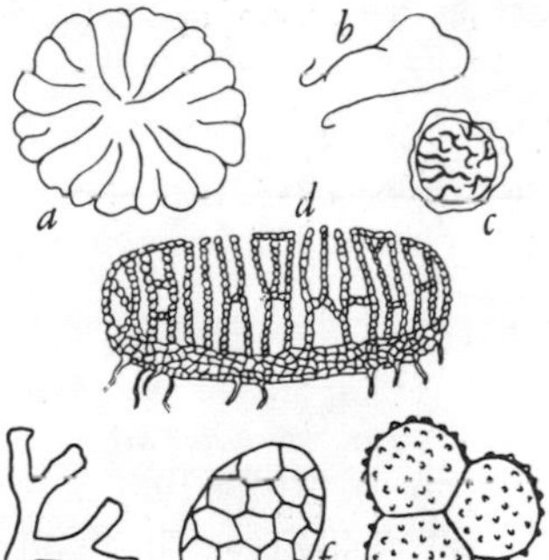

Figure 316

Fig. 316. *Riccia frostii*. a, plant; b, lobe enlarged, with capsule; c, spore; d, section of thallus. About 1 cm. in diameter; Vermont to Washington, California, New Mexico, South America. e, portion of thallus of *R. sullivantii;* f, spore; Eastern United States, Eurasia. g, spore of *R. curtisii;* North Carolina to Florida and Texas.

21b Lobes of thallus slender (1 mm. wide), usually wide apart. Spores winged, reticulate, with 5 to 8 areoles across the spore. Fig. 316. ....*Riccia sullivantii*

22a (b, c) Plant deeply cut on both sides of a stem-like midrib into ruffled, leaf-like lobes. Fig. 318. Family FOSSOMBRONIACEAE. Genus *Fossombronia* 23

22b Plant with shallow marginal lobes, with lumps of blue-green algae imbedded here and there, and with bottle-shaped gemma-containers; or tiny star-shaped gemmae. Fig. 317. Family BLASIACEAE .... Genus *Blasia*

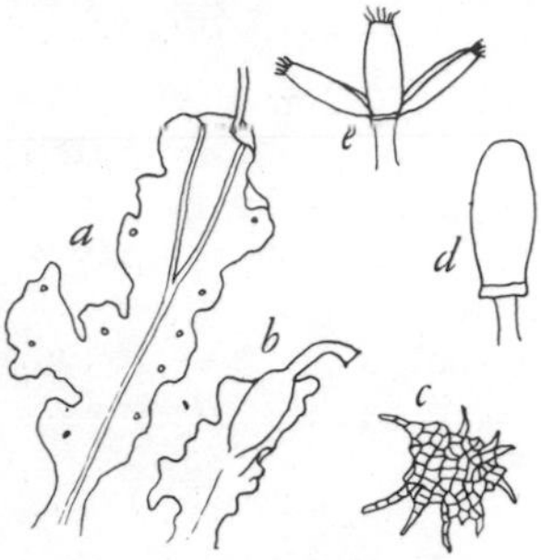

Figure 317

Fig. 317. *Blasia pusilla.* a, plant; b, gemma-bottle; c, star-shaped gemma; d, capsule; e, opened capsule. Often in sods covering many square feet of freshly exposed damp clay. Capsules ripen in late April in Iowa. Greenland to Alaska, Pennsylvania, Iowa, New Mexico, California, Europe, Asia, Australia.

22c Margins of plant even, or wavy but not regularly lobed. The plant itself may be variously lobed or branched. Figs. 319-322 25

23a Elaters few and imperfect or none. Spores .036-.046 mm., pale brown, reticulate, with 6-7 meshes across the spore. Massachusetts to Texas, Europe .... *Fossombronia cristula*

23b Elaters perfect, with spiral bands 24

24a Spores with ridges not forming a network. Fig. 318 .... *Fossombronia wondraczekii*

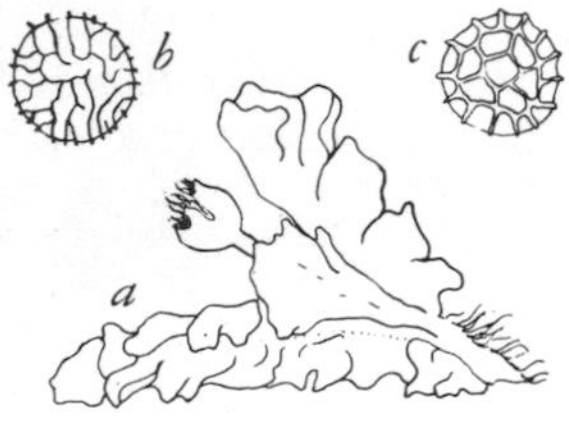

Figure 318

Fig. 318. *Fossombronia wondraczekii.* a, plant; b, spore; c, spore of *F. foveolata.* Eleven species are known from North America. The name of the first one here illustrates the international aspect of Science! The species is known from Europe, Asia and Africa, as well as from the eastern United States.

24b Spores covered with a distinct network with 5-6 meshes across the spore. North America, Europe. Fig. 318.... *Fossombronia foveolata*

25a Midrib well defined, bulging like a cord along lower side of plant, the rest of the thallus only 1 cell thick. Figs. 319, 320 26

25b Midrib ill defined, merely the gradually thickened central part of the plant, which is 1 cell thick only at the extreme margin if at all. Figs. 321, 322 30

26a Plant 1 to 2 mm. wide, much longer than wide, of very even width, forking. Sex organs underneath. On trees, leaves or damp ground. Fig. 320. Family METZGERIACEAE, Genus *Metzgeria*..........27

26b Plant 3 to 4 mm. wide, often very irregularly lobed; sex organs on upper side, along midrib. On wet peaty ground. Fig. 319. Family PALLAVICINIACEAE ....Genus *Pallavicinia*

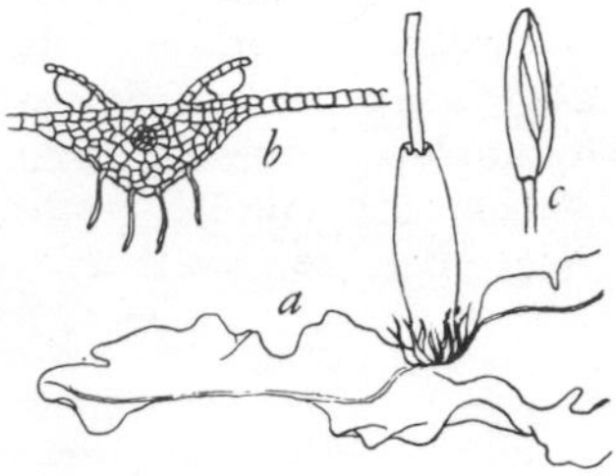

Figure 319

Fig. 319. *Pallavicinia lyellii.* a, plant; b, section of antheridial shoot; c, capsule. Thallus 4-5 mm. wide, with a central strand of small cells in the midrib. Worldwide. *Moerckia flotowiana* inhabits northern North America and Europe. The thallus lacks the central strand in the midrib, and the sporangium is thicker walled; otherwise like *Pallavicinia*. Two other species of *Moerckia* occur in North America.

27a Thallus with hairs on both upper and lower surfaces............ ....*Metzgeria pubescens*

27b Without hairs on upper surface..............................28

28a Under side of midrib 2 cells wide. Marginal hairs in pairs, curved and hooked. Hairs confined to margins and midrib............ ....*Metzgeria hamata*

28b Under side of midrib 3-7 cells wide...........................29

29a Marginal hairs in pairs. Thallus 2 mm. wide, the cells .045 x .06 mm. Fig. 320..............................*Metzgeria conjugata*

29b Marginal hairs single. Thallus 1 mm. wide, the cells .035 x .042 mm. Fig. 320..............................*Metzgeria furcata*

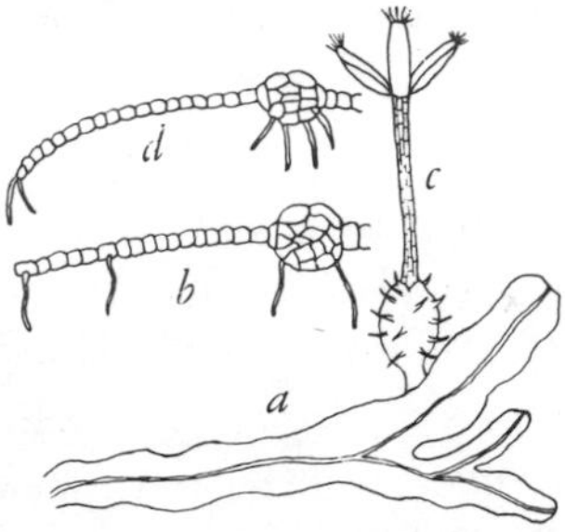

Figure 320

Fig. 320. *Metzgeria furcata.* a, plant; b, cross section of thallus; c, involucre, seta, open capsule with elaters; d, section of thallus of *M. conjugata.* Both of these, the first 1 mm. wide, the second 2 mm. wide, have worldwide distribution. Six other species are almost as far spread, but not so commonly seen.

30a Plant 4 to 16 mm. wide, usually crowded in wide (10-50 cm.) patches on moist shaded ground. Elaters attached at base of capsule. Fig. 321............................Family PELLIACEAE, Genus *Pellia*

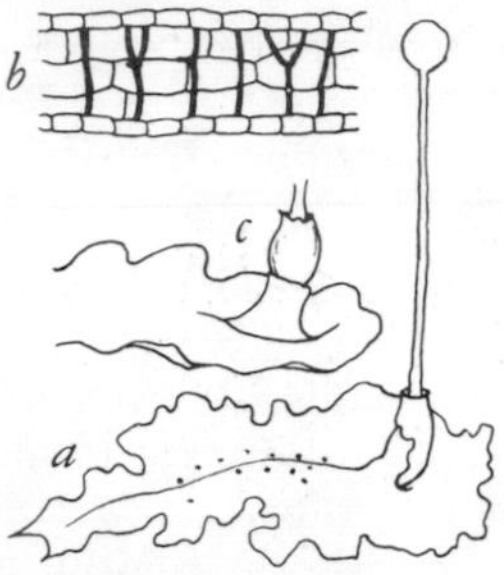
Figure 321

Fig. 321. *Pellia epiphylla*. a, plant; b, section of thallus with thickened bands; c, fruiting tip of *P. neesiana* showing cylindric involucre. *P. endiviaefolia* lacks the thickened bands, but has the cylindric involucre. All three are circumboreal, south to North Carolina and Texas., apparently avoiding lime. *P. epiphylla* is the most common.

30b Plant 1-5 mm. wide, variously lobed or branched, in very wet places or in shallow water. Elaters attached to apex of capsule (tips of valves). Fig. 322.......Family RICCARDIACEAE, Genus *Riccardia*

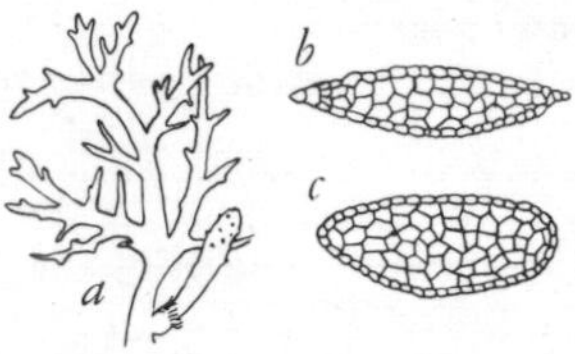
Figure 322

Fig. 322. *Riccardia multifida*. a, plant; b, cross section of thallus; c, section of thallus of *R. palmata*. Little branchy thalli, among other mosses or in crowds, in water or very wet places. Rarely found in fruit. *R. pinguis* is 2-10 mm. wide. All of our 5 species are of circumboreal or world-wide distribution.

31a Leaves deeply divided into many threads or rows of cells. Figs 323-326 32

31b Leaves entire, or toothed, or divided at tip into 2, 3 or 4 lobes. Figs. 327-372 35

32a Basal part of leaf showing 2 major lobes, each 6-20 cells wide. Fig. 323......................................Genus *Ptilidium*

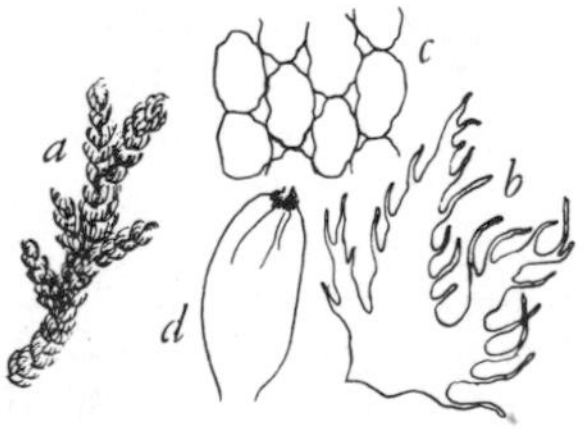
Figure 323

Fig. 323. *Ptilidium pulcherrimum*. a, plant; b, leaf; c, cells of leaf; d, perianth. Creeping over rotten wood, often amongst other mosses; often purplish brown. *P. ciliare* has wider leaf-lobes, 15 to 20 cells at base of lobe, against 6 to 10 cells for the preceding species; it is more upright, in deep tufts. Both of these are circumboreal, south to Pennsylvania and Illinois. *P. californicum*, with only 3 to 12 hair-tipped divisions per leaf, ranges from California to Idaho and Alaska.

32b Basal part of leaf 1-4 cells wide. Figs. 324-326.................33

33a Plant large (covering 2 to 55 cm. or more); leaves much divided into very many filiform divisions. Fig. 324........Genus *Tricholea*

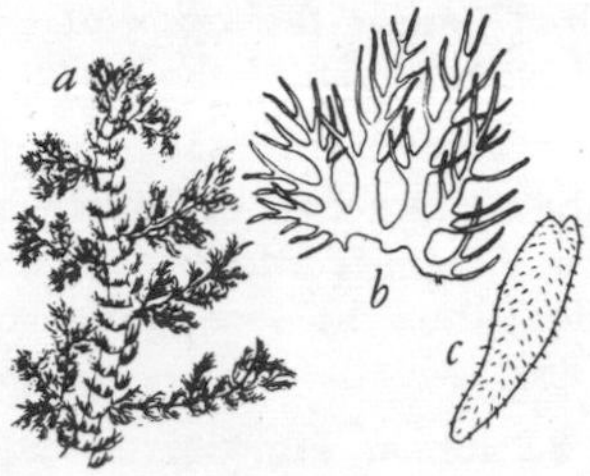

Figure 324

Fig. 324. *Tricholea tomentella.* a, plant; b, leaf; c, perianth. Stems hairy; underleaves similar to upper leaves. In beautiful pale green or yellowish mats on wet ground. Newfoundland to Virginia, Tennessee and Wisconsin. Europe, Asia, Samoa, Tahiti!

33b Small slender plants: leaves with 2-4 filamentous divisions. Figs. 325, 326 34

34a Basal part of divisions 2 cells wide. Fig. 325..Genus *Microlepidozia*

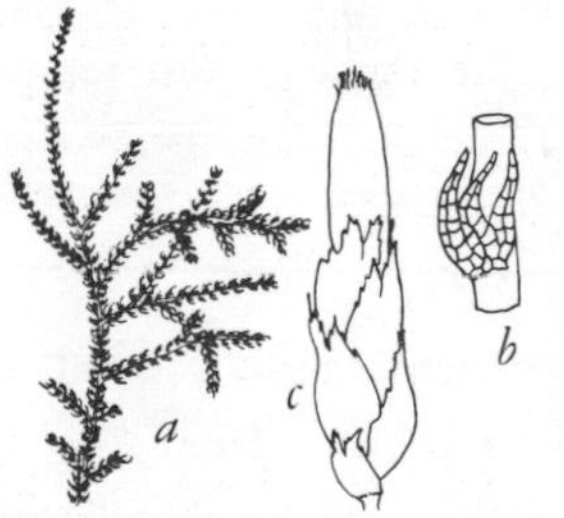

Figure 325

Fig. 325. *Microlepidozia sylvatica.* a, plant; b, leaf; c, perianth. Minute films on peaty soil in woods; New England to Florida. *M. setacea,* with leaves 4-parted, is found in northeastern United States, Europe and Asia.

34b Basal part of divisions only 1 cell wide. Fig. 326..............
....................................Genus *Blepharostoma*

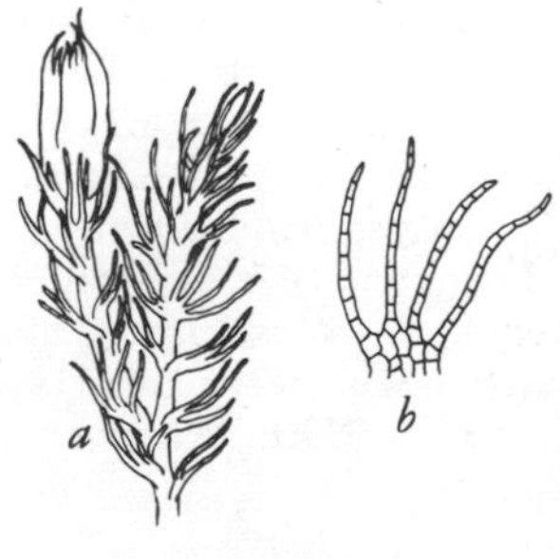

Figure 326

Fig. 326. *Blepharostoma trichophyllum.* a, plant; b, leaf. Fine threads on peaty, mossy ground, moist and shady. Frequently fruiting. Greenland to Alaska, New Jersey, Iowa, Colorado, (to 10,000 ft. altitude) and California; Europe; Asia. *B. arachnoideum* (British Columbia to California and Montana) has 2 or 3 divisions, with cells nearly twice as long as those of the preceding species (.04-.07 mm.).

35a Leaves flat or curved, not sharply folded. Figs. 327-354..........36

35b Leaves two-lobed and folded, one lobe pressed firmly against the other. Figs. 355-372..........65

36a Leaves incubous: attached obliquely to the stem so that the edge of leaf on upper surface of stem is attached nearer the apex of the stem than the lower edge; thus the leaf slopes toward the base of the stem. Figs. 327-330..........37

36b Leaves transversely attached, or succubous: attached obliquely so that the edge of the leaf on upper surface of stem is attached nearer the base of the stem than the lower edge; thus the leaf slopes toward the apex of the stem. Figs. 331-354..........43

37a Leaves divided half way or more into 3-6 lobes. Fig. 327.......... Genus *Lepidozia*

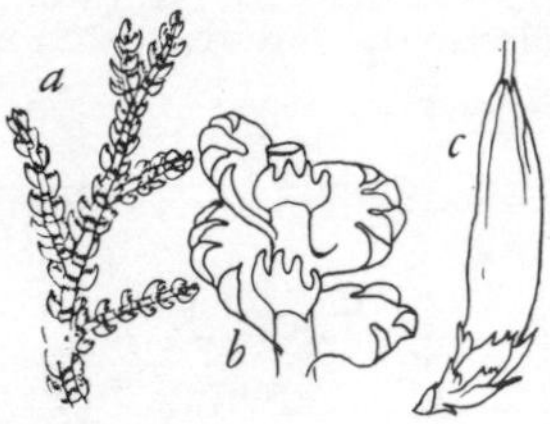

Figure 327

Fig. 327. *Lepidozia reptans.* a, plant; b, leaves and underleaves; c, perianth. Pale filmy growths on shaded, damp sandy soil or rocks, frequent. Newfoundland to Alaska, California, Mexico and North Carolina. Europe. Three other species are reported from North America.

37b Leaves entire or notched, not divided half way. Figs. 328-330...38

38a Leaves 3-toothed at apex, firm, green or brown. Figs. 328, 329. Genus *Bazzania*..........39

38b Leaves entire or 2-toothed, pale and watery; cells large (.03-.055 mm.). Fig. 330. Genus *Calypogeia*..........40

39a Leaves firmly attached to stem. Fig. 328........*Bazzania trilobata*

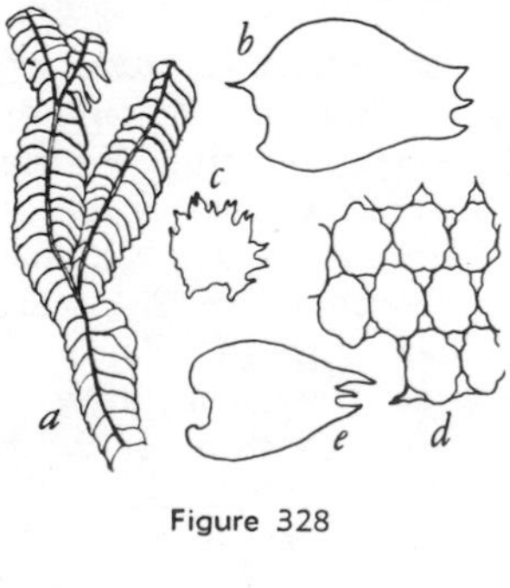

Figure 328

Fig. 328. *Bazzania trilobata.* a, plant; b, leaf; c, underleaf; d, cells of leaf; e, leaf of *B. tricrenata.* Common on moist shaded logs or rocks, often in patches 2 feet across. The leaves bend down when dry; very rarely fruiting. East of the 95th meridian. Europe. In Washington State *B. tricrenata* is frequent. Five other species are recorded for North America.

39b Many leaves broken off leaving parts of stem bare. Underleaves wider than long, wavy or toothed on the sides. Fig. 329.......... ....*Bazzania denudata*

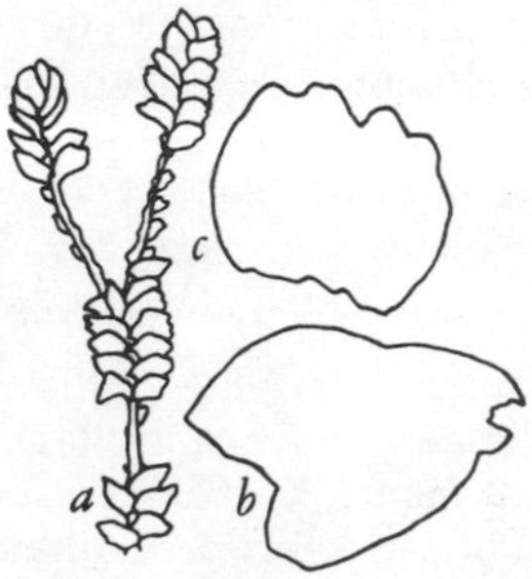

Figure 329

Fig. 329. *Bazzania denudata*. a, shoot; b, leaf; c, underleaf. Small plants, 2 mm. wide, 10-30 mm. long. Greenland to Alaska, Washington, Ohio and South Carolina.

40a Leaves all 2-toothed or 2-lobed at apex. Lobes of underleaves narrowly acute, with a tooth on each side...................... ....*Calypogeia sullivantii*

40b Leaves entire or very shallowly 2-pointed. Lobes of underleaves never slenderly acute.......................................41

41a Marginal cells of leaves about twice as long as wide. Sinus of underleaves shallow or lacking.............*Calypogeia neesiana*

41b Marginal cells hardly longer than wide.......................42

42a Underleaves 2-lobed, the margins entire. Fig. 330.............. ....*Calypogeia trichomanis*

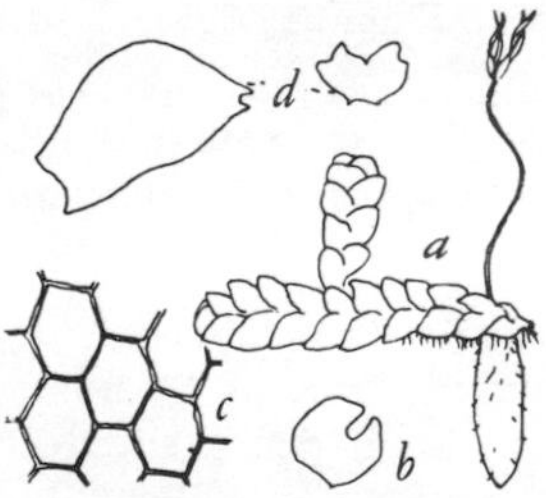

Figure 330

Fig. 330. *Calypogeia trichomanis*. a, shoot from dorsal surface, with subterranean "perigynium" and sporophyte; b, underleaf; c, cells of leaf; d, leaf and underleaf of *C. fissa*. Shoots very flat, on damp peaty soil or rotten wood, often among other mosses. The curious subterranean "perigynium" is unique; found in spring. Pretty much all over this continent and Europe. The species merge into one another, and are hardly distinguishable.

42b Underleaves 2-lobed, with a tooth or bulge on one or both sides. Fig. 330.................................*Calypogeia fissa*

43a **Leaves entire, not at all lobed or toothed (bracts around the perianth are excluded). Figs. 331-335 .... 44**

43b **Leaves 2- or more lobed, or toothed on the margin. Figs. 337-354 . . 48**

44a **(b, c) Perianth triangular, split in three at the top, overtopped by the larger, obovate calyptra (archegonium) when sporophyte emerges, borne on a short branch; underleaves present, conspicuous, 2-lobed; antheridia in axils of leaves in groups along the stem. Fig. 331. .... Genus *Chiloscyphus***

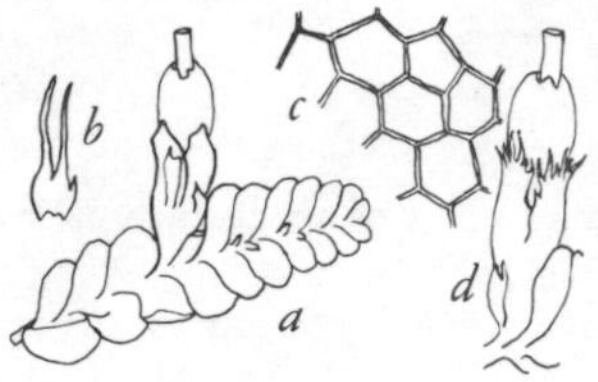

Figure 331

Fig. 331. *Chiloscyphus polyanthus.* a, plant; b, underleaf; c, cells of leaf; d, perianth and calyptra of *C. pallescens.* One of our largest liverworts, often in beds several inches across on moist shaded banks; margin of leaf often concave at apex. Sporophytes in early May in Iowa. Labrador to Alaska, North Carolina, Missouri and California. Europe. *C. pallescens* is paler, and in wetter places, Quebec to British Columbia, North Carolina, New Mexico and Oregon. Europe. *C. rivularis* grows attached to stones in cold rivulets; underleaves greatly reduced.

44b **Similar to the above, but calyptra remaining deep within the perianth, which terminates a main shoot; antheridia just below the perianth. Fig. 340 .... *Lophocolea heterophylla,* No. 52a**

44c **Underleaves absent or minute and lanceolate. Figs. 332-335 ..... 45**

45a **Branches from under side of stem; leaves circular, rather rigid, tending to stand on edge facing one another; dioicous; antheridia on short branches. Fig. 332 .... Genus *Odontoschisma***

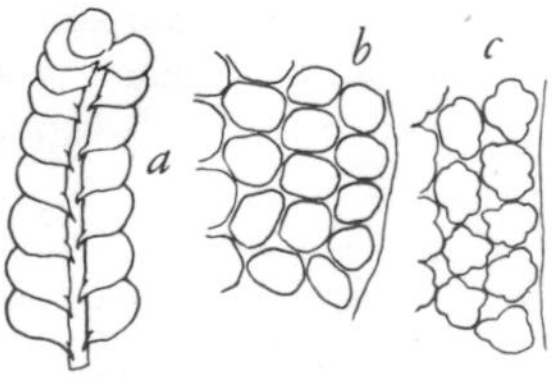

Figure 332

Fig. 332. *Odontoschisma prostratum.* a, plant; b, cells of leaf; c, cells of *O. denudatum.* Common on damp peaty soil; often bearing slender leafless branches (flagella); perianth on a short branch, but rarely seen. Northeastern to Ohio and South America. *O. denudatum* extends from Florida and Alabama to Greenland, Iceland and Europe. Compare *Jamesoniella,* No. 46a.

45b Branches axillary; leaves cordate to oblong, lying flat when wet; cell walls thin all around; antheridia grouped along the main stem, or on a branch. Figs. 333-335..............................46

46a Mouth of perianth contracted, and fringed with many-celled hairs. Fig. 333....................................Genus *Jamesoniella*

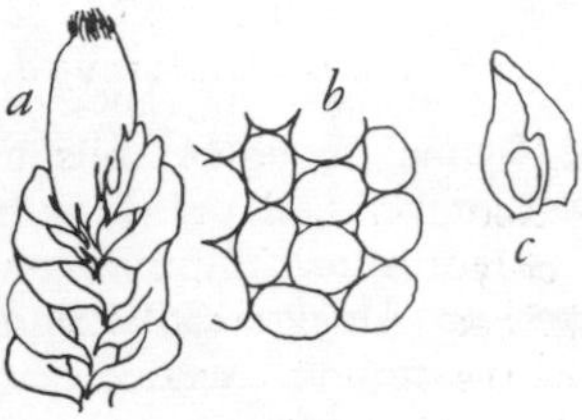

Figure 333

Fig. 333. *Jamesoniella autumnalis.* a, plant with perianth and bracts; b, cells of leaf; c, leaf that bears an antheridium. Common on moist sandstone or earth, usually with other mosses, Greenland to British Columbia, Washington, Missouri and Alabama. Europe. Dioicous. Antheridia at the end of a special shoot, or in patches along the stem, in 4-6 pairs of bracts, each bract with 1 or 2 teeth on the upper margin. Perianth on the end of a main shoot. These characters will distinguish this from *Odontoschisma* or *Chiloscyphus.* Sporophytes in September.

46b Mouth of perianth plaited but not fringed. Figs. 334, 335. Genus *Jungermannia* 47

47a Leaves broadly cordate; cell walls thin, without trigones; perianth slender, spindle-shaped. Fig. 334.........*Jungermannia cordifolia*

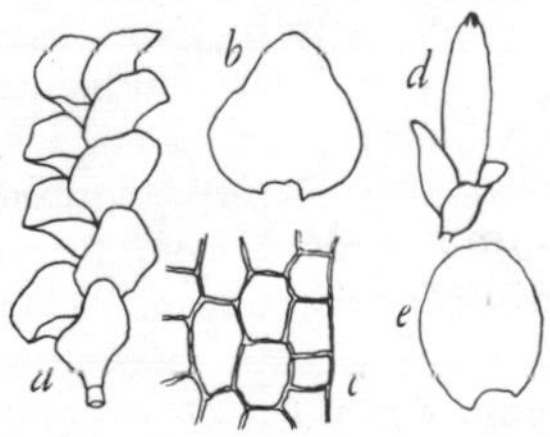

Figure 334

Fig. 334. *Jungermannia cordifolia.* a, plant; b, leaf; c, cells of leaf; d, perianth; e, leaf of *J. pumila.* Tiny green films on moist sandstone or wet soil, Greenland to Alaska, California, Wisconsin and New York. Iceland, Europe, Asia, South America. *J. pumila* is larger, about 1 mm. wide; similar range.

47b Leaves oblong-rectangular; trigones distinct, bulging into the cells; perianth cylindric, nearly flat across the top; with a short tubular mouth. Fig. 335........................*Jungermannia lanceolata*

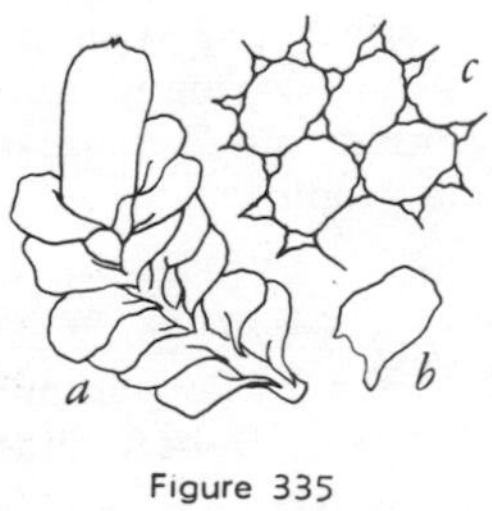

Figure 335

Fig. 335. *Jungermannia lanceolata.* a, plant; b, leaf; c, cells of leaf. In thin mats among mosses. Stems to 3 cm. long; cells .03-.048 mm. Monoicous; antheridia just below the perianth. Labrador to Alaska, Washington and North Carolina. Europe, Asia. Twelve species of *Jungermannia* are now recognized in North America. Formerly this genus included nearly all of the leafy liverworts.

48a Leaves toothed, at least on distal margin. Figs. 336-338........49

48b Margins not toothed, but the leaf 2-4-lobed. Figs. 339-354.......51

49a Leaves long-decurrent on upper side of stem, with margins turned back. Large plants. Figs. 337, 338. Genus *Plagiochila*..........50

49b Leaves nearly transversely attached, crowded, bluish green. Stem thick and fleshy. Fig. 336......................*Lophozia incisa*

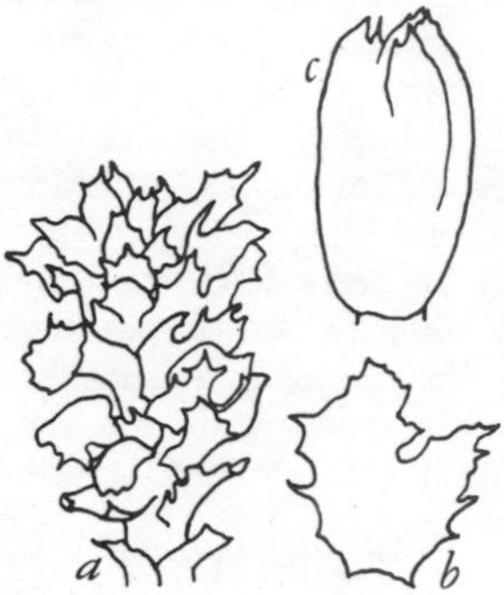

Figure 336

Fig. 336. *Lophozia incisa.* a, shoot; b, leaf; c, perianth. Stems about 14 cells in diameter from left to right, 9 or 10 cells from dorsal to ventral side. Rhizoids numerous. Greenland to Alaska, California, New Mexico, North Carolina, Mexico; Eurasia.

50a Teeth of leaf more than 10, small to obsolete; leaves broadly ovate. Fig. 337................................*Plagiochila asplenioides*

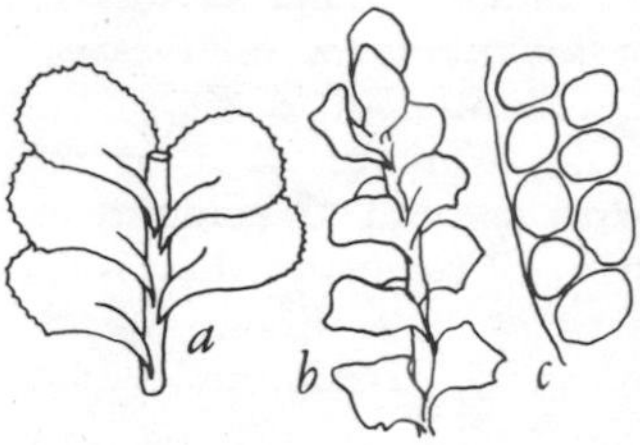

Figure 337

Fig. 337. *Plagiochila asplenioides.* a, wet shoot; b, dry shoot; c, cells of leaf. Variable as to size, up to 4 or 5 mm. wide, yellowish green, in peculiar pleated sods, or among other mosses. Rarely fruiting. Leaves usually entire in Mid-west; United States and Canada; Mexico; Europe. Common.

50b Teeth fewer than 10, large and several-celled; leaves narrowly ovate. Fig. 338............................*Plagiochila sullivantii*

Figure 338

Fig. 338. *Plagiochila sullivantii.* a, shoot; b, leaf; c, cells of leaf. There are several of these spinose species, varying to simply bi-lobed leaves. This one is found from New Hampshire to Florida and Tennessee. A large genus in the tropics.

51a (b, c) Underleaves easily found, split nearly to the base; perianth 3-angled, at the end of a main shoot, with 3 fringed lobes. Figs. 340, 341. Genus *Lophocolea*...............................52

51b Underleaves easily found, lanceolate, Fig. 339..Genus *Harpanthus*

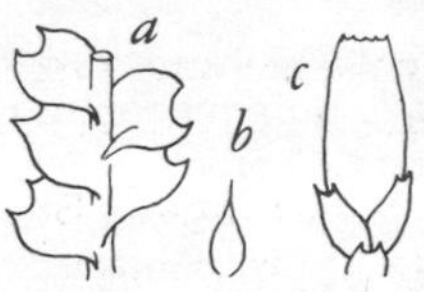

Figure 339

Fig. 339. *Harpanthus scutatus.* a, shoot; b, underleaf; c, perianth. Pale, close to the substrate, often mistaken for the next. On damp ground or rotten wood, Labrador to British Columbia, Wisconsin, Tennessee and North Carolina. Europe.

51c Underleaves small or absent. Figs. 342-354....................53

52a Leaves broadest at middle or distal end, wtih 2 short acute lobes, or emarginate or entire. Fig. 340...........*Lophocolea heterophylla*

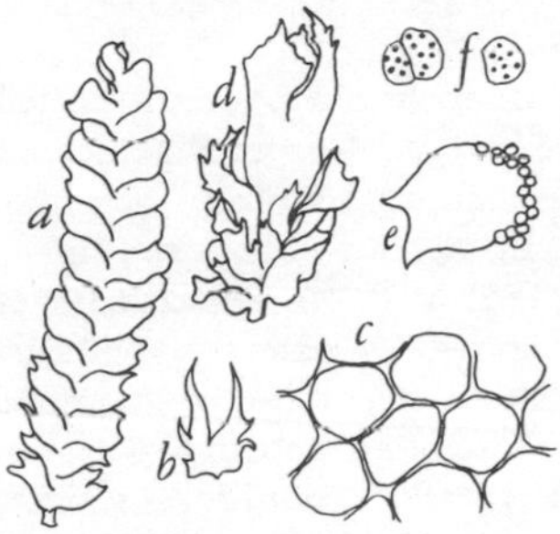

Figure 340

Fig. 340. *Lophocolea heterophylla.* a, plant; b, underleaf; c, cells of leaf; d, perianth; e, leaf of *L. minor* with gemmae; f, gemmae. Common on shaded banks or rotten wood, United States and southern Canada; Europe. Perianths mature in autumn; sporophytes come up in spring, or in January in the laboratory. *L. minor* is about half as large as the former species.

52b Leaves broadest at base, divided into two long-acuminate lobes. Fig. 341..............................*Lophocolea bidentata*

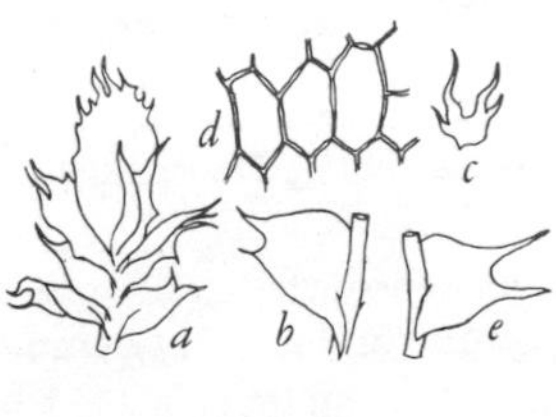

Figure 341

Fig. 341. *Lophocolea bidentata.* a, shoot; b, leaf; c, underleaf; d, cells of leaf; e, leaf of *L. cuspidata.* The first is dioicous and rarely fruits; the second is monoicous and usually has perianths; otherwise they are very much alike. On moist earth, old logs and stumps, over most of North America and Europe.

53a (b, c, d) Leave broad, with 3 or 4 large triangular lobes. Figs. 344-347 54

53b Leaves with 3 (-2) very unequal lobes, one margin much larger and more convex than the other. Fig. 342...........Genus *Tritomaria*

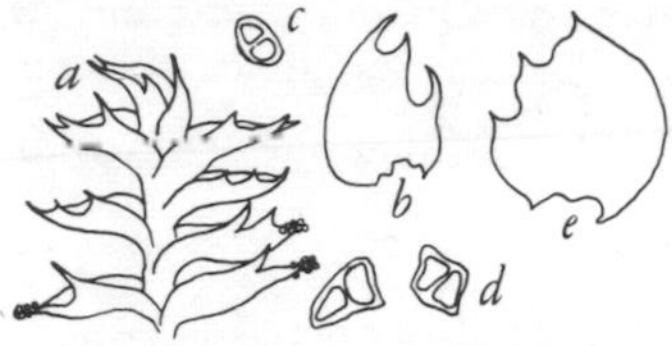

Figure 342

Fig. 342. *Tritomaria exsecta.* a, shoot; b, leaf; c, gemma; d, gemmae of *T. exsectiformis;* e, leaf of *T. quinquedentata.* The first two are small, erect plants, 5 10 mm. tall, the gemmae reddish; the second has cells .022-.024 mm. across, the first .010-.017 mm. The third is larger, stems 2-5 cm. long; gemmae 2-celled, angular. Northern United States (North Carolina, Tennessee, Iowa) to Alaska. Europe.

53c Leaves two-lobed. Figs. 348-354..............................57

53d Leaves entire or broadly and shallowly emarginate; perianth united at base with neighboring leaves. Fig. 343......Genus *Plectocolea*

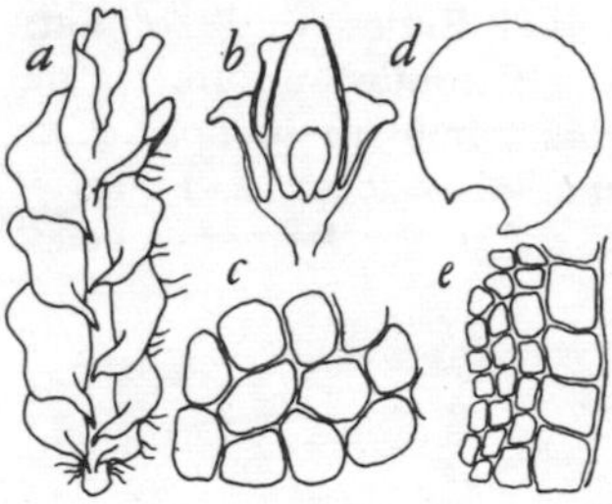

Figure 343

Fig. 343. *Plectocolea hyalina.* a, shoot with perianth; b, section of perianth; c, cells of leaf; d, leaf of *P. crenulata;* e, marginal cells of same. When the extreme marginal cells seem to lie below the next cells within, so that the margin will not lie flat, we have *P. crenuliformis.* On moist soil or rocks, often covering a foot of surface in pure stand. Dioicous. Sporophytes in April in Iowa. United States east of Rocky Mountains. Mexico. Europe. *P. rubra* is the usual form on our northwest coast.

54a Leaves flat when wet; lobes usually obtuse; lower margin of leaf without hairlike appendages (cilia). Fig. 344..*Barbilophozia barbata*

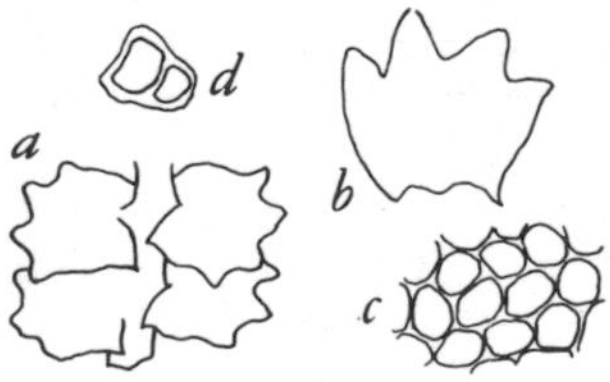

Figure 344

Fig. 344. *Barbilophozia barbata.* a, shoot; b, leaf; c, cells of leaf; d, gemma. A large liverwort, on moist rocks and banks, across the continent northward: Michigan, Colorado, Washington, and in Europe. Underleaves usually absent.

54b **Lower margin of leaf with 2-4 cilia; leaves wrinkled; lobes acuminate; underleaves present, cleft in two, ciliate-margined. Figs. 345-347 ....55**

55a **Cells of cilia much longer than broad. Fig. 345..** ***Barbilophozia hatcheri***

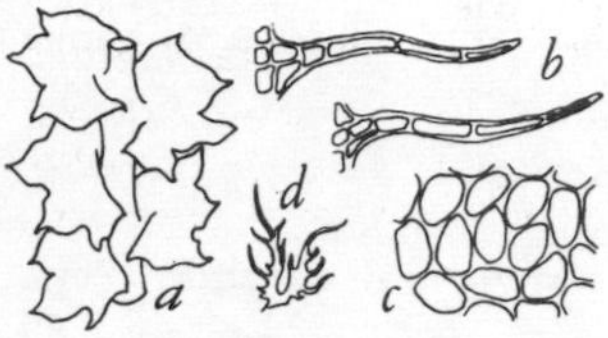

Figure 345

Fig. 345. *Barbilophozia hatcheri.* a, shoot; b, cilia; c, cells of leaf; d, underleaf. Large species of our northwest. *B. lycopodioides* has leaves 4-5-lobed, with shorter lobes, and rarely with gemmae. Both are found also in Europe.

55b **Cells of cilia about as broad as long. Figs. 346, 347. Genus *Orthocaulis* 56**

56a **Leaves 3-lobed about 1/3 of length. Fig. 346..*Orthocaulis floerkei***

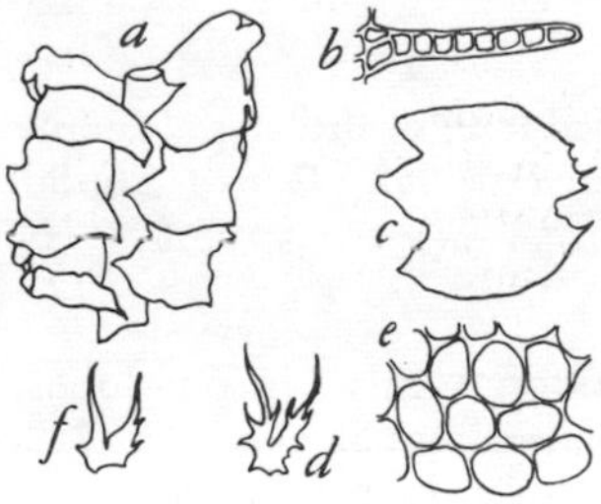

Figure 346

Fig. 346. *Orthocaulis floerkei.* a, shoot; b, cilium; c, leaf; d, underleaf; e, cells of leaf; f, underleaf of *O. kunzeanus.* Large species of northern distribution. Europe. This, with the preceding number and the following are called *Lophozia* in all of the older texts.

56b **Leaves 4-lobed about 1/2 of length. Fig. 347..** ***Orthocaulis quadrilobus***

Figure 347

Fig. 347. *Orthocaulis quadrilobus.* a, leaf; b, cilium; c, underleaf. Gemmae rare, variously shaped. Arctic-alpine. Europe.

57a Leaves with long-acuminate lobes, the lower margin rolled over to form a sac; very slender plants; Fig. 348........Genus *Nowellia*

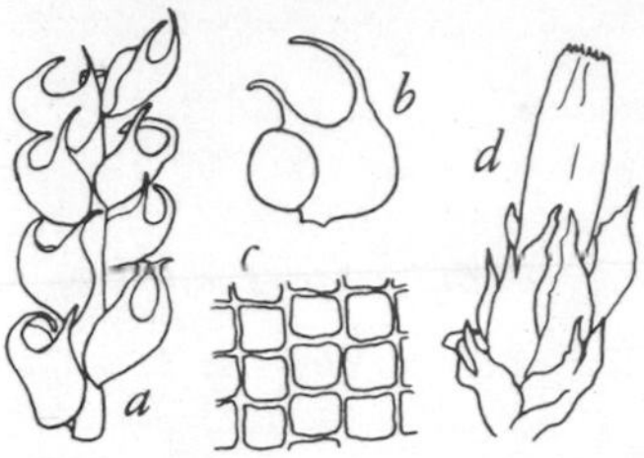

Figure 348

Fig. 348. *Nowellia curvifolia*. a, shoot; b, leaf; c, cells of leaf; d, perianth with bracts. The curious leaves are unique. On wet rotten wood or wet peat, Newfoundland to North Carolina, Iowa and Minnesota. Europe, Asia. Known from only one spot in Iowa, on a vertical face of moist sandstone.

57b Lobes acute or obtuse, not acuminate; leaves not saccate. Figs. 349-354 58

58a Extremely slender plants, 0.5-1.0 mm. wide or smaller. Figs. 349-351 59

58b Larger; shoots, with leaves, more than 0.5 mm. wide; leaves transversely attached or nearly so. Figs. 352-354..................62

59a Leaves obliquely attached to stem, often decurrent; stems covered with a layer of large transparent cells. Figs. 349, 350. Genus *Cephalozia* 60

59b Leaves transversely attached, scarcely wider than the stem, deeply cut into two acute lobes; stems opaque. Fig. 351. Genus *Cephaloziella* 61

60a Leaves divided half or more into two slender, nearly parallel lobes, not decurrent; cells .035-.05 mm. in diameter; monoicous. Fig. 349. ....*Cephalozia bicuspidata*

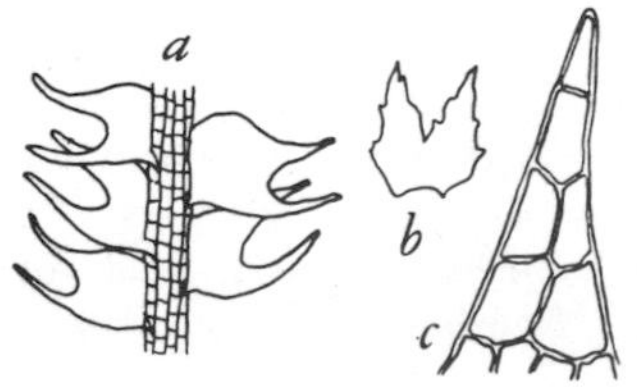

Figure 349

Fig. 349. *Cephalozia bicuspidata*. a, shoot; b, bract; c, apex of lobe. The long parallel lobes of the leaves easily characterize this species. It often has erect, small leafed "flagella". Greenland to Alaska, California, Mexico, Florida, Europe, Asia, Africa.—*C. lammersiana* (Maine; British Columbia to Oregon, Eurasia) does not have flagella.

60b Leaves divided about 1/3 into two short converging lobes, decurrent; cells .025-.03 mm. in diameter; dioicous. Fig. 350........ ....*Cephalozia media*

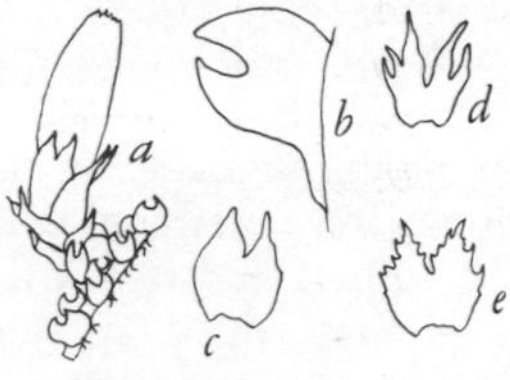

Figure 350

Fig. 350. *Cephalozia media.* a, shoot; b, leaf; c, bract; d, bract of C. *connivens;* e, bract of C. *catenulata.* These tiny plants are widespread over North America, Europe and Asia. C. *connivens* has leaf cells .04-.06 mm. and is monoicous. C. *catenulata* .016-.021 mm., dioicous. In bogs on peat, dead wood or tussocks of sedge.

61a Underleaves distinct; lobes of leaf 2-4 cells wide at base; perianth fusiform, with 3-6 folds; dioicous. Fig. 351..*Cephaloziella hyssacea*

61b Underleaves absent; lobes of leaf 6-8 cells wide at base; perianth cylndric, 4-5 ridged; monoicous. Fig. 351...................... ....*Cephaloziella hampeana*

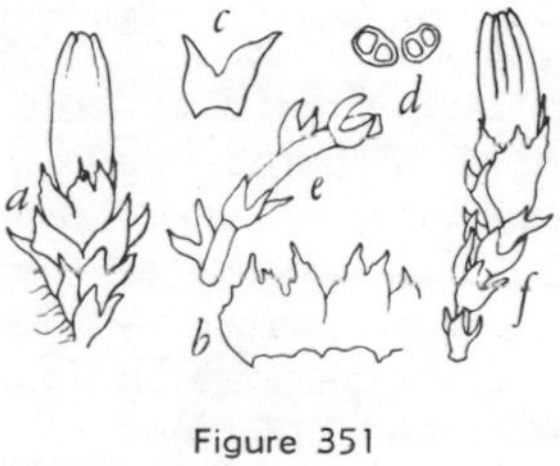

Figure 351

Fig. 351. *Cephaloziella byssacea.* a, shoot with perianth; b, bract; c, leaf; d, gemmae; e, shoot; f, perianth of C. *hampeana.* Thin films on peaty soil, or single strands among other mosses. Twenty-nine species are recorded from North America, but hardly anybody can tell them apart. One species may vary considerably.

62a Leaves nearly flat; lobes acute, mostly wide apart; gemmae common, angular. Fig. 354. Genus *Lophozia*......................64

62b Leaves decidedly concave, the two sides bent upward. Figs. 352, 353 63

63a Gemmae common, angular; leaves clasping stem at base; lobes acute. Fig. 352..........................Genus *Anastrophyllum*

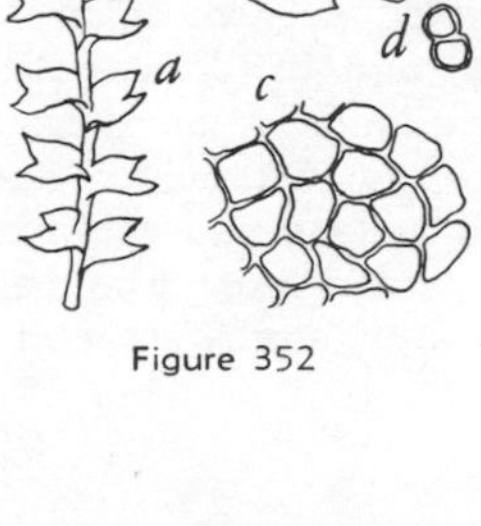

Figure 352

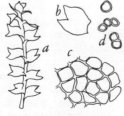

Fig. 352. *Anastrophyllum michauxii.* a, shoot; b, leaf; c, cells of leaf; d, gemmae. In dense brownish patches, creeping or erect, the stems about 1 cm. long. Cells of leaf .013-.014 mm. wide. On rotten wood or rocks, Labrador to North Carolina, Wyoming and Idaho.

63b Without gemmae; lobes obtuse. Fig. 353.......Genus *Marsupella*

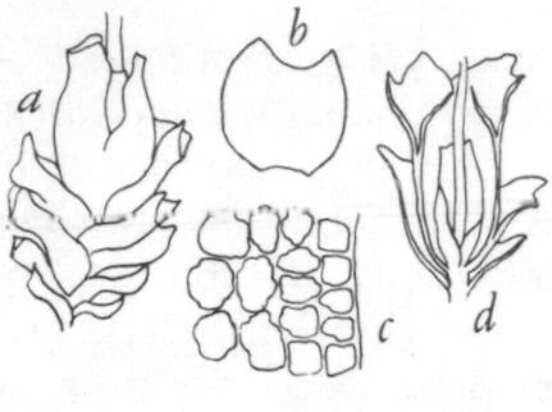

Figure 353

Fig. 353. *Marsupella emarginata.* a, shoot; b, leaf; c, cells of leaf; d, section of perianth and bracts. On moist banks and rocks, in loose mats; stems to 3 cm. long. In *M. emarginata* the outermost cells of the stem are thick walled and about the same size as the inner ones. In *M. sphacelata* the outer cells are thin walled and about twice as big as those within. Eight other species are recorded for North America, ranging across the continent in northern United States and northward; also in Europe. Perianths of this and the preceding are not often seen.

64a Bracts of involucre 2-5 lobed, with margins entire. Fig. 354.......
...*Lophozia ventricosa*

64b Bracts of involucre 3-5 lobed, with margins toothed. Fig. 354....
...*Lophozia excisa*

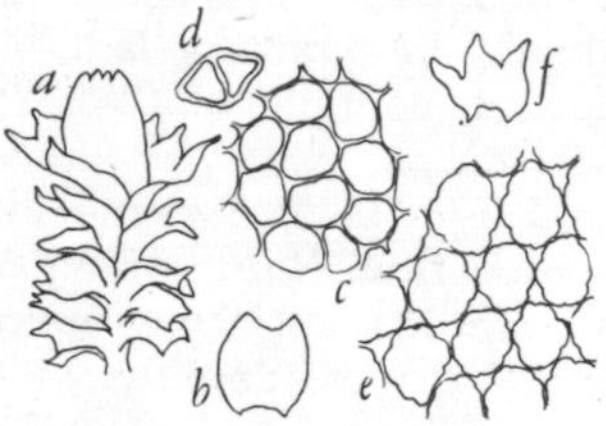

Figure 354

Fig. 354. *Lophozia ventricosa.* a, shoot with perianth; b, leaf; c, cells of leaf; d, gemma; e, cells of *L. porphyroleuca;* f, bract of *L. excisa.* These are thin films of green on soil among rocks or on trees, in patches an inch or two across. All three are spread clear across the northern United States and Canada, and in Europe.

65a Underlobe larger than upper, both approximately flat. Figs. 355-359 66

65b Underlobe smaller than upper and completely hidden by it, flat or sac-like. Figs. 360-372.......................................70

66a Larger lobe oblong-lanceolate; perianth cylindric and furrowed. Fig. 355 ....Genus *Diplophyllum*

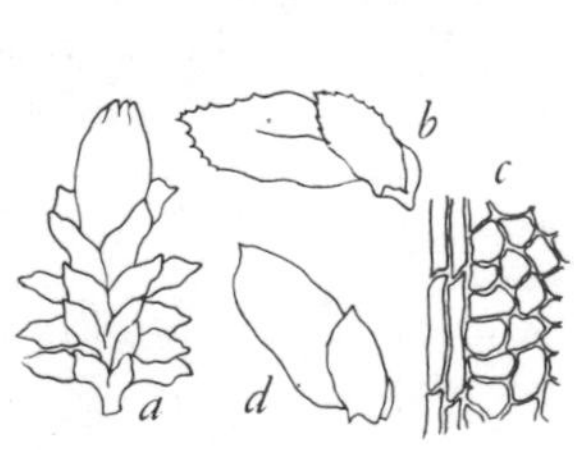

Figure 355

Fig. 355. *Diplophyllum albicans.* a, shoot with perianth; b, leaf; c, leaf-cells; d, leaf of *D. apiculatum.* Thin films on shaded peaty ground; *D. albicans* is common in England and Europe, and in Washington and Oregon. *D. apiculatum* is found from New England to Georgia, Oklahoma and Wisconsin. It lacks the elongated vein-like cells up the middle of the leaf. The corresponding plant on our northwest coast is *D. taxifolium.*

66b Larger lobe rounded-ovate; perianth with a wide flattened mouth. Figs. 356-359. Genus *Scapania*....................................67

67a Basal margin of smaller (upper) leaf-lobe with long, branched cilia. Fig. 356...................................*Scapania bolanderi*

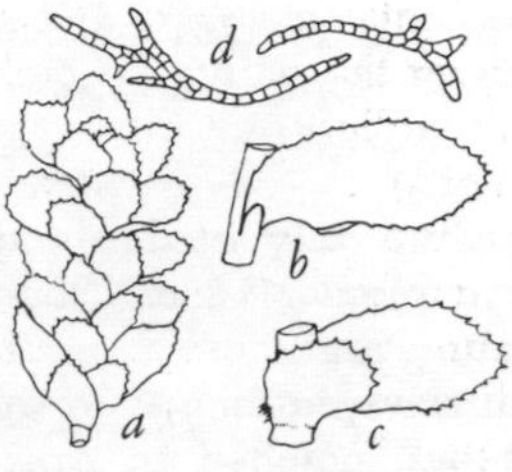

Figure 356

Fig. 356. *Scapania bolanderi.* a, shoot; b, leaf and under side of stem; c, leaf and upper side of stem; d, cilia from margin of leaf. Stems to 8 cm. long, leaves to 1 mm. Common on west coast; Washington, Oregon. On logs and stumps. The toothing of the leaves is like that of other species; the cilia are unique.

67b Basal margin entire or finely toothed, not ciliate. Figs. 357-359..68

68a Lower (larger) lobe of leaf with sharply toothed margin. Both upper and lower lobes decurrent. Fig. 357.......*Scapania nemorosa*

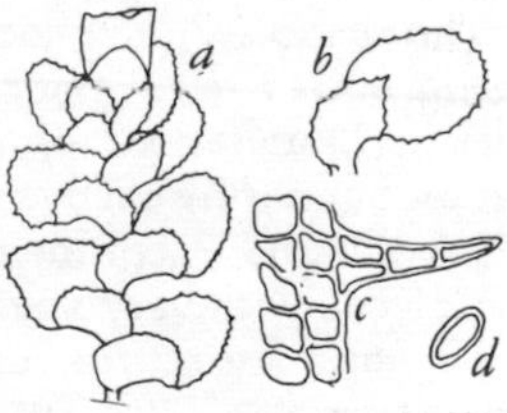

Figure 357

Fig. 357. *Scapania nemorosa.* a, shoot; b, leaf and upper surface of stem; c, margin of leaf; d, gemma. Widespread in North America and Europe, on moist soil or rocks, often covering many square feet. The tips of shoots are often covered with red-brown gemmae.

68b Lower lobe entire or wavy or with a few minute teeth at apex. Upper lobe not decurrent. Fig. 358, 359.....................69

69a Lower (larger) lobe of leaf entire or very finely toothed at apex, little or not at all decurrent. Fig. 358............*Scapania irrigua*

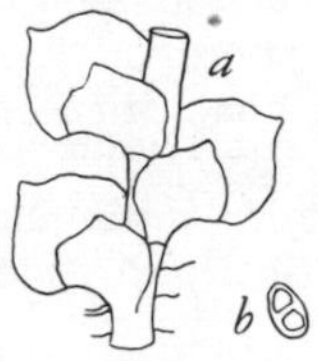

Figure 358

Fig. 358. *Scapania irrigua.* a, shoot; b, gemma. In marshes and bogs, among grasses, northern North America and Europe. *S. curta* has leaves longer than wide, with minute trigones, and rhizoids all along under side of stem.

69b Lower lobe with wavy margins, decidedly decurrent. Fig. 359.... .... *Scapania undulata*

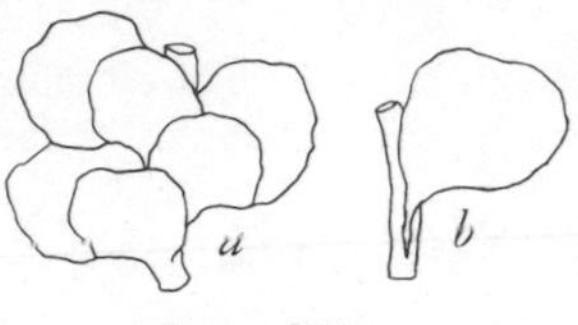

Figure 359

Fig. 359. *Scapania undulata.* a, shoot; b, leaf and lower side of stem. Submerged, on rocks, in brooks or springs, or on marshy ground or wet wood; all over North America. Europe. Twenty-four species of *Scapania* are recorded for North America.

70a (b, c) Underlobe of leaf tongue-shaped, attached only at one end; underleaf tongue-shaped, conspicuous. Large plants, 3-8 cm. long. Figs. 360-362. Family PORELLACEAE. Genus *Porella*..........71

70b Underlobe forming a sac or pouch, very narrowly attached to upper lobe (or rarely flat); underleaves present, notched at apex. Several archegonia in each perianth. Perianth obcordate, ridged lengthways, with a little tubular snout, Figs. 363-367. Family FRULLANIACEAE 73

70c Underlobe flat, its longest side attached to upper lobe. Figs. 368-372 85

71a Trigones large (in old leaves), bulging into the cells; plant glossy. Fig. 360.. *Porella navicularis*

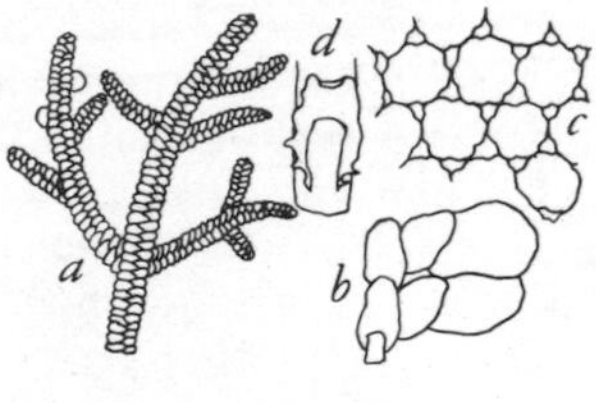

Figure 360

Fig. 360. *Porella navicularis.* a, shoot, from above; b, underleaves and underlobes; c, cells of leaf; d, underleaf of *P. cordaeana*. Common on our northwest coast, on trees and logs. *P. roellii* and *P. cordaena* also occur in our northwest, with very small trigones. *P. cordaeana* has very narrow underlobes.

71b Trigones small; surface of plant dull green, not glossy. Figs. 361, 362 72

72a Leaves closely overlapping; large plants on rocks, logs or trees. Fig. 361............................ *Porella platyphylloidea*

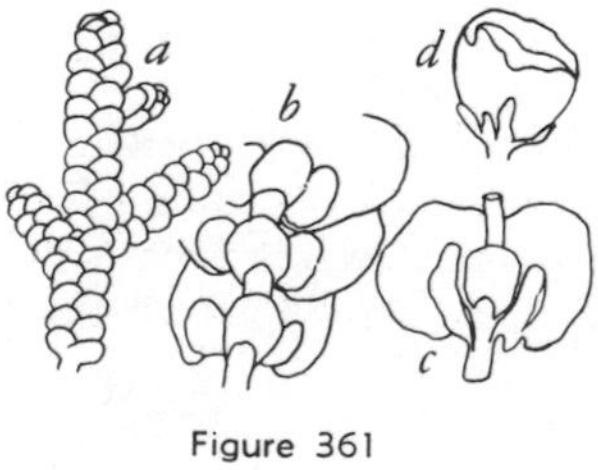

Figure 361

Fig. 361. *Porella platyphylloidea.* a, shoot; b, underlobes and underleaves; c, same of *P. platyphylla;* d, perianth. Stems to 8 cm. long, leaves to 1.5 mm.; often covering square feet of surface. The two named species are doubtfully distinguishable; both are widespread in North America and Europe. Dioicous.

72b Leaves scarcely touching; underlobe very small, tongue-shaped. Fig. 362 .... ***Porella pinnata***

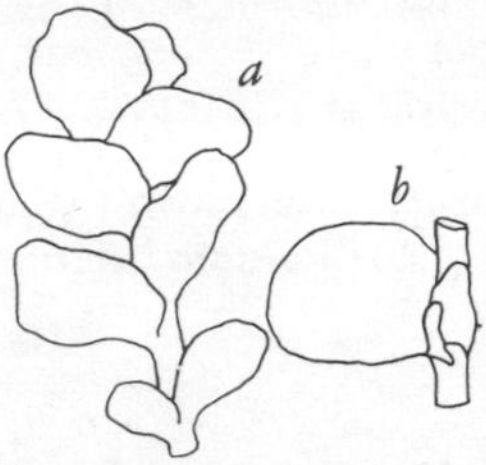

Figure 362

Fig. 362. *Porella pinnata.* a, shoot; b, underleaf and underlobe. In shallow streams, attached to rocks, constantly or frequently submerged. Widespread in eastern United States and Europe. In Texas it grows on trees and has sporophytes.

73a Plants dark green; dorsal lobe pointed; cell walls thin. Leaf subtending a branch partly attached to the branch. Fig. 363 .... ***Jubula pennsylvanica***

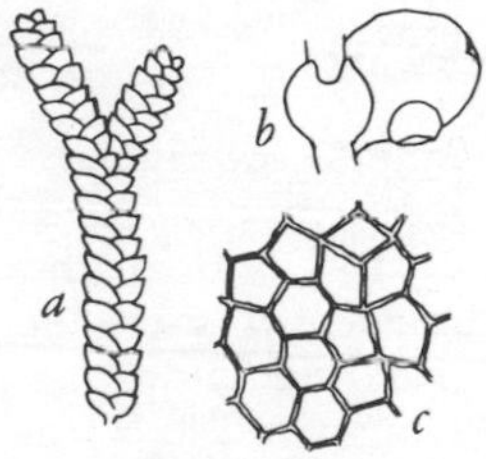

Figure 363

Fig. 363. *Jubula pennsylvanica.* a, shoot; b, underleaf and underlobe; c, cells of leaf. Nova Scotia to Georgia and Tennessee, on wet shaded rocks, frequent. The only species in North America.

73b Plants black to red-brown or green; dorsal lobe usually not pointed; cell walls usually thick, with conspicuous trigones and often with bead-like thickenings along the walls (intermediate thickenings). Leaf subtending a branch attached only to stem. Figs. 364-367. Genus *Frullania* **74**

74a With erect leafless shoots ("flagella"). Fig. 364 .... ***Frullania bolanderi***

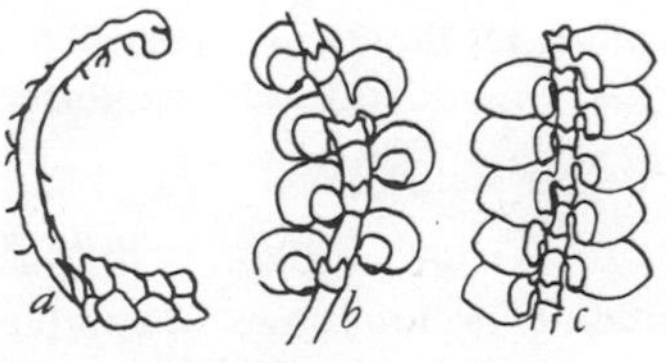

Figure 364

Fig. 364. *Frullania bolanderi.* a, plant with "flagellum"; b, under side of shoot. Maine to Iowa; California to British Columbia. Asia. c, under side of shoot of *F. kunzei;* South Carolina to Florida and Louisiana.

74b Without flagella 75

75a Apex of leaf acute. Paracysts sometimes present. Fig. 365 .... *Frullania nisquallensis*

75b Apex of leaf rounded 76

76a Underlobes flat, not sac-like. On rocks. Perianth unknown. Fig. 366 .... *Frullania riparia*

76b Underlobes usually sac-like 77

77a With paracysts: large red cells in the leaf 78

77b Without paracysts 81

78a Paracysts in a row, resembling a midrib. Dioicous 79

78b Paracysts scattered 80

79a Underleaves cordate or auriculate at base. Fig. 365 .... *Frullania asagrayana*

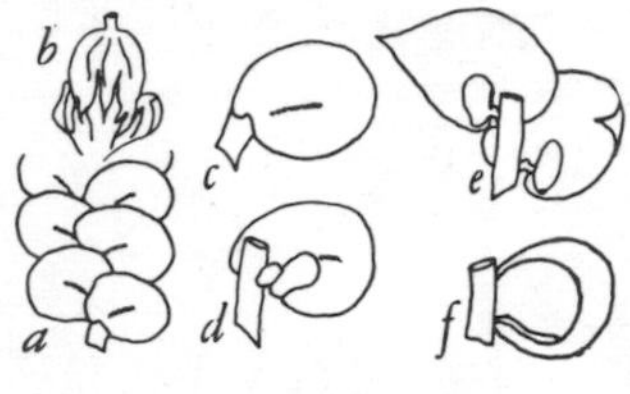

Figure 365

Fig. 365. *Frullania asagrayana*. a, shoot seen from above; b, perianth seen from beneath; c, leaf seen from above; d, leaf and underlobe; e, same of *F. nisquallensis;* f, leaf and underlobe of *F. oakesiana:* Newfoundland to Vermont and Minnesota. The first makes red-brown mats up to a foot across on bark, Newfoundland to Georgia, Oklahoma and Wisconsin. The second grows on rocks and trees, Alaska to northern California. *F. franciscana* of California, and *F. californica*, California to British Columbia, have a few enlarged cells in some of the leaves. Underleaves of the former have a tooth on each side, of the latter are entire.

79b Underleaves wedge-shaped or rounded to the base. Fig. 365 .... *Frullania franciscana*

80a Underleaves cordate or auriculate at base. Dioicous. Fig. 365 .... *Frullania californica*

80b Underleaves wedge-shaped or rounded to the base. Monoicous. Fig. 364 .... *Frullania kunzei*

81a (b, c) Leaf cells with trigones and intermediate thickenings. Dioicous 83

81b Leaf cells without trigones or intermediate thickenings. Monoicous; antheridial branch short, just below the perianth. Fig. 366. .... *Frullania inflata*

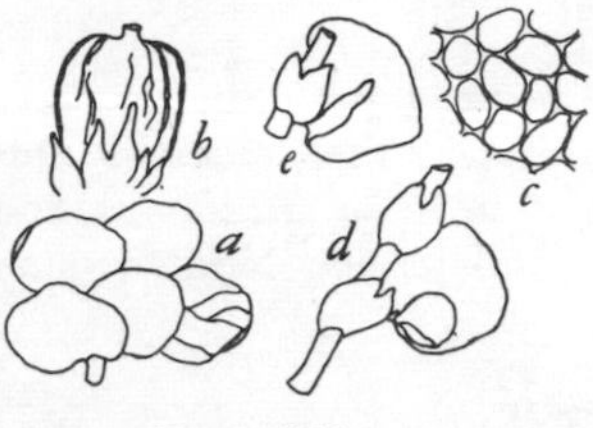

Figure 366

Fig. 366. *Frullania inflata.* a, shoot seen from above, with antheridial branch; b, perianth seen from beneath; c, cells of leaf; d, underlobe and underleaf; e, underlobe and underleaf of *F. riparia.* The first grows on trees, Connecticut to Florida, Arizona and Mexico. The second has about the same range, growing on rocks.

81c Leaf cells with trigones, without intermediate thickenings. Monoicous 82

82a Underlobe large, covering more than half of upper lobe. Fig. 365. .... *Frullania oakesiana*

82b Underlobe cylindrical, narrow, close to stem. Fig. 364......... .... *Frullania kunzei*

83a Upper lobe lying flat, wet or dry. Keels of perianth 4-8........ 84

83b Upper lobes spreading to squarrose when wet, curved down and clasping stem when dry. Keels of perianth 3, thin, high. Fig. 367. .... *Frullania squarrosa*

84a Underlobes wholly inflated. Intermediate thickenings numerous. Fig. 367................................ *Frullania eboracensis*

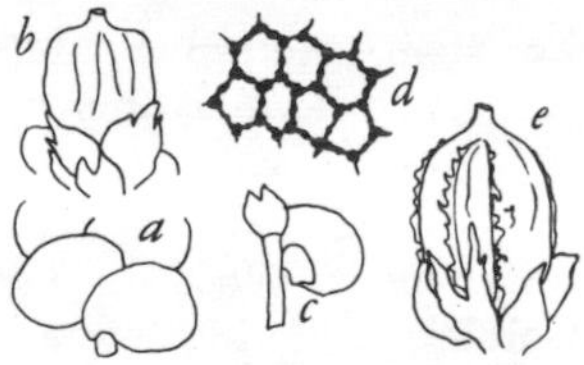

Figure 367

Fig. 367. *Frullania eboracensis.* a, shoot seen from above; b, perianth seen from below; c, leaf and underleaf seen from beneath; d, cells of leaf; e, perianth of *F. squarrosa.* The first is a small blackish plant with smooth perianth, and leaves closely overlapping, wet or dry. The second is much larger, red-brown, the leaves curved down when dry but spreading wide apart (squarrose) when wet; perianth tuberculate. Both are common in the eastern United States, on trees or old wood. Twenty-six species of Frullania are listed for North America.

84b Underlobes collapsed near their stalks. Intermediate thickenings few .... *Frullania brittoniae*

85a (b, c) Underleaves absent; rhizoids attached in tufts to underlobes; perianth flat. Figs. 368, 369. Family RADULACEAE. Genus *Radula*. *86*

85b Underleaves absent; leaves and ovoid, beaked perianth coarsely papillose. A minute plant, on bark or among other mosses. Our only papillose liverwort. Nova Scotia to Minnesota, Arkansas and the Gulf. Fig. 372.......... *Cololejeunea biddlecomiae*

85c Underleaves present, entire or notched; rhizoids in tufts attached to base of underleaf. Only one archegonium in each perianth. Perianths clavate, ridged lengthways near apex, with a little tubular snout. Figs. 370-372. Family LEJEUNEACEAE..........89

86a Dorsal lobe of leaf only 1.5 to 1.7 times the length of the ventral lobe, i.e. the ventral lobe large. Without gemmae. Fig. 369.......... *Radula bolanderi*

86b Dorsal lobe of leaf 1.4 to 2.5 times as long as the ventral lobe...87

87a Many leaves have the dorsal lobe broken off. Without gemmae. Fig. 368.......... *Radula obconica*

87b Dorsal lobes not broken off. Gemmae usually present..........88

88a Ventral lobe arching entirely across the stem, the tip broadly rounded. No perianths known. Fig. 368.......... *Radula andicola*

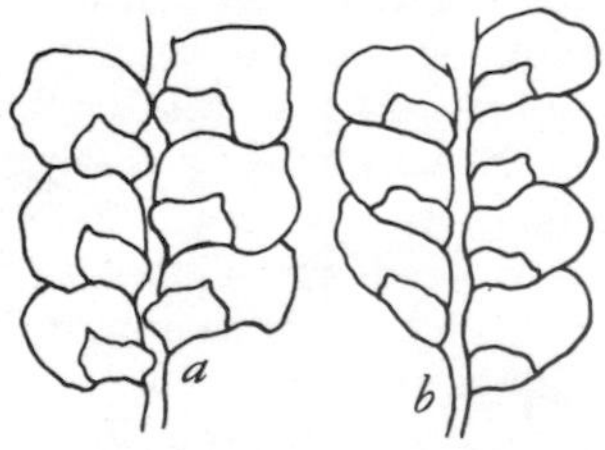

Figure 368

Fig. 368. *Radula andicola*. a, under side of shoot. On rocks, West Virginia to District of Columbia, Florida, Mexico, South America; b, under side of shoot of *R. obconica;* on rocks or trees, Maine to North Carolina, Louisiana and Minnesota. Twelve species of *Radula* are recognized in North America.

88b Ventral lobe arching about half way across stem, the tip acute to obtuse. Perianths common. Figs. 369.........*Radula complanata*

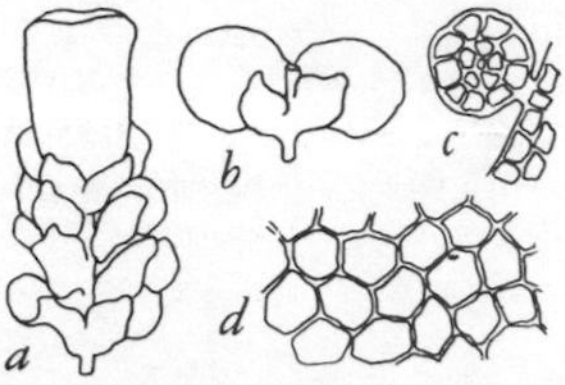

Figure 369

Fig. 369. *Radula complanata*. a, shoot with perianth; b, leaves from beneath; c, gemma; d, cells of leaf. On bark or stones throughout the United States and Europe. *R. bolanderi,* Washington and Oregon, has the margin of the leaf grown fast to the stem beneath.

89a Underleaves orbicular, entire, not lobed. On rocks and trees. Genus *Leucolejeunea* 90

89b Underleaves notched at apex to form 2 lobes................91

90a Margin of ventral lobe straight or slightly curved from tip to keel, the apical tooth 1-2 cells long. Fig. 370....*Leucolejeunea clypeata*

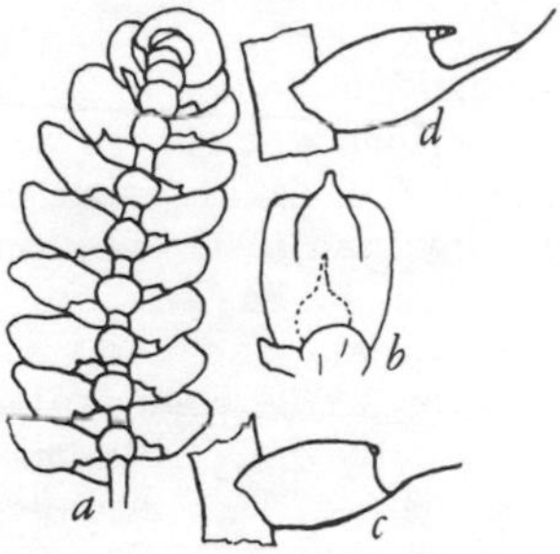

Figure 370

Fig. 370. *Leucolejeunea clypeata*. a, lower side of shoot; b, perianth; c, margin and tooth of underlobe. New Hampshire to Florida and Oklahoma; d, margin and tooth of *L. unciloba*. Rhode Island to Florida, Texas and South America.

90b Margin of ventral lobe deeply curved from tip to keel, the apical tooth 3-6 cells long, curved. Fig. 370.....*Leucolejeunea unciloba*

91a Leaves very small, less than .25 mm. long. Genus *Microlejeunea*. 92

91b Larger; leaves more than .25 mm. long. Genus *Lejeunea*......93

92a Underleaves .14 x .1 mm., cleft half way. Fig. 371............... ....*Microlejeunea laetevirens*

92b Underleaves 0.1 x 0.085 mm. or smaller, cleft more or less than half. Fig. 371................................*Microlejeunea ulicina*

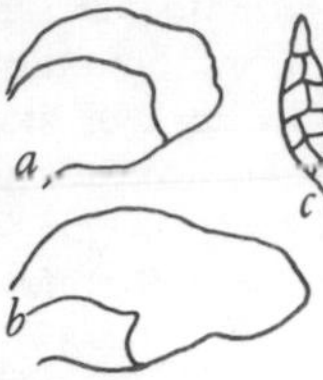

Figure 371

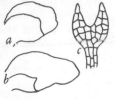

Fig. 371. *Microlejeunea ulicina.* a, under side of leaf; eastern United States and Europe; b, leaf and underlobe of *M. laetevirens,* same range; c, underleaf of *M. ulicina.*

93a Underleaves orbicular, widest at middle, about 0.15 mm. long. Spores .016-.028 mm., finely papillose. Fig. 372....*Lejeunea patens*

93b Underleaves ovate-orbicular, widest below the middle, about 0.2 mm. long. Spores 0.028-0.043 mm., coarsely papillose. Fig. 372...*Lejeunea cavifolia*

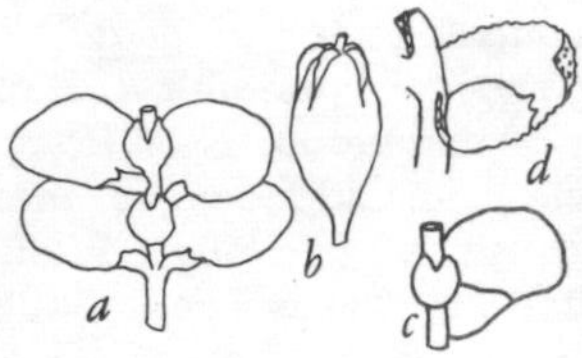

Figure 372

Fig. 372. *Lejeunea cavifolia.* a, under side of shoot; b, perianths; c, under side of shoot of *L. patens.* The first is found all over the United States and in Eurasia and Africa. The second is in eastern United States and Europe. d, leaf and underlobe of *Cololejeunea biddlecomiae;* eastern United States to Minnesota and Oklahoma; nine other species occur in North America. The old genus *Lejeunea,* with great numbers of species in the tropics, has been split into a number of genera of less unwieldly size. They are all minute plants, on rocks, bark or even on leaves of higher plants.

SYSTEMATIC LIST OF MOSSES AND LIVERWORTS

What's the use? — You may want a check list on which to check the species that you have identified. Another mark may show what is in your collection. And you may find space in which to write when and where you found the species. So little is known about the moss flora of any county in the United States that your record will be of real value. For only a half dozen States is there a published list of mosses that is anywhere near complete.

You may also want to know about the family relationships of the mosses. Here they are, family by family. We have followed in general the Check List for North America issued by the Sullivant Moss Society (now The American Bryological Society). In this list the Musci are treated "conservatively", that is, in as few families as possible. Probably most bryologists would now-a-days divide our Hypnaceae into a dozen families. The Hepaticae are divided into families and genera in a modern and up-to-date fashion — too many families and genera, and species too, some of us think. But here they are. And the sequence of families is considered "natural", that is, according to their blood relationship, so far as that can be done in a linear series.

No one has ever made a satisfactory key to Families of mosses. The only useful keys are to genera. You cannot get a view of the families from our keys. Hence this Systematic List. A key is at best a compromise; it becomes more and more useful as you use it more.

PHYLUM BRYOPHYTA (ATRACHEATA)

Green (photosynthetic) plants with a life-cycle consisting of an alternation of haploid (gametophyte) and diploid (sporophyte) phases. Eggs and sperms borne in gametangia with discrete multicellular walls (archegonia and antheridia). The gametophyte alone makes contact with the substratum, and bears the sporophyte at the point where the egg was borne and fertilized. Entirely without tracheids or tracheae.

CLASS 1. MUSCI MOSSES

Gametophyte with leaves and more or less of stem, the leaves 2-many ranked but never in two dorso-lateral rows. Leaves often with midrib and elongated cells. Archegonia acrogenous (the first one using up the apical cell of the shoot). Sporophyte usually firm and long-lived. Never having elaters.

Series 1. Sphagnobrya. Order 1. Sphagnales. FAMILY SPHAGNACEAE. Genus *Sphagnum*. Capsule globular, with columella not reaching the circular operculum, without peristome, opening explosively, raised above the leaves on a pseudopodium.

S. *affine* R. & C. Fig. 25
S. *capillaceum* (Weiss) Schrank Fig. 26
S. *cuspidatum* Ehrh. No. 5a
S. *girgensohnii* Russow Fig. 26
S. *magellanicum* Brid. Fig. 25
S. *palustre* L Fig. 25
S. *warnstorfii* Russow Fig. 26

Series 2. Andreaeobrya. Order 1. Andreaeales. FAMILY ANDREAEACEAE. Genus *Andreaea*. Capsule cylindrical, the columella incomplete, without operculum or peristome, opening by four longitudinal slits, raised above the leaves on a pseudopodium.

A. *rothii* W. & M. Fig. 27
A. *rupestris* Hedw. Fig. 27

Series 3. Eubrya. Capsule spherical or cylindrical or variously ribbed, with complete columella (except in *Archidium* and some minute mosses), without a pseudopodium. Mostly with operculum and peristome.

Division 1. Nematodonteae. Peristome teeth in one circle, each tooth composed of many cells lying lengthways of the tooth.

FAMILY TETRAPHIDACEAE.

Genus *Tetraphis*. Teeth four.
T. *geniculata* Girgens. Fig. 51
T. *pellucida* Hedw. Fig. 51.

FAMILY POLYTRICHACEAE. Teeth 32 to 64, their tips attached to a transverse membrane.

Genus *Atrichum*
A. *angustatum* (Brid.) Bry. Eur. Fig. 43
A. *crispum* (James) Sull. Fig. 44; no. 192a
A. *macmillani* (Holz.) Frye Fig. 43
A. *undulatum* (Hedw.) Beauv. Fig. 44
A. *undulatum* var. *altecristatum* R. & C. Fig. 44
A. *undulatum* var. *selwynii* (Aust.) Frye Fig. 44

Genus *Oligotrichum*
O. *aligerum* Nutt. Fig. 42
O. *parallelum* (Mitt.) Kindb. Fig. 42

Genus *Pogonatum*
P. alpinum (Hedw.) Roehl Fig. 46
P. brachyphyllum (Rich.) Beauv. Fig. 45
P. capillare (Rich.) Brid. Fig. 46
P. contortum (Schw.) Sull. No. 42a
P. pensilvanicum (Hedw.) Paris Fig. 45
P. urnigerum (Hedw.) Beauv. Fig. 46

Genus *Polytrichadelphus*
P. lyallii Mitt. Fig. 47

Genus *Polytrichum*
P. commune Hedw. Fig. 50
P. formosum Hedw. Fig. 49
P. gracile Smith Fig. 49
P. juniperinum Hedw. Fig. 48
P. norvegicum Hedw. Fig. 47
P. ohioense R. & C. Fig. 50
P. piliferum Hedw. Fig. 48

Division 2. Arthrodonteae. Peristome teeth in one circle, with or without an inner circle of membrane, teeth or filaments. The teeth are made of cell walls and show transverse markings. Or peristome lacking.

Subdivision 1. Haplolepideae. With only one circle of teeth. Each tooth consists of the fused walls of two adjacent circles of cells: the outer cell-wall extends the entire width of the tooth; the inner side of the tooth is derived from two cells and therefore shows a longitudinal zigzag line marking the boundaries of these cells (Fig. 373). Or peristome lacking, but with characters of leaf and/or capsule and/or spores which prove relationship to some family with peristome.

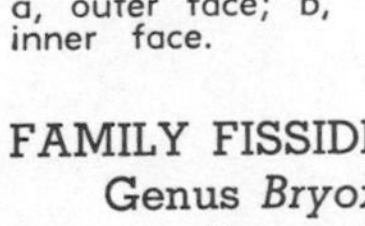

Fig. 373. Tooth of Haplolepideae. a, outer face; b, inner face.

FAMILY FISSIDENTACEAE
Genus *Bryoxiphium*
B. norvegicum (Brid.) Mitt. Fig. 33

Genus *Fissidens*
F. adiantoides Hedw. Fig. 38
F. bryoides Hedw. Fig. 37

F. bushii Card. & Ther. Fig. 39
F. cristatus Wils. Fig. 38, 39
F. debilis Schw. Fig. 35
F. donnellii Aust. Fig. 36
F. garberi Lesq. & James Fig. 36
F. grandifrons Brid. Fig. 35
F. julianus (Mont.) Schimp. Fig. 35
F. limbatus Sull. Fig. 37
F. minutulus Sull. Fig. 37
F. obtusifolius Wils. Fig. 36
F. osmundioides Hedw. Fig. 39
F. polypodioides Hedw. No. 26c
F. ravenelii Sull. Fig. 36
F. rufulus Bry. Eur. Fig. 34
F. subbasilaris Hedw. Fig. 38
F. taxifolius Hedw. Fig. 39
F. viridulus (W. & M.) Wahlenb. No. 25b

FAMILY ARCHIDIACEAE

Genus *Archidium*
A. ohioense Schimp. Fig. 99

FAMILY DITRICHACEAE

Genus *Bruchia*
B. brevifolia Sull. Fig. 103, 104
B. flexuosa (Sw.) C. Muell. Fig. 104
B. ravenelii Wils. Fig. 103, 104
B.. sullivanti Aust. Fig. 103, 104
B. texana Aust. Fig. 104

Genus *Ceratodon*
C. purpureus (Hedw.) Brid. Fig. 91, 127; No. 158a, 183b

Genus *Distichium*
D. capillaceum (Hedw.) Bry. Eur. Fig. 32
D. inclinatum (Hedw.) Bry. Eur. Fig. 32

Genus *Ditrichum*
D. cylindricum (Hedw.) Grout Fig. 128
D. flexicaule (Schw.) Hampe Fig. 130
D. flexicaule var. *brevifolium* (Kindb.) Grout. Fig. 130
D. lineare (Sw.) Lindb. Fig. 108
D. pallidum (Hedw.) Hampe Fig. 129
D. pusillum (Hedw.) E.G.B. Fig. 108

Genus *Pleuridium*
P. acuminatum Lindb. Fig. 102
P. subulatum (Hedw.) Lindb. Fig. 102

Genus *Trematodon*
- *T. ambiguus* (Hedw.) Hornsch. Fig. 125
- *T. longicollis* Mx. Fig. 125

FAMILY SELIGERIACEAE

Genus *Blindia*
- *B. acuta* (Hedw.) Bry. Eur. Fig. 113

Genus *Seligeria*
- *S. calcarea* (Hedw.) Bry. Eur. Fig. 107
- *S. campylopoda* Kindb. Fig. 107
- *S. doniana* (Smith) C.M. Fig. 107
- *S. pusilla* (Hedw.) Bry. Eur. Fig. 107

FAMILY DICRANACEAE

Genus *Arctoa*
- *A. starkei* (W. & M.) Grout Fig. 114

Genus *Brothera*
- *B. leana* (Sull.) C. Muell. Fig. 122

Genus *Campylopus*
- *C. flexuosus* Brid. Fig. 121

Genus *Dichodontium*
- *D. pellucidum* (Hedw.) Schimp. Fig. 57

Genus *Dicranella*
- *D. herminieri* Besch. Fig. 109
- *D. heteromalla* (Hedw.) Schimp. Fig. 131
- *D. hilariana* (Mont.) Mitt. Fig. 109
- *D. rufescens* (Smith) Schimp. Fig. 110
- *D. schreberi* (Hedw.) Schimp. Fig. 132
- *D. squarrosa* (Schrad.) Schimp. See Fig. 132. No. 185a
- *D. varia* (Hedw.) Schimp. Fig. 110

Genus *Dicranodontium*
- *D. denudatum* (Brid.) E.G.B. Fig. 121

Genus *Dicranoweisia*
- *D. cirrata* (Hedw.) Lindb. Fig. 112
- *D. crispula* (Hedw.) Lindb. Fig. 112

Genus *Dicranum*
- *D. bergeri* Bland. Fig. 60
- *D. bonjeani* DeNot. Fig. 117
- *D. bonjeani* var. *alatum* Barnes Fig. 117
- *D. condensatum* Hedw. Fig. 59, 120
- *D. drummondii* C. Muell. Fig. 60

D. flagellare Hedw. Fig. 119
D. fulvum Hook. Fig. 58, 118
D. fulvum var. *viride* (S. & L.) Grout Fig. 58
D. fuscescens Turn. Fig. 59, 120
D. majus Smith Fig. 116
D. montanum Hedw. Fig. 61
D. muhlenbeckii Bry. Eur. Fig. 60
D. rhabdocarpum Sull. Fig. 118
D. rugosum (Hoffm.) Brid. Fig. 116
D. scoparium Hedw. Fig. 117
D. spurium Hedw. Fig. 58
D. strictum Schleich. Fig. 114

Genus *Oncophorus*
O. polycarpus (Hedw.) Brid. Fig. 115
O. virens (Hedw.) Brid. Fig. 115
O. wahlenbergii Brid. Fig. 115

Genus *Oreoweisia*
O. serrulata (Funck) DeNot. Fig. 57

Genus *Paraleucobryum*
P. longifolium (Hedw.) Loeske Fig. 122

Genus *Rhabdoweisia*
R. denticulata (Brid.) Bry. Eur. Fig. 126
R. denticulata var. *americana* Culman Fig. 126

FAMILY LEUCOBRYACEAE

Genus *Leucobryum*
L. albidum (Brid.) Lindb. Fig. 29
L. glaucum (Hedw.) Schimp. Fig. 29

Genus *Octoblepharum*
O. albidum Hedw. Fig. 28

FAMILY ENCALYPTACEAE

Genus *Encalypta*
E. ciliata Hedw. Fig. 77
E. procera Bruch No. 90a
E. rhabdocarpa Schw. Fig. 76
E. streptocarpa Hedw. Fig. 76
E. vulgaris Hedw. Fig. 77

FAMILY POTTIACEAE

Sub-family Trichostomoideae: Leaves mostly narrow, with upper cells small and obscure and basal ones narrow. Midrib with stereids both above and below the guide cells.

Genus *Astomum*
A. muhlenbergianum (Sw.) Grout Fig. 75

Genus *Barbula*
B. convoluta Hedw. Fig. 92
B. cruegeri Sond. Fig. 79, 92
B. cylindrica (Tayl.) Schimp. Fig. 93
B. fallax Hedw. Fig. 93
B. unguiculata Hedw. Fig. 79, 92
B. vinealis Brid. Fig. 93

Genus *Didymodon*
D. recurvirostris (Hedw.) Jenn. Fig. 91
D. tophaceus (Brid.) Jur. Fig. 90
D. trifarius (Hedw.) Brid. Fig. 91; No. 183a

Genus *Eucladium*
E. verticillatum (Brid.) Bry. Eur. Fig. 95

Genus *Gymnostomum*
G. aeruginosum Smith Fig. 97
G. calcareum N. & H. Fig. 97
G. recurvirostrum Hedw. Fig. 97

Genus *Hyophila*
H. tortula (Schw.) Hampe Fig. 54

Genus *Pleurochaete*
P. squarrosa (Brid.) Lindb. No. 118a

Genus *Timmiella*
T. anomala (Bry. Eur.) Limpr. Fig. 54

Genus *Tortella*
T. fragilis (H. & W.) Limpr. Fig. 94
T. humilis (Hedw.) Jenn. Fig. 94
T. tortuosa (Turn.) Limpr. Fig. 94

Genus *Trichostomum*
T. cylindricum (Bruch) C. Muell. Fig. 96

Genus *Weisia*
W. viridula Hedw. Fig. 84

Sub-family Pottioideae: Leaves usually broad and blunt, with upper cells comparatively large and lower cells broad and colorless. Midrib with stereids only below the guide cells (dorsal).

Genus *Acaulon*
A. rufescens Jaeg. Fig. 75; No. 30a

Genus *Aloina*
A. rigida var. *pilifera* (Bry. Eur.) Limpr. Fig. 41

Genus *Crossidium*
- *C. squamigerum* (Viv.) Jur. Fig. 41

Genus *Desmatodon*
- *D. coloradensis* Grout Fig. 82
- *D. latifolius* (Hedw.) Brid. Fig. 81
- *D. obtusifolius* (Schw.) Jur. Fig. 82
- *D. plinthobius* Sull. & Lesq. Fig. 81
- *D. porteri* James Fig. 82

Genus *Merceya*
- *M. latifolia* Kindb. Fig. 78
- *M. ligulata* (Spruce) Schimp. Fig. 78

Genus *Phascum*
- *P. cuspidatum* var. *americanum* R. & C. Fig. 75

Genus *Pottia*
- *P. heimii* (Hedw.) Fuern. Fig. 80; 187a
- *P. truncata* (Hedw.) Fuern. Fig. 142

Genus *Pterigoneurum*
- *P. subsessile* (Brid.) Jur. Fig. 41

Genus *Tortula*
- *T. bistratosa Flowers* No. 97a
- *T. bolanderi* (Lesq.) Broth. Fig. 83
- *T. fragilis* Tayl. Fig. 79
- *T. mucronifolia* Schw. Fig. 146
- *T. muralis* Hedw. Fig. 83
- *T. obtusissima* (C. Muell.) Mitt. No. 100b
- *T. pagorum* (Milde) DeNot. Fig. 79
- *T. princeps* DeNot. Fig. 83
- *T. ruralis* (Hedw.) Smith Fig. 83
- *T. subulata* Hedw. Fig. 80

FAMILY CALYMPERACEAE

Genus *Syrrhopodon*
- *S. floridanus* Sull. Fig. 56
- *S. texanus* Sull. Fig. 56

FAMILY GRIMMIACEAE

Genus *Braunia*
- *B. californica* Sull. Fig. 64
- *B. secunda* (Hook.) Bry. Eur. Fig. 64

Genus *Grimmia*
- *G. affinis* Hornsch. Fig. 140
- *G. alpestris* Nees Fig. 137

G. alpicola Hedw. Fig. 136
G. anodon Bry. Eur. Fig. 139
G. apocarpa Hedw. Fig. 136
G. calyptrata Hook. Fig. 140
G. commutata Hueben. Fig. 137
G. laevigata (Brid.) Brid. Fig. 138
G. maritima Turn. No. 169a
G. montana Bry. Eur. Fig. 137
G. ovalis Lindb. Fig. 137, 140
G. pilifera Beauv. Fig. 139
G. plagiopodia Hedw. Fig. 139
G. raui Aust. Fig. 138
G. torquata Hornsch. No. 171a
G. trichophylla Grev. Fig. 140
G. wrightii Aust. Fig. 138

Genus *Hedwigia*
H. ciliata Hedw. Fig. 63
H. ciliata forma *viridis* (Bry. Eur.) Jones Fig. 63

Genus *Pseudobraunia* Fig. 64

Genus *Ptychomitrium*
P. drummondii Sull. No. 168b
P. gardneri Lesq. No. 168b
P. incurvum (Muhl.) Sull. Fig. 13. No. 168b
P. leibergii Best No. 168a

Genus *Rhacomitrium*
R. aciculare Brid. Fig. 133
R. canescens Brid. Fig. 62
R. fasciculare (Hedw.) Brid. Fig. 134
R. heterostichum (Hedw.) Brid. Fig. 133
R. lanuginosum (Hedw.) Brid. Fig. 133
R. varium (Mitt.) Lesq. & James Fig. 134

Genus *Scouleria*
S. aquatica Hook. Fig. 135
S. marginata E.G.B. Fig. 135

FAMILY EPHEMERACEAE

Genus *Ephemerum*
E. cohaerens (Hedw.) Hampe Fig. 40
E. crassinervium (Schw.) C.M. Fig. 40, 101
E. serratum (Hedw.) Hampe No. 31a
E. sessile (Bry. Eur.) Rabenh. Fig. 40
E. spinulosum Schimp. Fig. 40

Genus *Nanomitrium*
N. austinii (Sull.) Lindb. Fig. 101

FAMILY DISCELIACEAE

Genus *Discelium*

D. nudum (Dicks.) Brid. Fig. 160

Sub-division 2. Heterolepideae. Two distinct but wholly unrelated families of uncertain relationship.

FAMILY SPLACHNACEAE: Teeth composed of 2 or 3 layers of cells, and showing transverse lines, or peristome lacking.

Genus *Splachnum*

S. ampullaceum Hedw. Fig. 52

S. luteum Hedw. Fig. 52

Genus *Tayloria*

T. serrata (Hedw.) Bry. Eur. Fig. 53

Genus *Tetraplodon*

T. mnioides (Hedw.) Bry. Eur. Fig. 53

T. pennsylvanicus (Brid.) Sayre Fig. 53

FAMILY BUXBAUMIACEAE: Inner peristome is a conical, pleated membrane, open at the top; outer peristome is a circle of stiff threads, or lacking. Capsule unsymmetric.

Genus *Buxbaumia*. With seta and double peristome.

B. aphylla Hedw. Fig. 30

Genus *Diphyscium*

D. foliosum (Hedw.) Mohr Fig. 30; No. 50b

Sub-division 3. Diplolepideae. Peristome in 2 circles, as noted under Arthrodonteae. The structure of the teeth is exactly the reverse of that of the Haplolepideae, so that they have a zigzag line on the outer face and transverse lines across the inner (Fig. 374). The outer peristome may be imperfect or lacking, or the inner may be imperfect or lacking, but the other characters of the plant will prove its relationship to some family with complete peristome.

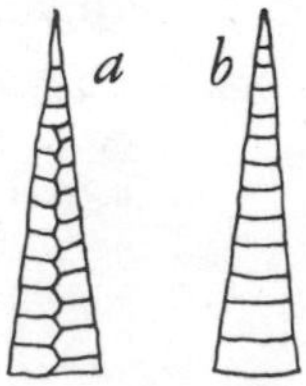

Fig. 374. Tooth of Diplolepideae. a, outer face; b, inner face.

1. **Acrocarpi.** Sporophytes borne at the apex of a stem or branch, subtended by leaves that are similar in texture to those below. Plants with upright stems, or more or less spreading.

FAMILY FUNARIACEAE

Genus *Aphanorhegma*
A. patens (Hedw.) Lindb. Fig. 106
A. serratum (H. & W.) Sull. Fig. 105, 106

Genus *Entosthodon*
E. drummondii Sull. Fig. 161

Genus *Funaria*
F. americana Lindb. Fig. 164
F. calvescens Schw. Fig. 163
F. flavicans Mx. Fig. 163
F. hygrometrica Hedw. Fig. 163
F. hygrometrica var. *convoluta* Hampe See Fig. 163
F. serrata Brid. Fig. 164

Genus *Physcomitrium*
P. hookeri Hampe Fig. 162
P. immersum Sull. Fig. 105
P. pyriforme Brid. Fig. 162
P. turbinatum (Mx.) Brid. Fig. 162

Genus *Pyramidula*
P. tetragona (Brid.) Fig. 100

FAMILY SCHISTOSTEGACEAE

Genus *Schistostega*
S. pennata (Hedw.) Hook. & Tayl. Fig. 31

FAMILY ORTHOTRICHACEAE

Genus *Amphidium*
A. californicum (Hampe) Broth. Fig. 74
A. lapponicum (Hedw.) Schimp. Fig. 74
A. mougeotii (Bry. Eur.) Schimp. Fig. 74

Genus *Drummondia*
D. prorepens (Hedw.) Jenn. Fig. 98

Genus *Macromitrium*
M. mucronifolium Hook. & Grev. Fig. 56

Genus *Orthotrichum*
O. affine Brid. No. 78b
O. anomalum Hedw. Fig. 71

O. *consimile* Mitt. Fig. 72
O. *cupulatum* (Hoffm.) Brid. Fig. 71
O. *elegans* Hook. & Grev. Fig. 69
O. *hallii* Sull. & Lesq. Fig. 72
O. *laevigatum* Zett. Fig. 69
O. *lyellii* H. & T. Fig. 68
O. *macounii* Aust. Fig. 69
O. *obtusifolium* Brid. Fig. 67
O. *ohioense* S. & L. Fig. 73
O. *pulchellum* Brunton Fig. 72
O. *pumilum* Dicks. Fig. 73
O. *pusillum* Mitt. Fig. 73
O. *rupestre* Schleich. Fig. 70
O. *sordidum* Sull. No. 78b
O. *speciosum* Nees Fig. 68, 69
O. *strangulatum* Schw. Fig. 71
O. *texanum* Sull. Fig. 70
O. *texanum* var. *globosum* Lesq. Fig. 70

Genus *Schlotheimia*
S. *sullivantii* C. Muell. Fig. 98

Genus *Ulota*
U. *americana* (Beauv.) Limpr. Fig. 65
U. *crispa* (Hedw.) Brid. Fig. 65
U. *ludwigii* Brid. Fig. 65
U. *obtusiuscula* C. M. & Kindb. Fig. 66
U. *phyllantha* Brid. Fig. 66

Genus *Zygodon*
See Fig. 74

FAMILY TIMMIACEAE

Genus *Timmia*
T. *austriaca* Hedw. Fig. 55
T. *megapolitana* Hedw. Fig. 55

FAMILY AULACOMNIACEAE

Genus *Aulacomnium*
A. *androgynum* Schw. Fig. 85
A. *heterostichum* (Hedw.) Bry. Eur. Fig. 143
A. *palustre* (W. & M.) Schw. Fig. 85

FAMILY BARTRAMIACEAE

Genus *Anacolia*
A. *menziesii* (Turn.) Paris Fig. 88

Genus *Bartramia*
B. *ithyphylla* Brid. Fig. 89

B. pomiformis Hedw. Fig. 89, 143
B. stricta Brid. Fig. 89

Genus *Catoscopium*
C. nigritum Brid. Fig. 141

Genus *Philonotis*
P. americana Dism. Fig. 87
P. fontana (Hedw.) Brid. Fig. 87
P. longiseta (Rich.) E. G. B. Fig. 86
P. sphaericarpa Brid. Fig. 86

Genus *Plagiopus*
P. oederi (Brid.) Limpr. Fig. 111

FAMILY MEESIACEAE

Genus *Amblyodon*
A. dealbatus (Hedw.) P. B. No. 214a

Genus *Meesia*
M. triquetra (Hook. & Tayl.) Aongstr. Fig. 159
M. uliginosa Hedw. Fig. 159

FAMILY BRYACEAE

Genus *Bryum*
B. argenteum Hedw. Fig. 149
B. bicolor Dicks. Fig. 149
B. bimum Schreb. Fig. 152
B. caespiticium Hedw. Fig. 151
B. capillare Hedw. Fig. 151
B. cernuum (Sw.) Lindb. Fig. 148
B. crassirameum R. & C. Fig. 152
B. *cuspidatum* (Bry. Eur.) Schimp. See Fig. 151
B. miniatum Lesq. Fig. 150
B. pallens (Brid.) Roehl Fig. 148
B. pendulum (Hornsch.) Schimp. Fig. 148
B. pseudotriquetrum (Hedw.) Schw. Fig. 152 (=B. bimum Schreb.)
B. sandbergii Holz. Fig. 150
B. turbinatum (Hedw.) Sm. No. 201a
B. uliginosum (Brid.) Bry. Eur. Fig. 148
B. weigelii Spreng Fig. 150

Genus *Leptobryum*
L. pyriforme (Hedw.) Schimp. Fig. 123

Genus *Pohlia*
P. annotina (Hedw.) Loeske Fig. 145
P. annotina var. *decipiens* Loeske Fig. 145

P. carnea Lindb. Fig. 144
P. cruda (Hedw.) Lindb. No. 188a
P. delicatula (Hedw.) Andr. Fig. 144
P. elongata Hedw. Fig. 145
P. nutans (Hedw.) Lindb. Fig. 145
P. proligera Lindb. Fig. 145
P. rothii (Correns) Broth. Fig. 145
P. wahlenbergii (W. & M.) Andr. Fig. 144

Genus *Rhodobryum*
R. roseum (Hedw.) Limpr. Fig. 147

FAMILY MNIACEAE

Genus *Cinclidium*
C. stygium Sw. Fig. 153

Genus *Mnium*
M. affine Bland. Fig. 154
M. cuspidatum Hedw. Fig. 150, 154
M. drummondii Br. & Sch. No. 206a
M. glabrescens Kindb. Fig. 153
M. hornum Hedw. Fig. 155
M. insigne Mitt. No. 207a
M. marginatum P. B. Fig. 156
M. medium Bry. Eur. Fig. 154
M. menziesii (Hook.) C. M. Fig. 158
M. orthorhynchum Brid. Fig. 156
M. punctatum Hedw. Fig. 153
M. punctatum var. *elatum* Schimp. Fig. 153
M. serratum Brid. Fig. 156
M. spinulosum Bry. Eur. Fig. 156
M. stellare Hedw. Fig. 157
M. venustum Mitt. Fig. 154

FAMILY RHIZOGONIACEAE

Genus *Rhizogonium*
R. spiniforme (Hedw.) Bruch Fig. 124

2. Pleurocarpi: Sporophyte borne on a special short branch subtended by greatly modified leaves (perichaetium). Plants always much branched, with stems usually prostrate and creeping.

FAMILY HYPNACEAE

Genus *Amblystegiella*
A. confervoides (Brid.) Loeske Fig. 260
A. subtilis (Hedw.) Loeske Fig. 260

Genus *Amblystegium*
A. americanum Grout See Fig. 222
A. compactum (C. M.) Aust. Fig. 222
A. juratzkanum Schimp. See Fig. 217, 220
A. serpens (Hedw.) Bry. Eur. Fig. 220
A. varium (Hedw.) Lindb. Fig. 217, 219, 221

Genus *Bestia*
B. breweriana (Lesq.) Grout Fig. 211

Genus *Brachythecium*
B. acutum (Mitt.) Sull. See Fig. 244
B. albicans (Hedw.) Bry. Eur. Fig. 244
B. campestre Bry. Eur. See Fig. 243
B. collinum (Schleich.) Bry. Eur. Fig. 250 No. 60a
B. collinum var. *idahense* (R. & C.) Grout Fig. 250
B. flagellare (Hedw.) Jenn. Fig. 246
B. flexicaule R. & C. See Fig. 244
B. lamprochryseum C. M. & Kindb. Fig. 240
B. leibergii Grout Fig. 242
B. nelsoni Grout Fig. 248
B. oxycladon (Brid.) J. & S. Fig. 241, 243
B. oxycladon var. *dentatum* (L. & J.) Grout Fig. 241
B. plumosum (Sw.) Bry. Eur. Fig. 246
B. populeum (Hedw.) Bry. Eur. Fig. 246
B. reflexum (Starke) Bry. Eur. Fig. 245 No. 60a
B. rivulare Bry. Eur. Fig. 240, 248 No. 73a
B. rutabulum (Hedw.) Bry. Eur. Fig. 247, 248 No. 42b
B. salebrosum (W. & M.) Bry. Eur. Fig. 241, 243, 244
B. starkei (Brid.) Bry. Eur. See Fig. 245
B. velutinum (Hedw.) Bry. Eur. Fig. 249

Genus *Brotherella*
B. recurvans (Mx.) Fleisch. Fig. 264
B. roellii (R. & C.) Fleisch. See Fig. 264

Genus *Bryhnia*
B. graminicolor (Brid.) Grout Fig. 166
B. novae-angliae (S. & L.) Grout Fig. 166

Genus *Calliergon*
C. cordifolium (Hedw.) Kindb. Fig. 205; No. 72a

Genus *Calliergonella*
C. cuspidata (Brid.) Loeske Fig. 268
C. schreberi (Brid.) Grout Fig. 269

Genus *Camptothecium*
C. aeneum (Mitt.) J. & S. No. 60b
C. lutescens (Hedw.) Bry. Eur. Fig. 230
C. nitens (Hedw.) Schimp. Fig. 229
C. pinnatifidum (S. & L.) J. & S. See Fig. 230

Genus *Campylium* cf. Fig. 265
- *C. chrysophyllum* (Brid.) Bryhn Fig. 216
- *C. hispidulum* (Brid.) Mitt. Fig. 256
- *C. polygamum* (Bry. Eur.) Bryhn Fig. 227, 266
- *C. stellatum* (Hedw.) L. & Jens. Fig. 227, 266

Genus *Chamberlainia*
- *C. acuminata* (Hedw.) Grout Fig. 236
- *C. cyrtophylla* (Kindb.) Grout Fig. 236

Genus *Cirriphyllum*
- *C. boscii* (Schw.) Grout Fig. 209
- *C. cirrosum* (Schw.) Grout Fig. 209
- *C. piliferum* (Hedw.) Grout Fig. 209

Genus *Climacium* No. 42b, 50a
- *C. americanum* Brid. Fig. 195
- *C. dendroides* (Hedw.) W. & M. Fig. 195
- *C. kindbergii* (R. & C.) Grout Fig. 195

Genus *Cratoneuron*
- *C. commutatum* (Hedw.) Roth Fig. 197
- *C. filicinum* (Hedw.) Roth Fig. 197

Genus *Drepanocladus*
- *D. aduncus* (Hedw.) Warnst. Fig. 202; No. 53b
- *D. aduncus* var. *kneiffii* (Bry. Eur.) Warnst. Fig. 202
- *D. aduncus* var. *polycarpus* (Bland.) Warnst. Fig. 202
- *D. exannulatus* (Guemb.) Warnst. Fig. 203
- *D. fluitans* (Hedw.) Warnst. See Fig. 203
- *D. intermedius* (Lindb.) Warnst. Fig. 201
- *D. revolvens* (C. M.) Warnst. See Fig. 201
- *D. sendtneri* (Schimp.) Warnst. See Fig. 202
- *D. uncinatus* (Hedw.) Warnst. Fig. 210
- *D. vernicosus* (Lindb.) Warnst. Fig. 210

Genus *Entodon*
- *E. brevisetus* (H. & W.) J. & S. Fig. 286
- *E. cladorrhizans* (Hedw.) C. M. Fig. 290
- *E. compressus* (Hedw.) C. M. Fig. 291
- *E. drummondii* (Bry. Eur.) J. & S. See Fig. 290
- *E. seductrix* (Hedw.) C. M. Fig. 286

Genus *Eurhynchium*
- *E. diversifolium* (Schl.) Bry. Eur. Fig. 234
- *E. fallax* (R. & C.) Grout (= *E. substrigosum* Kindb.) Fig. 234
- *E. hians* (Hedw.) J. & S. Fig. 233
- *E. oreganum* (Sull.) J. & S. Fig. 231
- *E. praelongum* Bryhn See Fig. 231
- *E. pulchellum* (Hedw.) Jenn. (= *E. strigosum* of MFNA)

E. riparioides (Hedw.) Jenn. (= *E. rusciforme* of MFNA) Fig. 232
E. rusciforme (Neck.) Milde Fig. 232; No. 48a (= *riparioides* (Hedw.) Jenn.)
E. serrulatum (Hedw.) Kindb. Fig. 224
E. stokesii (Turn.) Bry. Eur. See Fig. 231
E. strigosuum (Hoffm.) Bry. Eur. Fig. 233 (=E. *pulchellum* (Hedw.) Jenn.)
E. strigosum var. *praecox* (Hedw.) Husnot Fig. 234.
E. strigosum var. *robustum* Roell See Fig. 233

Genus *Heterophyllium*
H. haldanianum (Grev.) Kindb. Fig. 275
H. nemorosum (Koch) Kindb. See Fig. 275

Genus *Homalotheciella*
H. subcapillata (Hedw.) Card. Fig. 237

Genus *Homalothecium*
H. nevadense (Lesq.) R. & C. See Fig. 228
H. nuttallii (Wils.) Grout Fig. 228

Genus *Homomallium*
H. adnatum (Hedw.) Broth. Fig. 259

Genus *Hygroamblystegium*
H. fluviatile (Sw.) Loeske Fig. 206
H. irriguum (Wils.) Loeske Fig. 219, 221
H. irriguum var. *spinifolium* (Schimp.) Grout See Fig. 206
H. noterophilum (Sull.) Warnst. Fig. 206
H. orthocladon (Beauv.) Grout Fig. 219, 221

Genus *Hygrohypnum* No. 42b
H. bestii (R. & B.) Broth. Fig. 271
H. dilatatum (Wils.) Loeske Fig. 274; No. 129b
H. eugyrium (Bry. Eur.) Loeske Fig. 273
H. molle (Schimp.) Loeske See Fig. 274
H. montanum (Wils.) Broth. Fig. 271
H. novae-caesareae (Aust.) Grout Fig. 272; No. 134c
H. novae-caesareae var. *badense* Herz. Fig. 272
H. ochraceum (Turn.) Loeske Fig. 270
H. palustre (Hedw.) Loeske Fig. 271, 273

Genus *Hylocomium*
H. brevirostre (Beauv.) Bry. Eur. Fig. 198
H. pyrenaicum (Spruce) Lindb. See Fig. 198
H. splendens (Hedw.) Bry. Eur. Fig. 172, 198
H. umbratum (Hedw.) Bry. Eur. Fig. 198

Genus *Hypnum*
H. arcuatum Lindb. (= *H. patientiae* Lindb.)
H. callichroum Brid. See Fig. 277

H. circinale Hook. Fig. 282
H. crista-castrensis Hedw. Fig. 279
H. cupressiforme Hedw. Fig. 283
H. cupressiforme var. *filiforme* Brid. See Fig. 283
H. curvifolium Hedw. Fig. 281
H. fertile Sendt. See Fig. 284
H. imponens Hedw. Fig. 284
H. molluscum Hedw. Fig. 280; No. 10a
H. pallescens (Hedw.) Bry. Eur. Fig. 285
H. patientiae Lindb. Fig. 276 (= *H. arcuatum* of MFNA)
H. pratense Koch See Fig. 276
H. reptile Mx. Fig. 285
H. revolutum (Mitt.) Lindb. Fig. 278
H. subimponens Lesq. Fig. 277
H. vaucheri Lesq. Fig. 283

Genus *Leptodictyum*
L. brevipes (Card. & Ther.) Broth. Fig. 226
L. riparium (Hedw.) Warnst. Fig. 217, 225, 227, 244 No. 43b
L. riparium forma *fluitans* (L. & J.) Grout Fig. 225
L. riparium forma *laxirete* (C. & T.) n. comb. Fig. 225, 226
L. riparium forma *longifolium* (Schultz) Grout See Fig. 225
L. riparium forma *obtusum* (Grout) Grout Fig. 226
L. sipho (Beauv.) Broth. See Fig. 225
L. trichopodium (Schultz) Warnst. Fig. 217
L. trichopodium var. *Kochii* (Bry. Eur.) Broth. Fig. 217
L. vacillans (Sull.) Broth. Fig. 226

Genus *Plagiothecium*
P. denticulatum (Hedw.) Bry. Eur. Fig. 294
P. denticulatum var. *aptychus* (Spruce) Grout Fig. 294
P. deplanatum (Sull.) Grout Fig. 297
P. elegans (Hook.) Sull. Fig. 298
P. geophilum (Aust.) Grout Fig. 296
P. micans (Sw.) Paris Fig. 298
P. piliferum (Sw.) Bry. Eur. Fig. 295
P. roeseanum (Hampe) Bry. Eur. Fig. 292; No. 134c
P. ruthei Limpr. Fig. 294
P. striatellum (Brid.) Lindb. Fig. 265
P. sylvaticum (Brid.) Bry. Eur. See Fig. 294
P. undulatum (Hedw.) Bry. Eur. Fig. 293

Genus *Platygyrium*
P. repens (Brid.) Bry. Eur. Fig. 261

Genus *Porotrichum*
P. alleghaniense (C. M.) Grout Fig. 207

Genus *Pseudisothecium*
- *P. myosuroides* (Hedw.) Grout Fig. 235
- *P. stoloniferum* (Hook.) Grout Fig. 235

Genus *Pylaisia* cf. Fig. 262
- *P. intricata* (Hedw.) Bry. Eur. See Fig. 287
- *P. polyantha* Bry. Eur. Fig. 288
- *P. selwynii* Kindb. Fig. 287
- *P. subdenticulata* Bry. Eur. Fig. 288

Genus *Rhytidiadelphus*
- *R. loreus* (Hedw.) Warnst. Fig. 289; No. 134L
- *R. squarrosus* (Hedw.) Warnst. See Fig. 289; No. 129a
- *R. triquetrus* (Hedw.) Warnst. Fig. 168; No. 129a

Genus *Rhytidiopsis*
- *R. robusta* (Hook.) Broth. Fig. 171, 196

Genus *Rhytidium*
- *R. rugosum* (Hedw.) Kindb. Fig. 165

Genus *Sciaromium*
- *S. lescurii* (Sull.) Broth. Fig. 208
- *S. fryei* Williams See Fig. 208

Genus *Scleropodium*
- *S. caespitosum* (Wils.) Bry. Eur. Fig. 239
- *S. cespitans* (C. Muell.) L. F. Koch Fig. 239
- *S. colpophyllum* (Sull.) Grout See Fig. 239
- *S. illecebrum* (Hedw.) Bry. Eur. See Fig. 238
- *S. obtusifolium* (Hook.) Kindb. Fig. 238

Genus *Scorpidium*
- *S. scorpioides* (Hedw.) Limpr. Fig. 267

Genus *Sematophyllum* cf. Fig. 259, 264, 272
- *S. adnatum* (Mx.) E. G. B. Fig. 262
- *S. caespitosum* (Hedw.) Mitt. Fig. 262
- *S. carolinianum* (C.M.) E. G. B. Fig. 263
- *S. marylandicum* (C. M.) E. G. B. Fig 263

FAMILY LESKEACEAE

Genus *Anomodon*
- *A attenuatus* (Hedw.) Hueben. Fig. 186
- *A. minor* (Beauv.) Lindb. Fig. 185
- *A. rostratus* (Hedw.) Schimp. Fig. 183
- *A. rugelii* (C. M.) Keissl. Fig. 186
- *A. tristis* (Cesati) Sull. Fig. 184
- *A. viticulosus* (Hedw.) H. & T. Fig. 185

Genus *Claopodium*
- *C. crispifolium* (Hook.) R. & C. Fig. 182
- *C. whippleanum* (Sull.) R. & C. Fig. 182

Genus *Haplohymenium*
- *H. triste* (Cesati) Kindb. Fig. 184

Genus *Helodium*
- *H. blandowii* (W. & M.) Warnst. Fig. 189
- *H. paludosum* (Sull.) Aust. Fig. 189

Genus *Herpetineurum*
- *H. toccoae* (Sull. & Lesq.) Card. Fig. 212

Genus *Heterocladium*
- *H. heteropteroides* Best Fig. 174
- *H. heteropterum* (Bruch) Bry. Eur. Fig. 174

Genus *Leskea* cf. Fig. 259
- *L. arenicola* Best. Fig. 188
- *L. australis* Sharp See No. 28a
- *L. gracilescens* Hedw. Fig. 188
- *L. nervosa* (Schw.) Myrin Fig. 187, 64a
- *L. obscura* Hedw. Fig. 188
- *L. polycarpa* Hedw. Fig. 188
- *L. tectorum* (Braun) Lindb. See Fig. 187

Genus *Lindbergia*
- *L. brachyptera* var. *austinii* (Sull.) Grout Fig. 181

Genus *Myurella*
- *M. careyana* Sull. Fig. 176
- *M. julacea* (Schw.) Bry. Eur. See Fig. 176

Genus *Pseudoleskea*
- *P. atrovirens* Bry. Eur. Fig. 180
- *P. incurvata* (Hedw.) Dix. Fig. 167
- *P. oligoclada* Kindb. No. 7a
- *P. patens* (Lindb.) Limpr. Fig. 180
- *P. radicosa* (Mitt.) L. & J. Fig. 167
- *P. rigescens* (Wils.) Lindb. Fig. 180

Genus *Pterigynandrum*
- *P. filiforme* Hedw. Fig. 170

Genus *Thelia*
- *T. asprella* Sull. Fig. 178
- *T. hirtella* (Hedw.) Sull. Fig. 179
- *T. lescurii* Sull. Fig. 178

Genus *Thuidium*
- *T. abietinum* (Brid.) Bry. Eur. Fig. 192
- *T. alleni* Aust. Fig. 193

T. delicatulum (Hedw.) Mitt. Fig. 193, 194
T. microphyllum (Hedw.) Best Fig. 190
T. minutulum (Hedw.) Bry. Eur. Fig. 191
T. philiberti Limpr. Fig. 193
T. pygmaeum Bry. Eur. Fig. 191
T. recognitum (Hedw.) Lindb. Fig. 194
T. scitum (Beauv.) Aust. Fig. 192
T. virginianum (Brid.) Lindb. Fig. 190, 194

FAMILY HOOKERIACEAE

Genus *Hookeria*
H. acutifolia Hook. Fig. 258
H. lucens (Hedw.) Smith. Fig. 258

FAMILY NECKERACEAE

Genus *Homalia*
H. jamesii Schimp. Fig. 223

Genus *Neckera*
N. douglasii Hook. Fig. 301
N. menziesii Hook. Fig. 299
N. pennata Hedw. Fig. 300
N. undulata Hedw. Fig. 299

FAMILY LEUCODONTACEAE

Genus *Leptodon*
L. nitidus Sull. See Fig. 214
L. ohioensis Sull. See Fig. 214
L. trichomitrion (Hedw.) Mohr Fig. 214

Genus *Leucodon*
L. brachypus Brid. Fig. 254
L. julaceus (Hedw.) Sull. Fig. 255
L. sciuroides (Hedw.) Schw. Fig. 255

Genus *Pterogonium*
P. gracile (Hedw.) Bry. Eur. Fig. 169

FAMILY CRYPHAEACEAE

Genus *Alsia*
A. californica (H. & A.) Sull. Fig. 199

Genus *Antitrichia*
A. californica Sull. Fig. 213
A. curtipendula (Hedw.) Brid. Fig. 213; No. 41b

Genus *Cryphaea*
C. glomerata Schimp. Fig. 177
C. nervosa (H. & W.) Bry. Eur. See Fig. 177

Genus *Dendroalsia*
D. abietina (Hook.) E. G. B. Fig. 173

FAMILY FABRONIACEAE

Genus *Anacamptodon*
A. splachnoides (Froehl.) Brid. Fig. 218

Genus *Clasmatodon*
C. parvulus (Hampe) Sull. Fig. 215

Genus *Fabronia*
F. ciliaris (Brid.) Brid. Fig. 257
F. gymnostoma Sull. & Lesq. No. 102c
F. imperfecta Sharp No. 102c
F. pusilla Raddi Fig. 257
F. ravenelii Sull. See Fig. 257
F. wrightii Sull. No. 102c

Genus *Schwetschkeopsis*
S. denticulata (Sull.) Broth. Fig. 175

FAMILY FONTINALACEAE

Genus *Brachelyma*
B. subulatum (Beauv.) Schimp. Fig. 204

Genus *Dichelyma*
D. capillaceum Bry. Eur. Fig. 200
D. falcatum (Hedw.) Myr. Fig. 198
D. uncinatum Mitt. Fig. 198

Genus *Fontinalis*
F. antipyretica Hedw. Fig. 251
F. antipyretica var. *gigantea* Sull. See Fig. 251
F. dalecarlica Bry. Eur. Fig. 252
F. duriaei Schimp. Fig. 253
F. lescurii Sull. Fig. 253
F. neomexicana S. & L. See Fig. 251
F. novae-angliae Sull. See Fig. 252

CLASS 2. HEPATICAE LIVERWORTS

Gametophyte a thallus, or if leafy with leaves in 2 equal dorsolateral rows, often with a third ventral row. Leaves without midrib; cells mostly isodiametric, with several chloroplasts. Archegonia acrogenous or anacrogenous. Sporophyte fragile, evanescent, usually with spirally marked elaters among the spores.

Order Jungermanniales

FAMILY PTILIDIACEAE

Genus *Blepharostoma*
B. arachnoideum Howe Fig. 326
B. trichophyllum (L) Dumort. Fig. 326

Genus *Ptilidium*
P. californicum (Aust.) U. & C. See Fig. 323
P. ciliare (L) Hampe See Fig. 323
P. pulcherrimum (Web.) Hampe Fig. 323

Genus *Tricholea (Trichocolea)*
T. tomentella (Ehrh.) Dumort. Fig. 324

FAMILY LEPIDOZIACEAE

Genus *Bazzania*
B. denudata (Torr.) Trev. Fig. 329
B. tricrenata (Wahl.) Trevis. Fig. 328
B. trilobata (L) S. F. Gray Fig. 328

Genus *Lepidozia*
L. reptans (L) Dumort. Fig. 327

Genus *Microlepidozia*
M. setacea (Web.) Joerg. See Fig. 325
M. sylvatica (Evans) Joerg. Fig. 325

FAMILY CALYPOGEIACEAE

Genus *Calypogeia*
C. fissa (L) Raddi Fig. 330
C. neesiana (M. & C.) K. Muell. Fig. 330
C. sullivantii Aust. Fig. 330
C. trichomanis (L) Corda Fig. 330

FAMILY CEPHALOZIACEAE

Genus *Cephalozia*
C. bicuspidata (L) Dumort. Fig. 349
C. catenulata (Hueben.) Spruce Fig. 350
C. connivens (Dicks.) Lindb. Fig. 350
C. lammersiana Spruce Fig. 349
C. media Lindb. Fig. 350

Genus *Nowellia*
N. curvifolia (Dicks.) Mitt. Fig. 348

Genus *Odontoschisma*
O. denudatum (Nees) Dumort. Fig. 332
O. prostratum (Sw.) Trevis. Fig. 332, 333

FAMILY CEPHALOZIELLACEAE

Genus *Cephaloziella*
C. byssacea (Roth) Warnst. Fig. 351
C. hampeana (Nees) Schiffn. Fig. 351

FAMILY JUNGERMANNIACEAE

Genus *Anastrophyllum*
A. michauxii (Web.) Buch Fig. 352

Genus *Barbilophozia*
B. barbata (Schmid.) Loeske Fig. 344
B. hatcheri (Evans) Loeske Fig. 345
B. lycopodioides (Wallr.) Loeske See Fig. 345

Genus *Jamesoniella*
J. autumnalis (DC) Steph. Fig. 332, 333

Genus *Jungermannia*
J. cordifolia Hook. Fig. 334
J. lanceolata L. Fig. 335
J. pumila With. Fig. 334

Genus *Lophozia*
L. excisa (Dicks.) Dumort. Fig. 354
L. incisa (Schrad.) Dum. Fig. 336
L. porphyroleuca (Nees) Schiffn. Fig. 354
L. ventricosa (Dicks.) Dumort. Fig. 354

Genus *Orthocaulis*
O. floerkei (W. & M.) Buch Fig. 346
O. kunzeanus (Hueben.) Buch Fig. 346
O. quadrilobus (Lindb.) Buch Fig. 347

Genus *Plectocolea*
P. crenulata (Smith) Evans Fig. 343
P. crenuliformis (Aust.) Mitt. Fig. 343
P. hyalina (Lyell) Mitt. Fig. 343
P. rubra (Gottsche) Evans See Fig. 343

Genus *Tritomaria*
T. exsecta (Schmid.) Schiffn. Fig. 342
T. exsectiformis (Breidl.) Schiffn. Fig. 342
T. quinquedentata (Huds.) Buch Fig. 342

FAMILY HARPANTHACEAE

Genus *Chiloscyphus*
C. pallescens (Ehrh.) Dumort. Fig. 331
C. polyanthus (L) Corda Fig. 331, 333
C. rivularis (Schrad.) Loeske Fig. 331

Genus *Harpanthus*
H. scutatus (W. & M.) Spruce Fig. 339

Genus *Lophocolea*
L. bidentata (L) Dumort. Fig. 341
L. cuspidata (Nees) Limpr. Fig. 341
L. heterophylla (Schrad.) Dumort. Fig. 340; No. 44b
L. minor Nees Fig. 340

FAMILY MARSUPELLACEAE

Genus *Marsupella*
M. emarginata (Ehrh.) Dumort. Fig. 353
M. sphacelata (Gies.) Dum. Fig. 353

FAMILY PLAGIOCHILACEAE

Genus *Plagiochila*
P. asplenioides (L) Dumort. Fig. 337
P. sullivantii Gottsche Fig. 338

FAMILY SCAPANIACEAE

Genus *Diplophyllum*
D. albicans (L) Dumort. Fig. 355
D. apiculatum (Evans) Steph. Fig. 355
D. taxifolium (Wahlenb.) Dumort. See Fig. 355

Genus *Scapania*
S. bolanderi Aust. Fig. 356
S. curta (Mart.) Dumort. See Fig. 358
S. irrigua (Nees) Dumort. Fig. 358
S. nemorosa (L) Dumort. Fig. 357
S. undulata (L) Dumort. Fig. 359

FAMILY PORELLACEAE

Genus *Porella*
P. cordaeana (Hueben.) Evans 360
P. navicularis (L. & L.) Lindb. Fig. 360
P. pinnata L. Fig. 362
P. platyphylla (L) Lindb. Fig. 361
P. platyphylloidea (Schwein.) Lindb. Fig. 361
P. roellii Steph. See Fig. 360

FAMILY RADULACEAE

Genus *Radula*
R. andicola Steph. Fig. 368
R. bolanderi Gottsche See Fig. 369
R. complanata (L) Dumort. Fig. 369
R. obconica Sull. Fig. 368

FAMILY FRULLANIACEAE

Genus *Frullania*

F. asagrayana Mont. Fig. 365
F. bolanderi Aust. Fig. 364
F. brittoniae Evans No. 84b
F. californica (Aust.) Evans See Fig. 365
F. eboracensis Gottsche Fig. 367
F. franciscana Howe See Fig. 365
F. inflata Gottsche Fig. 366
F. kunzei Lehm. & Lindenb. Fig. 364
F. nisquallensis Sull. Fig. 365
F. oakesiana Aust. Fig. 365
F. riparia Hampe Fig. 366
F. squarrosa (R. Bl. & N.) Dumort. Fig. 367

Genus *Jubula*

J. pennsylvanica (Steph.) Evans Fig. 363

FAMILY LEJEUNEACEAE

Genus *Cololejeunea*

C. biddlecomiae (Aust.) Evans Fig. 372

Genus *Lejeunea*

L. cavifolia (Ehrh.) Lindb. Fig. 372
L. patens Lindb. Fig. 372

Genus *Leucolejeunea*

L. clypeata (Schwein.) Evans Fig. 370
L. unciloba (Lindenb.) Evans Fig. 370

Genus *Microlejeunea*

M. laetevirens (Nees & Mont.) Evans Fig. 371
M. ulicina (Tayl.) Evans Fig. 371

Order Metzgeriales

FAMILY FOSSOMBRONIACEAE

Genus *Fossombronia*

F. cristula Aust. No. 23a
F. foveolata Lindb. Fig. 318
F. wondraczekii (Corda) Dum. Fig. 318

FAMILY PELLIACEAE

Genus *Pellia*

P. endiviaefolia (Dicks.) Dum. Fig. 321
P. epiphylla (L) Corda Fig. 321
P. neesiana (Gottsche) Limpr. Fig. 321

FAMILY BLASIACEAE

Genus *Blasia*

B. pusilla L. Fig. 317

FAMILY PALLAVICINIACEAE

Genus *Moerckia*

M. flotowiana (Nees) Schiffn. Fig. 319

Genus *Pallavicinia*

P. lyellii (Hook.) S. F. Gray Fig. 319

FAMILY METZGERIACEAE

Genus *Metzgeria*

M. conjugata Lindb. Fig. 320
M. furcata (L) Dumort. Fig. 320
M. hamata Lindb. No. 28a
M. pubescens (Schrank) Raddi No. 27a

FAMILY RICCARDIACEAE

Genus *Riccardia*

R. multifida (L) S. F. Gray Fig. 322
R. palmata (Hedw.) Carruth. Fig. 322
R. pinguis (L) S. F. Gray See Fig. 322

Order Marchantiales

FAMILY MARCHANTIACEAE

Genus *Asterella*

A. ludwigii (Schw.) Underw. Fig. 312
A. tenella (L) Beauv. Fig. 312

Genus *Clevea*

C. hyalina (Somm.) Lindb. Fig. 309

Genus *Conocephalum*

C. conicum (L) Wiggers Fig. 307

Genus *Lunularia*

L. cruciata (L) Dumort. Fig. 306

Genus *Mannia*

M. californica (Gottsche) Wheeler See Fig. **310**
M. fragrans (Balb.) Frye & Clark Fig. 310

Genus *Marchantia*

M. domingensis Lehm. & Lindenb. Fig. 305
M. paleacea Bertol. Fig. 305
M. polymorpha L. Fig. 305

Genus Preissia
P. quadrata (Scop.) Nees. Fig. 308

Genus *Reboulia*
R. hemisphaerica (L) Raddi Fig. 311

FAMILY RICCIACEAE

Genus *Riccia*
R. beyrichiana Hampe Fig. 315
R. curtisii James Fig. 316
R. dictyospora Howe Fig. 315
R. fluitans L. Fig. 314
R. frostii Aust. Fig. 316
R. membranacea Gottsche & Lindenb. No. 18a
R. sullivantii Aust. Fig. 316

Genus *Ricciocarpus*
R. natans (L) Corda Fig. 313

Order Sphaerocarpales

FAMILY SPHAEROCARPACEAE

Genus *Sphaerocarpus*
S. texanus Aust. Fig. 302

CLASS 3. ANTHOCEROTAE. HORNWORTS.

Gametophyte a thallus, each cell containing one large chloroplast (in our species). Archegonia anacrogenous, fused into the thallus. Sporophyte long-lived, cylindrical, growing for a long time (months) at the base, splitting in two above, disclosing a central fiber (columella) surrounded by spores and irregular, 2-4-celled, smooth elaters. Columella incomplete as in Sphagnum.

Order Anthocerotales

FAMILY ANTHOCEROTACEAE

Genus *Anthoceros*. Sporophyte erect
A. crispulus (Mont.) Douin No. 7b
A. fusiformis Aust. Fig. 304
A. laevis L. Fig. 304
A. punctatus L. Fig. 304

Genus *Notothylas*. Sporophyte short, horizontal
N. orbicularis (Schwein.) Sull. Fig. 303

INDEX AND PICTURED-GLOSSARY

It should be noted that all generic names begin with a capital while the species names begin with a small letter. Both are italicized. The numbers which follow refer to pages.

A

Acaulon 51, 193
rufescens 33, 51, 193
Acrocarpi 8, 19, 197
ACROCARPOUS: having the sporophyte at the end of a stem or ordinary leafy branch. Fig. 375. 20, 21, 25.

Figure 375

ACUMEN: the tapering narrow point of an acuminate leaf.
ACUMINATE: tapering in the manner of Fig. 376. Note curvature of margin of leaf.

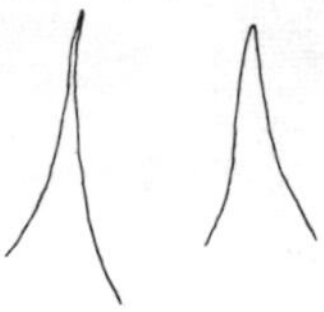

Figure 376

ACUTE: ending in a sharp angle, less than 90°. Fig. 377.

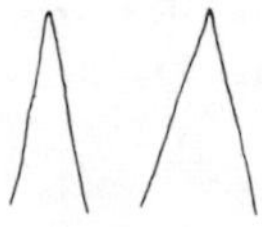

Figure 377

ALAR CELLS: the cells at the basal angle of the leaf. Fig. 378.

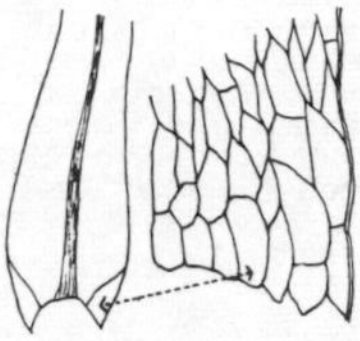

Figure 378

Aloina 193
rigida 33, 34, 193
var. *pilifera* 193
Alsia 112, 207
californica 112, 207
Amblyodon 199
dealbatus 93, 199
Amblystegiella 138, 200
confervoides 138, 200
subtilis 138, 200
Amblystegium 120, 201
americanum 121, 201
compactum 121, 201
juratzkanum 119, 121, 201
serpens 121, 201
varium 119, 120, 121, 201
Amphidium 197
californicum 50, 197
lapponicum 50, 197
mougeotii 50, 197
Anacamptodon 208
splachnoides 120, 208
Anacolia 198
menziesii 58, 198
Anastrophyllum 177, 210
michauxii 177, 210
Andreaea 7, 19, 23, 188
rothii 25, 188
rupestris 25, 188
Andreaeaceae 7, 188
Andreaeales 7, 188
Andreaeobrya 7, 21, 188
ANNULUS: a ring of thick walled cells between the mouth of the capsule and the lid, like the rubber gasket on a jar. Fig. 379.

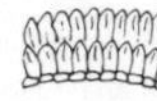

Figure 379

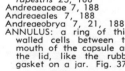

Anomodon 20, 106, 205
attenuatus 107, 205
minor 107, 205
rostratus 106, 205
rugelii 107, 205
tristis 106, 205
viticulosus 107, 205
ANTHERIDIUM: the male reproductive organ containing the sperms. Fig. 380. 3, 13, **16**

Figure 380

Anthoceros 157, 214
crispulus 158, 214
fusiformis 157, 214
laevis 6, 7, 157, 214
punctatus 157, 158, 214
Anthocerotaceae 157, 214
Anthocerotae 7, 22, 157, 214
Anthocerotales 20, 21, 157, 214
Antitrichia 118, 207
californica 118, 207
curtipendula 112, 118, 207
APEX: the tip; the end opposite to the point of attachment.
Aphanorhegma 197
patens 66, 95, 197
serratum 66, 95, 197
APICAL: belonging to the apex or tip.
APICULATE: ending in an abrupt, short, sharp point, but not stiff. Fig. 381.

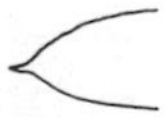

Figure 381

APOPHYSIS: see hypophysis.
APPENDICULATE: of cilia with small transverse spurs

at intervals along the margin. Fig. 382.

Figure 382

ARCHEGONIUM: the female reproductive organ containing the egg. Fig. 383.

Figure 383

AREOLE: one space or mesh of a network.

AURICLE: a lobe or bulge at the base of a leaf. Fig. 384.

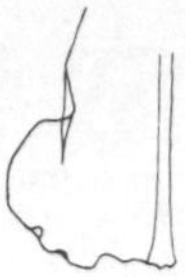

Figure 384

AUTOICOUS: having male and female organs on the same plant, the antheridia in a cluster just below the archegonia, or somewhere else along the shoot, or on a large or small branch. 13
AWN: a bristle at the tip of a leaf. 12

B

BEAK: a prolonged narrow tip of an operculum. Fig. 385.

Figure 385

BIFID: two-cleft to about the middle.
BILOBED: with two divisions, especially rounded ones.

BOG: a watery mass of decayed vegetation with acid reaction.

BORDERED: having the margin different from the rest of the leaf either in shape or color of cells. Fig. 386.

Figure 386

BRACT: a special leaflike structure at the base of a reproductive organ or cluster, 16.
BRACTEOLE: a small bract; a modified underleaf.

BROOD-BODIES: detachable cells or organs which give rise vegetatively to new plants; **gemmae.**

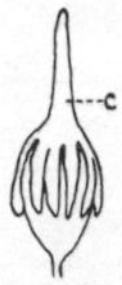

Figure 387

Figure 388

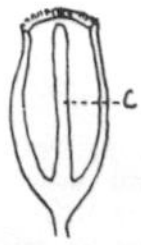

Figure 389

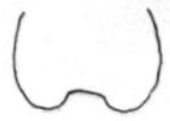

Figure 390

Figure 391

Figure 392

Figure 393

Figure 394

E

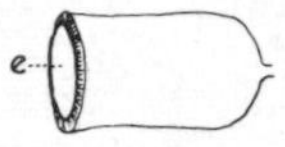

Figure 395

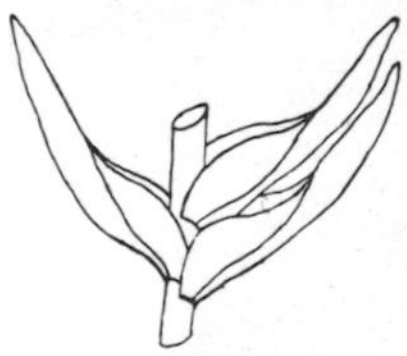

Figure 396

Figure 397

F

Figure 398

G

H

HYALINE: colorless and clear.
HYDRIC: of very wet habitat, or in water.

HYPOPHYSIS: a swelling of the seta immediately under the capsule. Fig. 399.

Figure 399

I

IMMERSED: of the capsule when the perichaetial leaves project beyond it. Fig. 400.

Figure 400

INCRASSATE: with thickened walls.
INCUBOUS: leaves overlapping like shingles on a roof if base of plant is at ridge and apex at the eaves. Fig. 401. 14, 20, 21

Figure 401

INFLATED: of alar cells which are enlarged much beyond the size of neighboring cells. Fig. 402.

Figure 402

INVOLUCRE: a protective covering around the calyptra or perianth formed of bracts or a short tube.
INVOLUTE: having the margins rolled inward (upward). Fig. 403.

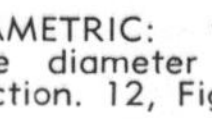

Figure 403

ISODIAMETRIC: with the same diameter in every direction. 12, Fig. 404.

Figure 404

J

JULACEOUS: cylindrical, and smooth or downy. Fig. 405.

Figure 405

K

KEEL: a sharp ridge as when a leaf is folded along the midrib or main division. Fig. 406.

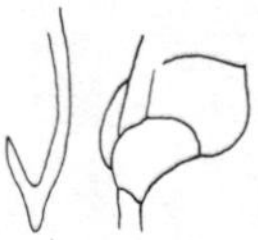

Figure 406

L

LACINIATE: slashed; cut into narrow lobes. Fig. 407.

Figure 407

LAMELLA: (pl. ae) thin sheets of cells usually standing perpendicular to the surface of a leaf. Fig. 408.

Figure 408

LAMINA: the flat, green part of the leaf; blade.
LANCEOLATE: lance-shaped; 4-6 times longer than wide, broadest at base and tapering to a point. Fig. 409.

Figure 409

M

N

tween seta and urn. Fig. 410n. (See Fig. 13).

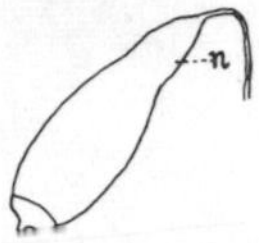

Figure 410

NODOSE: with rounded thickenings at intervals.

O

OBOVATE: similar to ovate, but broadest at the distal end.
OBTUSE: blunt or rounded at the end. Fig. 411.

Figure 411

OPERCULUM: the lid or cover of the capsule. Fig. 412.

Figure 412

OVAL: broadly elliptical. Fig. 413.

Figure 413

OVATE: egg-shaped, with the broader end downward. Fig 414.

Figure 414

P

PAPILLA: a tiny lump or knob on a cell wall. (See Fig. 15) 10
PAPILLOSE: rough with papillae. Fig. 415.

Figure 415

PARACYST: an enlarged or brightly colored cell, very different from the surrounding cells.

PARAPHYLLIA: thread-like or tiny leaf-like growths among the leaves. Fig. 416. 20

Figure 416

PAROICOUS: with antheridia in axils of perichaetial leaves just below the archegonia. 13

PELLUCID: translucent.
PERCURRENT: reaching to the apex but not beyond; percurrent costa. Fig. 417.

Figure 417

PERIANTH: a sheath surrounding the archegonia or young sporophyte. Fig. 418. 6, 16

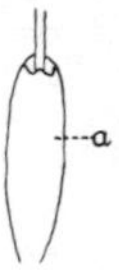

Figure 418

PERICHAETIUM: the special leaves or bracts surrounding the archegonium or base of the seta. Fig. 419.

Figure 419

Figure 420

Figure 421

Figure 422

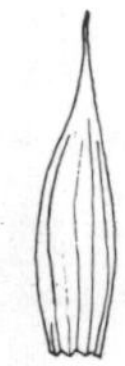

Figure 423

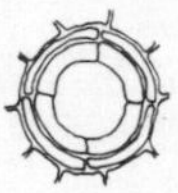

Figure 424

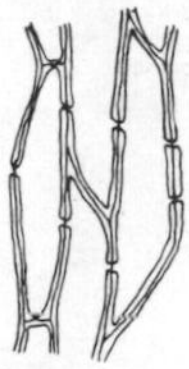

Figure 425

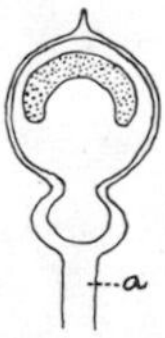

Figure 426

Figure 427

Figure 428

Figure 429

Figure 430

Figure 431

SPERM: the active, coiled, male reproductive cell or gamete. 3
Sphaerocarpaceae 156, 214
Sphaerocarpales 7, 20, 21, 156, 214
Sphaerocarpus 156, 214
texanus 156, 214
Sphagnaceae 7, 187
Sphagnales 7, 187
Sphagnobrya 7, 21, 187
Sphagnum 5, 19, 23-25, 187
affine 24, 188
capillaceum 25, 188
cuspidatum 24, 188
girgensohnii 24, 25, 188
magellanicum 24, 188
palustre 24, 188
warnstorfii 24, 25, 188
SPINDLE-SHAPED: tapering to each end. Fig. 432.

Figure 432

SPINOSE: having spines.
Splachnaceae 8, 21, 39, 196
Splachnum 196
ampulloceum 39, 196
luteum 39, 196
SPORANGIUM: the capsule.
SPORE: a microscopic reproductive body, in mosses 1-celled and borne in the capsule. (See Fig. 13). 2, 13, 15
SPOROPHYTE: the spore-bearing part or phase, composed of foot, seta and capsule. (See Fig. 13). 3, 4, 13
SQUARROSE: of leaves with midrib bent back at right angles to the stem. Fig. 433.

Figure 433

STEREID: a slender fiber cell with walls thicker than the lumen, in the midrib or margin of a leaf.
STERILE: without sporophyte or spores.
STOMA: (pl. stomata) an opening through the epidermis bordered by two special cells. Fig. 434. 4

Figure 434

STRUMA: a swelling on one side of the base of a capsule. Fig. 435.

Figure 435

STRUMOSE: having a struma.
SUBSTRATUM: the material on which the plant grows.
SUCCUBOUS: with leaves overlapping like shingles on a roof if base of plant is at eaves and apex at the ridge. (See Fig. 19.) 14, 20, 21
Sullivant 17, 18
SWAMP: low ground saturated with water, but usually not covered with it, producing more or less of shrubs and trees.
SYNOICOUS: with antheridia and archegonia mingled. 13
Syrrhopodon 41, 194
floridanus 41, 194
texanus 41, 194
Systematic List 187

T

Tayloria 196
serrata 40, 196
TERETE: cylindrical; round in cross section.
TESSELATE (*d*): marked in checkered squares. Fig. 436.

Figure 436

TETRAD: a group of four spores forming a three sided pyramid (tetrahedron).
Tetraphidaceae 188
Tetraphis 21, 188
geniculata 39, 188
pellucida 39, 188
Tetraplodon 196
mnioides 40, 196
pennsylvanicus 40, 196
Thalloid 20
THALLUS: a plant body not differentiated into stem and leaf. Fig. 437.

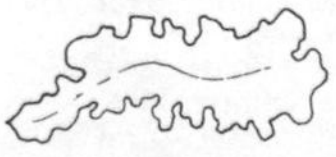

Figure 437

Thelia 103, 206
asprella 103, 206
hirtella 104, 206
lescurii 103, 206
Thuidium 20, 105, 108, 206
abietinum 109, 206
alleni 109, 206
delicatulum 109, 110, 207
microphyllum 108, 207
minutulum 109, 207
philiberti 109, 207
pygmaeum 109, 207
recognitum 110, 207
scitum 109, 207
virginianum 108, 110, 207
Timmia 198
austriaca 41, 198
megapolitana 41, 198
Timmiaceae 198
Timmiella 193
anomala 40, 193
TOOTH: (teeth) the processes composing the peristome, or the outer row of such processes when the peristome is double. Fig. 438.

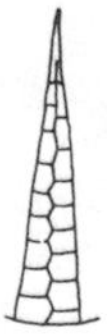

Figure 438

Tortella 60, 193
fragilis 61, 193
humilis 61, 193
tortuosa 61, 193
Tortula 54, 55, 194
bistratosa 55, 194
bolanderi 55, 194
fragilis 53, 194
mucronifolia 87, 194
muralis 55, 194
obtusissima 56, 194
pagorum 53, 194
princeps 55, 56, 194

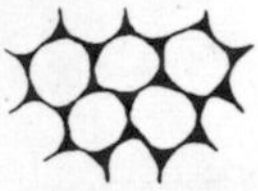

Figure 439

Figure 440

U

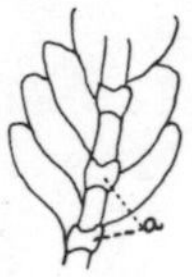

Figure 441

Figure 442

V

W

X

Z